LOW-CALORIE PRODUCTS

*An industry–university co-operation Symposium organised
under the auspices of the National College of Food Technology
(Department of Food Science and Technology), University of Reading,
25–26 March 1987*

THE SYMPOSIUM COMMITTEE

GORDON G. BIRCH, B.Sc., Ph.D., D.Sc.(Lond.), F.R.S.C., C.Chem., M.R.S.H.
Reader, National College of Food Technology (Department of Food Science and Technology), Food Studies Building, University of Reading, Whiteknights, Reading, Berks. RG6 2AP

GEOFFREY CAMPBELL-PLATT, B.Sc., Ph.D., F.I.F.S.T.
Professor of Food Technology, National College of Food Technology (Department of Food Science and Technology), Food Studies Building, University of Reading, Whiteknights, Reading, Berks. RG6 2AP

J. KNIGHTS, M.Sc.
PFW Ltd, PO Box 18, Greenford, Middlesex UB6 7JH

M. G. LINDLEY, Ph.D.
Tate and Lyle PLC, Group Research and Development, Philip Lyle Memorial Research Laboratory, PO Box 68, Reading, Berks. RG6 2BX

K. J. PARKER, M.A., D.Phil.(Oxon.), F.R.S.C., C.Chem.
'Murrens', Reading Road, Crowmarsh Gifford, Wallingford, Oxon. OX10 8EN

E. J. ROLFE, B.Sc., M.Chem.A., F.R.S.C., C.Chem., F.I.F.S.T.
Principal, National College of Food Technology (Department of Food Science and Technology), Food Studies Building, University of Reading, Whiteknights, Reading, Berks. RG6 2AP

Mrs B. A. SHORE
c/o National College of Food Technology (Department of Food Science and Technology), Food Studies Building, University of Reading, Whiteknights, Reading, Berks. RG6 2AP

LOW-CALORIE PRODUCTS

Edited by

G. G. BIRCH and M. G. LINDLEY

ELSEVIER APPLIED SCIENCE
LONDON and NEW YORK

ELSEVIER APPLIED SCIENCE PUBLISHERS LTD
Crown House, Linton Road, Barking, Essex IG11 8JU, England

Sole Distributor in the USA and Canada
ELSEVIER SCIENCE PUBLISHING CO., INC.
52 Vanderbilt Avenue, New York, NY 10017, USA

WITH 49 TABLES AND 73 ILLUSTRATIONS

© 1988 ELSEVIER APPLIED SCIENCE PUBLISHERS LTD
© 1988 A/S KØBENHAVNS PEKTINFABRIK—Paper 3

British Library Cataloguing in Publication Data

Low-calorie products.
1. Low calorie food. Production
I. Birch, G. G. (Gordon Gerard), *1934–*
II. Lindley, M. G.
664′.63

Library of Congress Cataloging-in-Publication Data

Low-calorie products.

'An industry–university co-operation symposium
organised under the auspices of the National College of
Food Technology (Department of Food Science and
Technology), University of Reading, 25–26 March
1987'— Prelim. p.
  Bibliography: p.
  Includes index.
  1. Low-calorie diet—Congresses.   2. Food—Caloric
content—Congresses.   I. Birch, G. G. (Gordon Gerard)
II. Lindley, M. G.   III. National College of Food
Technology. Dept. of Food Science and Technology.
RM222.2.L66   1988   664′.63   87-36404

ISBN 1-85166-161-1

Special regulations for readers in the USA

Typeset by Keyset Composition, Colchester
Printed in Great Britain at the University Press, Cambridge

List of Contributors

D. P. ATKINS
Food Science Division, Ministry of Agriculture, Fisheries and Food, Horseferry Road, London SW1P 2AE, UK

J. E. BLUNDELL
Biopsychology Group, Department of Psychology, University of Leeds, Leeds LS2 9JT, UK

I. R. DAVIES
AFRC Institute of Food Research, Norwich Laboratory, Colney Lane, Norwich NR4 7UA, UK

N. FINER
Guy's and St Thomas's Hospitals (University of London), Division of Medicine, 4th Floor, Hunt's House, Guy's Hospital, London SE1 9RT, UK

C. GEISSLER
Department of Food and Nutritional Sciences, King's College, University of London, Campden Hill Road, London W8 7AH, UK

B. G. HENDLEY
KAE Development Ltd, 7 Arundel Street, London WC2R 3DR, UK

A. J. HILL
Biopsychology Group, Department of Psychology, University of Leeds, Leeds LS2 9JT, UK

D. C. HOBBS
Pfizer Central Research, Eastern Point Road, Groton, Connecticut 06340, USA

B. HOMLER
The NutraSweet® Company, 601 East Kensington Road, Mount Prospect, Illinois 60056, USA

H. W. HOUGHTON
Schweppes International Ltd, Schweppes House, 105 Brook Road, Dollis Hill, London NW2 7DS, UK

G. LIVESEY
AFRC Institute of Food Research, Norwich Laboratory, Colney Lane, Norwich NR4 7UA, UK

J. A. METCALFE
British Diabetic Association, 10 Queen Anne Street, London W1M 0BD, UK

P. R. MURRAY
Pfizer Chemicals Europe & Africa, 10 Dover Road, Sandwich, Kent CT13 0BN, UK

P. J. ROGERS
Biopsychology Group, Department of Psychology, University of Leeds, Leeds LS2 9JT, UK

G.-W. VON RYMON LIPINSKI
Hoechst AG, D-6230 Frankfurt/Main 80, Federal Republic of Germany

Y. SCHUTZ
Institute of Physiology, University of Lausanne, CH-1005 Lausanne, Switzerland

V. SEYMOUR
KAE Development Ltd, 7 Arundel Street, London WC2R 3DR, UK

P. J. STRÄTER
Palatinit® Süssungsmittel GmbH, Wormser Str. 11, D-6719 Obrigheim/Pfalz, Federal Republic of Germany

M. G. TORDOFF
Monell Chemical Senses Center, 3500 Market Street, Philadelphia, Pennsylvania, 19104, USA

J. E. TRUDSØ
The Copenhagen Pectin Factory Ltd, DK-4623 Lille Skensved, Denmark

R. A. WILBEY
Department of Food Science and Technology, University of Reading, Whiteknights, PO Box 226, Reading RG6 2AP, UK

M. WOLKSTEIN
Reach Associates Inc., 75 South Orange Avenue, South Orange, New Jersey 07079, USA

Contents

PROCEEDINGS OF PREVIOUS SYMPOSIA

Glucose Syrups and Related Carbohydrates, edited by G. G. Birch, L. F. Green and C. B. Coulson, 1970.

Sweetness and Sweeteners, edited by G. G. Birch, L. F. Green and C. B. Coulson, 1971.

Health and Food, edited by G. G. Birch, L. F. Green and L. G. Plaskett, 1972.

Molecular Structure and Function of Food Carbohydrate, edited by G. G. Birch and L. F. Green, 1973.

Vitamin C, edited by G. G. Birch and K. J. Parker, 1974.

Food from Waste, edited by G. G. Birch, J. T. Worgan and K. J. Parker, 1975.

Intermediate Moisture Foods, edited by R. Davies, G. G. Birch and K. J. Parker, 1976.

Sensory Properties of Foods, edited by G. G. Birch, J. G. Brennan and K. J. Parker, 1977.

Sugar, Science and Technology, edited by G. G. Birch and K. J. Parker, 1978.

Food and Health: Science and Technology, edited by G. G. Birch and K. J. Parker, 1979.

Enzymes and Food Processing, edited by G. G. Birch, N. Blakebrough and K. J. Parker, 1980.

Nutritive Sweeteners, edited by G. G. Birch and K. J. Parker, 1981.

Dietary Fibre, edited by G. G. Birch and K. J. Parker, 1982.

Control of Food Quality and Food Analysis, edited by G. G. Birch and K. J. Parker, 1983.

Alcoholic Beverages, edited by G. G. Birch and M. G. Lindley, 1984.

Interactions of Food Components, edited by G. G. Birch and M. G. Lindley, 1985.

Developments in Food Flavours, edited by G. G. Birch and M. G. Lindley, 1986.

All published by Elsevier Applied Science Publishers.

1

Markets for Low-Calorie Foods

B. G. HENDLEY and V. SEYMOUR

KAE Development Ltd, London, UK

ABSTRACT

The markets for low-calorie foods in the UK amount to over £800 million currently. The term low-calorie is used to cover three distinct types of food products: first, products designed to aid in weight loss; second, reduced-calorie versions of normal foods and third, foods that are inherently low in calories.

The motivations for using low-calorie foods are also threefold: slimming, mainly for vanity; more general health considerations; and medical grounds. At any one time over 60% of the adult female population in the UK is slimming, either seriously or as a token gesture. Around 8% of the UK's adult population is medically obese, i.e. at least 20% over the average weight for their given frame. In Europe there are some 40 million obese people and at least the same again who are simply overweight. Medical motivations include heart conditions and diabetes where careful control of the diet can be essential.

The specialist slimming-food sector includes the traditional meal replacements and appetite suppressants; combined they are worth only £18m. The new VLCDs (Very Low-Calorie Diets) such as the Cambridge Diet are, however, much more successful, growing to £25m in only three years.

Reduced-calorie products, including ready meals, soft drinks, low-fat spread and bread, are worth £370 million currently (excluding skimmed milk and yogurt). Naturally low-fat products, in which skimmed milk and low-fat yogurt are included, account for more than £480m.

The booming market, therefore, is not attributable just to a sustained interest in slimming but a more widespread shift towards healthier foods with less fat and sugar and more fibre and therefore a net reduction in calorie intake.

LOW-CALORIE FOODS AND THE CONSUMER

Calorie reduction in the 1980s is an obsession for a large proportion of the populations of Western Europe and North America. Today, millions of Americans are trying to reduce their intake of calories, fat, cholesterol and sugar as well as of salt and additives. It is really a wonder that *any* food is sold at all in the US! Yet low-calorie food and drinks are expected to be worth about $40 billion by 1990!

Whilst the UK has not yet gone to such extremes about the constituents of its food, the trends are there. UK sales of low-calorie foods and drinks exceeded £800 million in 1986, with an estimated growth of approximately 5% per annum, and while the statement made a couple of years ago by a spokesman for the Advertising Standard Authority, '. . . there is no sign of any end to the public interest in the latest ways of slimming . . . even today, we hear of slimming potions, hoops and belts . . .' is still correct for a certain portion of the population, the larger trend is towards a more 're-educated' way of eating.

Consumer taste is shifting from specific slimming foods to a generally healthier diet—more fibre, less fat and sugar, and *therefore a net reduction* in calorie intake.

The term 'low-calorie' is widely used to cover three separate, quite distinct, types of food. First, there are those products specifically designed to aid in weight loss—the traditional meal replacement products such as Limmits and Slender and including appetite suppressants such as Ayds. This area has been widened in recent years with the introduction of the 'Very Low-Calorie Diets' or 'VLCDs', such as the Cambridge Diet.

The second distinct food type is the 'reduced-calorie' food and drink. These products are *lower* calorie versions of standard foods, such as low-calorie soup, hot chocolate, soft drinks, etc. Finally, there are those foods inherently low in fat, or calories, and hence, perceived to be earning the low-calorie label naturally by consumers.

Before looking more closely at these food markets, I would like to talk about the motivations of people using these different types of foods.

Despite recent shifts in consumer tastes, the major motivation for eating low-calorie foods is *slimming*, and the major motivation for slimming remains vanity. For instance, in a recent survey of consumers by Mintel, 55% of women dieters cited appearance as the key motive. Slimming activity encompasses, at any one time, well over 60% of the female population. Of course, the degree of this activity varies, from the 'thinking about going on a diet' all the way through to the avid dieter. The majority will follow, at least partially, some sort of plan suggested by an 'expert' and these plans or approaches are likely to include some 'slimming' products.

The spectrum encompasses those women who just wish to lose a few pounds so as to look good in this year's bikini, to those who are extremely overweight and have been on the diet/binge/diet cycle for years. It has been estimated that about 90% of adult women have at one time or another tried to slim. Of course, being overweight or weight-conscious is not solely a woman's prerogative! A study last year by the Royal College of Physicians estimated that 39% of *men* are overweight medically, as opposed to only 32% of women. But 8% of women were obese or very fat in terms of fat to body weight ratio, with only 6% of men being so.

It must be said that a large proportion of the 'vanity slimming' is seasonal. After Christmas is that traditional rush to lose those extra winter pounds and inches, and to make way for the ritual baring of the skin in the summer.

The second most popular motivation for eating low-calorie foods today is for 'health'. 'Health' is being used here in its broadest sense, implying a sense of fitness, well-being, and just generally being more in tune with one's body.

Today's consumers are becoming more educated about food and what it does. The trend is now towards those who are weight conscious as opposed to overweight . . . 'trimmers' rather than 'slimmers'. Manufacturers of slimming foods have begun to recognise this and to reposition their products on a 'healthy', 'good-tasting' platform. Many foods inherently low in calories or fat are now being consumed by a much wider audience.

Fitness in the physical activity sense has risen in the UK in recent years—today 54% of the population takes part in some type of sporting or physical activity. Approximately nine million people belong to a sports club and over three million adults *claim* to jog regularly. One in every five adults in the UK claims to have taken up a physical activity in the last three years for reasons of health and fitness. This equates to six million people between the ages of 16 and 54! There appear to be similarities in Europe as a whole with an estimated 170 million people taking part in sporting activities, and with 20 million Europeans claiming to jog regularly. Across Europe around 50 million adults have taken to exercise for reasons of health and fitness!

A more serious motivation for consuming low-calorie foods to slim is that of medical grounds. Heart disease and high blood pressure are very real health risks. Heart disease is still the number one killer in the UK today and obesity is a contributory factor to both high blood pressure and heart disease. Obesity is officially defined as being 20% over the average weight for a given build or frame. By this definition, some 8% of the UK population or over four million people are obese. Also, as mentioned before, there is a definite bias towards females. On a European basis, some 40 million people are probably officially obese, and a great number more are simply overweight.

However, health risks associated with excess weight do not only apply to the clinically obese. Studies have shown that even being mildly overweight can increase the risk of heart attack, diabetes in middle age, severe pain from arthritis and high blood pressure, as well as adding additional risks during pregnancy and surgery. Any one of these health risks is reason enough to try to reduce one's weight.

Diabetes mellitus should be extracted from the above medical conditions to be examined separately. Possibly, more so than with the other conditions, once a person is diagnosed as diabetic that condition becomes a way of life. There is no cure for diabetes, only methods of permanently adjusting your life style. The methods of keeping the disease under control are diet alone, diet plus tablets or diet plus injections, depending on what form of diabetes the individual has—whether insulin-dependent or insulin-independent.

There are 600 000 diagnosed diabetics in the UK of whom 250 000 are insulin-dependent. Sadly, 30 000 of these insulin-dependents are under 16 years of age. The British Diabetic Association estimates that a further 400 000–500 000 people have diabetes in a milder insulin-dependent form, and that a large majority of these are unaware that they are diabetic.

Internationally, diabetes is the world's third biggest killer disease—

after heart disease and cancer. There are an estimated 60 million people affected world-wide. Interestingly, the vast majority of these sufferers live in developed countries. The disease is uncommon in communities (such as the American Indians) living on traditionally processed foods. The presence of fibre in carbohydrate meals, whether in natural solid foods or as added supplements, reduces the body's insulin responses and often reduces the blood-sugar level. Limited data suggest that diabetic control is made easier by a high-fibre diet. The use of guar gum as an additive also seems to be effective. In the long run, replacing refined carbohydrate foods might also reduce the risk of diabetes by preventing or arresting obesity. But in the shorter term, these sufferers have to look to their diets, and to special dietetic foods to keep their health on an even keel. However, nutritionists believe a correctly balanced diet of standard foods is more beneficial than those products specially formulated, and, in fact, the British Diabetic Association is strongly in favour of the 'total client approach' and recommends that 'use of special diet foods be discouraged'. The BDA is currently encouraging manufacturers to increase the percentage of fibre-rich carbohydrate in their products and to continue to reduce fat and calorie content.

THE UK MARKET FOR LOW-CALORIE PRODUCTS

First, there are those products specifically designed to aid in weight loss—the traditional *specialist slimming food sector.*

The slimming products' market boomed in the 1960s when people (mainly women) wanted to achieve the 'Twiggy' look. At this point, many meal replacements and slimming aids were launched by pharmaceutical and health food companies. Today this sector is surprisingly small, given the consumers' continued interest in slimming. The traditional meal replacements market is worth approximately £15m per annum with slimming aids, such as appetite suppressants, at around the £3m mark. More importantly this sector shows little growth (Table 1).

For most people the perfect diet would guarantee a rapid loss of weight so that a resumption of 'normal eating' habits may be started again as quickly as possible. Despite the warnings of many experts who maintain that crash diets are dangerous, these are precisely what some consumers want.

Consumers want 'quick results' to such an extent that the VLCD

TABLE 1
UK Markets for Low-Calorie Foods

Specialist slimmers' foods	£m Retail selling price (RSP)
Meal replacements	15
Slimming aids	3
Very low-calorie	25
	43

Source: Mintel, KAE.

programmes have achieved a £25m market size in a few short years. Programmes such as the Cambridge Diet and the Micro Diet offer a plan of 330 calories, up to 380 calories now, with the introduction of Cambridge Meal Bars, which also guarantee your body all the essential nutrients and minerals it needs to stay healthy.

This dichotomy is one of the basic problems of the slimmers' markets. The intellectual, reasoned approach, versus the actual 'dream-fulfilment' element that pushes many consumers to diet in the first place. Any product that markets itself as an 'easy' option is bound to be a success for a while. Experience has shown that dieting alone will not usually result in permanent weight loss and in most cases only exercise combined with a nutritionally balanced diet will help to establish permanent results. But these results take time and there will always be an element of the population who do not wish to wait!

However, the VLCD boom aside, the appeal for the traditional meal replacement products has always been to the serious slimmers. This category is almost entirely women in the upper middle income group, and with the shift now towards better consumer information, better eating habits, and the keep fit influence, this market area is likely to decline in future years.

In today's market-place many *reduced-calorie* products already exist, including calorie-controlled meals, canned fruit, diet beverages, salad dressings, puddings, syrups, jams, jellies, snacks and so forth. This market is highly innovative in its methods of low-calorie alternative to traditional products.

Reduced-calorie foods can be produced by such techniques as portion control, increased water content, decreased fat content,

increased volume due to air incorporation, separation and reforma-
tion technology, addition of bulking ingredients such as fibre and a
decrease or substitution of sweetness; but, despite any elements of
'technological wizardry', reduced-calorie products form an extremely
large and buoyant market, estimated to be worth well over £300m in
1986 (Table 2).

TABLE 2
UK Markets for Low-Calorie Foods

Calorie-reduced foods	£m RSP
Soft drinks	130
Yellow fat spreads[a]	50
Bread and rolls	35
Ready meals	20
Other canned/frozen food	15
Breakfast cereals	10
Soups	10
Salad dressings	8
Jam	2
Artificial sweeteners	20
	300

[a]Excludes Flora, which is high in polyunsaturates but is not low-fat.
Source: Mintel, KAE.

The low-calorie soup market has grown steadily; today it is estimated at about £11m. Low-calorie, high-nutrition breakfast cereals
are also booming in the UK along with the more 'fibre-full' types of
museli and bran products. Frozen low-calorie convenience meals is
another growing sector. In the late 1970s both Findus and Weight
Watchers had a line of frozen calorie-counted meals which after
initial success began to decline, despite the fact that the overall frozen
ready-meal market was growing. Then, in 1984, Findus launched
'Lean Cuisine' acquired from its sister company, Stouffers, and that
brand grew to an estimated £10m after only nine months of sale.
'Lean Cuisine' was designed to appeal to the mass market, and had
low fat, low sugar, few preservatives, and only 300 calories per
serving.

Other companies such as Bird's Eye have followed suit. A definite
advantage of these tasty products is that they appeal not only to

slimmers, but also to other members of the family. The growth of chilled, reduced-calorie, ready meals is one which we have seen in the last few years. Own label brands such as Marks & Spencer and Waitrose have been leading influences here both in quality and in taste—picking up on the consumers' interest in fewer preservatives, and more 'natural' foods.

A rapid growth in low-calorie soft drinks in the past few years indicates not only a strong market for slimming drinks, but the generally increased health consciousness among soft drink consumers. The market's growth also indicates an appreciation for the improved flavour of such products since the introduction of 'aspartame'. The marketing and advertising of these products now tend to concentrate on taste and general fitness and health, rather than on the slimming aspect. A by-product of both these trends—increased health consciousness and improved product taste—is that the traditional summer peak in soft drink sales is lessening as the products are now increasingly bought for the whole family, for health reasons, for more year-round consumption.

The lower-calorie trend has become so apparent that even British Caledonia plans to offer its passengers the option of low-calorie menus. These menus will average one-half the calories of normal airline meals. (Available only in first or super executive classes of course.) In the USA, even low-calorie pizzas are now available!

The final type of 'low-calorie' foods are those which are inherently so—some vegetables, fruits, skimmed milk, cottage cheese, breads, potatoes, pasta, etc.—all of which, when eaten in moderation, are good for you, and are low in calories, or are perceived to be so . . . which in today's market, is the same thing. The two products most sold in the UK today are low-fat liquid milk (£315m in 1985) and yogurt (£165m in 1985). However, the UK still has a way to go. In France for instance 63% of all milk sales go into low-fat milk compared with only 8% in the UK! (See Table 3.)

The consumer's perceptions of foods as naturally low in calories are partially directed by the knowledge given out through the media, health education magazines, and the changing perceptions in the health area generally. Years ago, family doctors told slimmers to cut out bread and potatoes, whereas nowadays the advice is that these two items should be the *last* to go!

Consumers are bombarded with information of all types through diet books, marketing people, and even manufacturers. Another

TABLE 3
UK Market for Low-Calorie Foods

Inherently low-calorie foods (frequently used by slimmers)	£m RSP
Skimmed milk	320
Yogurt	165
Cottage cheese	30
	515

Source: Mintel, KAE.

perception which often influences their outlook, is whether a certain food looks 'fresh'. Putting items into the chilled food cabinets in supermarkets is an easy way for communicating the idea that a product is 'fresh' and therefore, in the consumer's eyes, more natural.

According to a report by Findus, nearly three-quarters of British adults are concerned about what they eat—both for the ingredients of processed food and for their effects on the body—and that consumers are developing a growing liking for tastes and textures that are natural. Foods naturally low in calories and low-in-calorie alternatives will continue to grow in popularity—particularly if manufacturers continue with new product development to improve the range and quality of products on offer.

To further develop low-calorie foods *and* to have those products successful in the market-place, a new product must equal or surpass the expected sensory properties of the food it imitates and therein lies the challenge for food technologists today.

2

Low-Calorie Soft Drinks

H. W. HOUGHTON

Schweppes International Ltd, London, UK

ABSTRACT

Low-calorie foods are usually analogues with half the calories of the more fattening regular products. Soft drinks are unique in that their low-calorie versions have almost no calories at all. Since there are no problems of bulk and texture they can be made by simply substituting the sugar by an intense sweetener. While saccharin was the only permitted sweetener in the UK and North America, their flavour was inferior and sales were a small percentage of the total soft drink sales. With the advent of aspartame the low-calorie sector has increased rapidly, now approaching a fifth of the total market for soft drinks.

In most countries soft drinks must be made only with sugars as the sweetening agent. Currently in the UK regular soft drinks must contain a certain minimum of sugar and the required sweetness can be made up with intense sweeteners. Mostly, low-calorie soft drinks are made without sugar, but the regulations allow small quantities, which can help the flavour.

The intense sweeteners used in soft drinks are saccharin, cyclamate, aspartame and acesulfame. Attempts to use others like neohesperidin, thaumatin and stevioside have failed. New sweeteners with promise are sucralose and alitame. Sweeteners can be employed on their own, and are done so for commercial reasons or because of legal restrictions. Technically a combination of sweeteners is best to give better flavour and greater stability, to reduce the potential daily intake of the population in calculations concerning the Acceptable Daily Intake (ADI), and not least for the undoubted benefits of synergy.

H. W. Houghton

INTRODUCTION

Most low-calorie foods are better designated as reduced-calorie since technically the food cannot be formulated or processed without some ingredients that yield calories. Soft drinks are unique in that their low-calorie versions have almost no calories at all. This allows the manufacturers to make such eye-catching claims as 'only 1 calorie per can'. They are easily made, the sugar is removed from the formulation and replaced by an intense sweetener. Some subtlety in re-formulation is required as I shall show later. When saccharin was the only permitted sweetener in the UK and North America the flavour was inferior to the sugar version and customers took their low-calorie soft drinks somewhat as a penance, part of the ethos of suffering deprivation when dieting. Sales were proportionately low, only about 4% of the total soft drinks market. With the advent of aspartame the low-calorie sector has increased rapidly. In the UK, regulations permitting the use of aspartame came into force in 1983 and from then up to 1986 sales volumes increased at a rate of 36% each year.

Table 1 shows the increase of aspartame used in soft drinks in the USA. Up until 1984 there was also an increase in usage of saccharin as most manufacturers were using the aspartame–saccharin mixture. The figures for 1985 show the change to all-aspartame formulations.

TABLE 1

USA: Changes in Sweeteners in Soft Drinks

			Sweetness equivalent to sugar	
Year	*Sugar*	*Fructose corn syrup*	*Saccharin*	*Aspartame*
		(kg per capita per annum)		
1975	10·8	2·3	2·7	0
1980	8·8	8·7	3·5	0
1981	7·6	10·5	3·6	0·1
1982	6·4	12·1	3·8	0·5
1983	4·8	13·9	4·3	1·6
1984	3·6	16·5	4·5	2·6
1985	1·3	19·7	2·7	5·0

Source: US Department of Agriculture.

These figures show that, currently, low-calorie drinks represent 27% of the volume of total soft drinks and some market analysts are forecasting 50% in the early 1990s. This table also shows another revolution in the American soft drinks industry, the almost complete removal of sucrose and its replacement by fructose corn syrup.

SOFT DRINK FORMULATIONS

The regulations for most countries only permit the use of sugar or carbohydrates in the standard soft drinks, but in the UK they may be sweetened with mixtures of carbohydrate and intense sweetener. Table 2 shows the formulation for a standard soft drink. Lemonade is the well-known clear, colourless drink and shares with cola the top-selling position in carbonated drinks. This is a typical formula but it does not represent any particular brand. It is sweetened with a mixture of sugar and saccharin. Since the regulations permit not more than 80 mg saccharin per litre, the saccharin content of 70 mg/litre in this formula is about the practical maximum. It is acidified to pH 2·6 with citric acid, the lemon flavouring is an alcoholic extract of essential oil of lemon and the three volumes of carbon dioxide are

TABLE 2
Lemonade

Ingredient	Standard	Low-calorie
Sugar kg/100 litres	7	0
Saccharin kg/100 litres	0·007	0·011
Aspartame kg/100 litres	–	0·017
Citric acid kg/100 litres	0·22	0·26
Sodium citrate kg/100 litres	–	0·05
pH	2·6	3·2
Lemon flavouring	+	+
Benzoic acid kg/100 litres	–	0·015
Carbon dioxide volumes	3·0	3·0
Calories per 100 ml	27	0·4

sufficient to preserve it from growth of yeast or mould, as well as providing the attractive sparkle.

The calorie count of 27/100 ml (kilocalories) is quite modest when compared to lager at 30, skimmed milk at 33, orange juice at 40 and low-fat yogurt at 60. Of course, we must also take into account the portion size. After drinking 100 ml of lemonade you are quite ready to drink another 100 ml and possibly even a third 100 ml. Whereas after 100 g of low-fat yogurt you have had quite enough.

The low-calorie lemonade is sweetened with a mixture of saccharin and aspartame and the quantities are designed so that each contributes about 50% of the sweetness. This should give the greatest synergy. To reduce the rate of hydrolysis of aspartame and consequent loss of sweetness we move the pH up to 3·2 by adding sodium citrate buffer. Then the citric acid must be increased to maintain the proper acid flavour. Because of the change in pH the product is more liable to spoilage so it must be preserved not only with carbon dioxide but with some benzoic acid as well. Bacteriological principles say that if you must use preservative then you must always use an adequate amount so this recipe has 150 mg/litre, the regulatory limit being 160 mg/litre. There are virtually no calories in this drink.

REGULATIONS

Table 3 shows the salient regulations that govern low-calorie soft drinks. The figure of 5·3 calories per 100 ml is derived from the 1964 regulations where it is stated as 1·5 calories per fluid ounce. Note the distinction between low-calorie and diabetic soft drinks. A drink with 50% orange juice would contain about 6% sugar and have 20 calories per 100 ml, but it could still be called a diabetic drink provided no cane or beet sugar was added.

Since 'low-calorie' is a recognised legal name it is not a slimming claim according to the labelling regulations; but most of us have a trade mark which constitutes a claim, for example 'Slimline' or 'Diet Coke', so the drink must be labelled with the standard energy statement in kilojoules and kilocalories per 100 ml. Nobody understands these figures so most of us helpfully put somewhere else on the label the actual amount of calories in the container. We must also put in the statement about the controlled diet.

The Americans have diet beverages or sugar-free beverages and

TABLE 3
Soft Drink Regulations: Low-Calorie

Soft Drink Regulations 1964

Low-calorie: contain not more than 5·3 kcal per 100 ml
no limitation on saccharin

Diabetic: contain no added sugar
no limitation on saccharin

Food Labelling Regulations 1984

Low-calorie is not a 'slimming claim'

'Slimming claims': mark with prescribed energy statement, i.e. less
than 50 kJ (12 kcal) per 100 ml
statement: 'can help slimming or weight control
only as part of a controlled diet'

Code of Federal Regulations 1986

Diet beverage or sugar-free beverage
—not more than 20·2 kcal per 100 ml
—declare presence of non-nutritive sweetener
—complete nutrition panel
—for saccharin declare: 'use of this product may be hazardous to your
health, this product contains saccharin which has been determined to
cause cancer in laboratory animals'
—for aspartame declare: 'phenylketonurics: contains phenylalanine'

---

their regulations are more elaborate: the complete nutrition panel means stating not only the calorie and carbohydrate content but also the fact that it contains no protein, no fat and less than 2% of the US Recommended Daily Allowance of a whole series of vitamins and minerals. There are also the warning labels about saccharin and aspartame. Removal of the long warning statement on saccharin was one of the factors (as well as commercial pressures) that caused a great part of the American low-calorie products to be reformulated solely with aspartame.

Table 4 shows the intense sweeteners that are available to us. Of the large number that have been tested and commercially launched, only four are currently being used in soft drinks. You will hear more later about acesulfame and aspartame, cyclamate is still used in many

TABLE 4
Intense Sweeteners

	UK CoT	JECFA and SCF max. ADI (mg/kg)
Acesulfame K	A	9
Aspartame	A	40
Cyclamate	B	11
Saccharin	B	2·5 (T)
Thaumatin	A	(T)
Miraculin	X	X
Monellin	X	X
Neohesperidin	X	X
Stevioside	X	X
Alitame		
Sucralose		

A = Substances that the available evidence suggests are acceptable for use in food.
B = Substances that on the available evidence may be regarded meanwhile as provisionally acceptable for use in food, but about which further information must be made available within a specified time for review.
(T) = A temporary ADI.
X = Not assessed or not given an ADI.

countries (though not in the UK or USA) and saccharin remains the most commonly used sweetener.

The Committee on Toxicity in the DHSS has given its approval to all of these and so has the Joint Expert Committee on Food Additives of the World Health Organization and the Scientific Committee for Food of the EEC. The approval of saccharin is temporary as the two committees are waiting to hear the results of further studies currently underway in the USA.

The next five sweeteners on the list are not technically suitable for soft drinks: thaumatin is better as a flavour enhancer. Miraculin and Monellin are extracts of the miracle berry and serendipity bush grown in Africa; they have no safety status. Neohesperidin is a chemical derivative of naringin extracted from grapefruit peels; it is only permitted in Belgium. Stevioside is an extract of the Paraguayan shrub and permitted in Japan. Alitame and sucralose are presently being assessed for safety before they receive permission for use and a commercial launch.

SYNERGY

When an intense sweetener is used alone its disadvantages show up unfavourably, for example the thin flavour and bitter after-taste in saccharin and the long-term instability of aspartame. In combination these disadvantages are reduced; there is a useful increase in both the sweetening power and the quality of the sweetness. It is important when talking about sweetening power to specify the sweetness level at which it is to be used and not the sweetening power at the threshold of taste, which is often quoted in brochures but is quite useless for calculation.

TABLE 5
Sweetening Power

Sucrose (%)	Sweetening power	
	Saccharin	Cyclamate
2	500×	40×
5	360×	36×
10	330×	33×
15	300×	27×
20	200×	24×

Table 5 shows the variation of sweetening power with the sweetness level calculated in percentage sucrose. For soft drinks it is best to use a sweetness level of 10% sucrose as most soft drinks are formulated around that mark. Using these principles Table 6 shows the sweetness formulation of a cola drink. This is not a cola drink found in the UK. The standard formula contains 11·4 kilograms sugar per 100 litres. The low-calorie version contains aspartame and saccharin. Using the standard sweetening power factors this drink has an equivalent sugar content of only 9 kilograms per 100 litres. In my experience that difference is due to synergy.

Table 7 shows the sweeteners in two orange drinks once formulated for neighbouring countries in Northern Europe having different

TABLE 6
Synergy in Sweeteners: A Cola Drink

		Sugar equivalent (kg/100 litres)
All-sugar formula:		
Sugar	=	11·4
Aspartame–saccharin formula:		
Aspartame 0·024 kg × 200	=	4·88
Saccharin 0·013 kg × 330	=	4·13
		9·0

TABLE 7
Synergy in Sweeteners: Two Orange Drinks

		Sugar equivalent (kg/100 litres)
First orange drink:		
Sugar 1·2 kg × 1	=	1·2
Saccharin 0·019 kg × 330	=	6·3
		7·5
Second orange drink:		
Sugar 1·2 kg × 1	=	1·2
Sorbitol 2·5 kg × 0·6	=	1·5
Saccharin 0·0047 kg × 330	=	1·6
Cyclamic acid 0·044 kg × 33	=	1·5
		5·8

regulations on sweeteners. The sugar–saccharin mixture gives an equivalent of 7·5 kg/100 litres. The second formulation includes sorbitol to improve 'mouthfeel' and the intense sweeteners are a combination of saccharin and cyclamate, 10 parts of cyclamate to 1 of saccharin giving a mixture of equal sweetness power. The sugar equivalent of only 5·8 shows there must be a very large contribution from synergy.

Laboratory tests can be more closely controlled with expert taste panels determining sweetness levels. Table 8 shows four variations of

TABLE 8
Synergy in Sweeteners: Laboratory Variations of an Orange Drink

	Sugar equivalent (kg/100 litres)
The all-sugar version:	
Sugar from fruit	0·6
Added sugar	10·5
	11·1
Cyclamate only:	
Sugar from fruit	0·6
Cyclamic acid 0·34 kg × 33 =	11·3
	11·9
Saccharin only:	
Sugar from fruit	0·6
Saccharin 0·032 kg × 330 =	10·5
	11·1
Cyclamate and saccharin:	
Sugar from fruit	0·6
Cyclamate 0·098 kg × 33 =	3·2
Saccharin 0·0084 kg × 330 =	2·8
	6·6

an orange drink; the first three have a single sweetener, namely sugar, cyclamate or saccharin. They are made up to give equal sweetness and the sugar equivalent confirms this. When cyclamate and saccharin are mixed, each to contribute about 50% of the sweetening power, the lower sugar equivalent shows the contribution due to synergy.

NEW INTENSE SWEETENERS

Alitame, being developed by Pfizer, and sucralose, being developed by Tate and Lyle in conjunction with Johnson and Johnson, are new intense sweeteners which we may use in years to come. Alitame is a dipeptide, aspartyl alanine, and it has the novel thietanyl amine attached (note its chemical similarity to aspartame which is aspartyl phenylalanine). It is very sweet so usage rates are going to be satisfactorily small and it is said to be more stable than aspartame. Currently the toxicological studies are under review by the Food and Drugs Agency in the USA.

Sucralose is chlorinated sucrose. It has a good-quality flavour and there is no question of its stability. Currently the toxicological studies are being reviewed by the Committee on Toxicity and the Food and Drugs Agency. Tate and Lyle have announced the sweetener to be

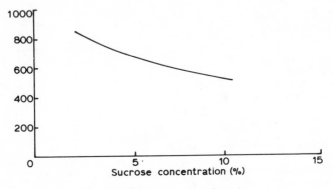

Fig. 1. Sucralose: sweetness intensity.

600 times more powerful than sugar but as Fig. 1 shows, its sweetening power is only 500× at the 10% sugar level and this seems the best level to use when formulating soft drinks. Table 9 shows a comparison of aspartame and sucralose formulated in a low-calorie tonic water. Much less sucralose is required and the formulation is simpler. The taste tests were done by an in-house expert panel and clearly the formulator had done his work well since he managed to get the flavour of both formulations identical. However, after six months the stability of the sucralose shows through and it is preferred.

Table 10 shows a similar study using a low-calorie orange drink and again the product development technologist has correctly formulated his products to give equivalently tasting drinks. In this case the loss of sweetness with aspartame is much more apparent and there is a very significant preference for the sucralose formulation after six months.

The advantages of using several sweeteners in a soft drink are not understood by the customer. She tends to count the number of

TABLE 9
Sucralose: Low-Calorie Orange Drink: Preference Results (%) using
Taste Panel

	Sugar equivalent (%)	*Taste panel preference (%)*	
		After manufacture	*After 6 months*
Aspartame:			
0·069 kg/100 litres × 200 = 13·8		33	10
Sucralose:			
0·028 kg/100 litres × 500 = 14·0		37	77
No preference		30	13

TABLE 10
Sucralose: Low-Calorie Tonic Water: Preference Results (%) using
Taste Panel

	Sugar equivalent (%)	*Taste panel preference (%)*	
		After manufacture	*After 6 months*
Aspartame:			
0·0425 kg/100 litres × 200 = 8·5		47	27
Sucralose:			
0·0162 kg/100 litres × 500 = 8·1		47	57
No preference		6	17

additives listed on the label and reject the product with the largest number even though, as I have shown, the total quantity of additive will be smaller. Government legislators are also prone to this misconception and want to reduce the number of permitted additives. Safety in terms of the concept of an Acceptable Daily Intake for each additive is best served by using a large number of additives in small quantities.

3

Use of Hydrocolloids in the Design of Low-Calorie Foods

J. E. TRUDSØ

The Copenhagen Pectin Factory Ltd, Lille Skensved, Denmark

ABSTRACT

Employing eating habits in Denmark as the example, problems and opportunities in the manufacture and marketing of low-calorie food products (from the point of view of food manufacturers) are identified and discussed with special attention to the use of pectin and carrageenan. The food products which require a revised product strategy by the food industry are dairy products, processed meat products, confectionery products, and products based on vegetable fat and butter. At the same time consumers must reduce their consumption of, especially, fresh red meat and refined sugar.

Examples of low-calorie food products incorporating pectin are low-calorie soft drinks, low-sugar jams and jellies; examples incorporating carrageenan are no-sugar jams and jellies, low-sugar confectionery, no-fat milk and low-fat processed meat products.

INTRODUCTION

In this paper, the term 'low-calorie' is treated as a relative term, since it does not make sense to describe, for instance, jams with 50% sugar or processed meat with 10% fat as 'low-calorie foods', unless you compare these to jams containing 65% sugar, or processed meat products with 30% fat, respectively.

With respect to hydrocolloids, which are—or may be—used for low-calorie food products, those manufactured by A/S Københavns

23

Pektinfabrik, viz. pectin and carrageenan, are selected for primary discussion.

THE DIETETIC BALANCE IN DENMARK

One may use statistics in many ways, for example as follows:

The average Danish male marries at the age of 26, and dies at the age of 72, whereas the average Danish female marries at the age of 22, and dies at the age of 78. Thus the average Danish female is 'programmed' to spend the last ten years of her life as a widow, because her husband has adopted some terrible eating habits and gets inadequate exercise.

To substantiate the unhealthy eating habits of the Danes, Table 1 lists the consumption of fat, sugar and alcohol.[1-5] Fat consumption has shown an increasing trend up to 1981, and it seems that the Danes are now gradually decreasing fat intake. However, fat still provides the Danes with around 57% of their required energy consumption, or more than twice the recommended amount. The consumption of both refined sugar and total sugar shows a decreasing trend, the total sugar intake being presently around 40 kg per capita, which is 80% more than recommended. Tables 2 and 3 list the food products primarily responsible for the fat and sugar intake of Danes.[6, 7]

Fresh milk products, fresh meat, vegetable fat and butter provide the Danes with 85% of their fat intake and should be the major items for decreased consumption or for change to lower-fat alternatives. However, processed meat products must also be brought into focus, especially since most manufacturers of meat products are increasing their processing level.

If all processed food products were without sugar, the sugar intake coming from fruit, juices and refined sugar would contribute around 8% of our daily energy need, which is close to the recommended 10%. On the other hand, if consumers stopped using refined sugar, fruit and juices would contribute 2% and processed food products 11% of our daily energy need. Thus, in order to reach an acceptable intake of sugar, the consumer will have to cut down on the use of refined sugar, and the food manufacturers will have to develop alternative products with reduced or no sugar content.

TABLE 1
Eating Habits each Year

Year	Consumption in kg/capita/year		
	Fat	Sugar	Alcohol
1970	58		6·6
1975	56	14	9·1
1981	66	13	9·6
1985	56	13	10·0

TABLE 2
Fat Intake from Foods

Food product	Consumption (kg/capita)	Fat content (%)	Fat (kg/capita)	% of fat consumption
Milk	131·2	3·5	4·6	8·2
Fresh red meat	29·0	20·0	5·8	10·4
Fresh poultry	7·4	10·0	0·7	1·3
Processed meat	34·7	25·0	8·7	15·5
Eggs	12·3	15·0	1·8	3·2
Vegetable fat	13·3	80·0	10·6	18·9
Butter	6·1	80·0	4·9	8·8
Cheese	9·4	15·0	1·4	2·5
Ice-cream	9·3	10·0	0·9	1·6
Cakes	9·4	30·0	2·8	5·0

TABLE 3
Sugar Intake from Foods

Food product	Consumption (kg/capita)	Sugar content (%)	Sugar (kg/capita)	% of sugar consumption
Jams	3·3	50·0	1·7	4·3
Confectionery	3·6	80·0	2·9	7·3
Ice-cream	9·3	15·0	1·4	3·5
Cakes	9·4	40·0	3·8	9·5
Fresh fruit	27·0	10·0	2·7	6·8
Fruit juices	14·5	10·0	1·5	3·8
Sugar	12·9	100·0	12·9	32·3
Soft drinks	55·0	10·0	5·5	13·8

PROBLEMS/OPPORTUNITIES

The manufacture of low-calorie foods involves a number of technical and economical problems, but certainly also a number of opportunities (Table 4). Since the major part of fat and sugar comes from products manufactured by the consumer, the food industry can solve only part of the dietetic problem by providing consumers with processed food products of a better nutritional composition. However, various attempts made by food manufacturers to market, in particular, products with a lower fat content have failed because consumers are not prepared to pay more for low-fat products than for their high-fat counterparts.

TABLE 4
Problems and Opportunities with Foods

Problems	Opportunities
Fat intake primarily comes from in-home preparation	Consumer awareness
	Processed fruit
A large part of sugar intake comes from in-home preparation	Dairy products
	Processed meat products
Food additives	Confectionery products
Legislation	Soft drinks
Substitute for fat	Hydrocolloids
Substitute for sugar	Vegetable fat
Consumer attitude	
Shelf life	

SUGGESTIONS

When removing fat and sugar from food products, the food manufacturer is faced with a number of technical and economic problems, some of which are:

Consistency/texture: Mouthfeel decreases when sugar is removed.
Spreadability decreases when fat is removed.
Mouthfeel decreases when fat is removed.

Taste: Sweetness decreases when sugar is removed.
                        Overall taste is altered when fat is removed.

Cost: Substitutes used for sugar and fat are more
                        expensive.

Legislation: Changes may require legislative
                        amendments.

Hydrocolloids like pectin and carrageenan are characterised by being able to impart consistency and texture to the water phase of food products, provided that the composition and processing of the food product are such as to provide these polysaccharides with proper conditions under which to perform. Both products have the property of increasing mouthfeel and pectin is already being used to restore the mouthfeel lost in artificially sweetened soft drinks when sugar is removed. Similarly, carrageenan has the property of increasing the mouthfeel of skim milk to a point where skim milk—from a mouthfeel point of view—resembles whole milk.

Presently, the consumption of soft drinks in Denmark is around 55 litres per capita, which represents a sugar consumption of 5–6 kg per year, or roughly 10% of the total sugar intake, whereas the consumption of low-calorie soft drinks, although increasing rapidly, is only 3 litres per capita.

It is relatively easy to convert soft drinks into low-calorie or indeed into no-calorie alternatives, because sugar acts primarily as a sweetener. It is more difficult to substitute sugar when sugar is also preventing bacteriological growth, as in jams and confectionery products. With respect to jams, practically all consumed in Denmark today contain less than 55% sugar, which has been possible only through the development of low-ester pectins and the use of preservatives. With low-ester pectin alone, it is still not possible to decrease the sugar content to less than 30%, so in cases where consumers demand 'no added sugar' preserves, other gelling agents are required. Such a gelling agent could be carrageenan, which is used today in artificially sweetened jams and jellies.

In confectionery products the sugar content is 80% or higher and, apart from providing sweetness and microbiological stability, sugar imparts consistency and texture. In low-pH confectionery, pectin and carrageenan may be used, especially when new confectionery concepts are introduced. By way of example, well-known table jellies or dessert jellies are marketed today in Japan as a new type of confectionery, where the sterilised jellies made with carrageenan are sold in units of 10–20 g. Furthermore, this product is packed in a laminate, which prevents it from drying out during storage.

The physical stability of confectionery products is largely dependent on the soluble solids content, and a decrease in the sugar level will demand other types of packaging material and the use of preservatives. However, many confectionery products have pH values at which food-approved preservatives have limited or no effect, and such products cannot be produced until a no-sugar soluble solid has been developed. One could in this context think of various hydrolysed proteins, but these would be significantly more expensive than sugar.

In ice-cream, sugars contribute with sweetness but what is perhaps more important, sugars decrease the freezing point of the mix, thus making the ice-cream 'spoonable' at freezing temperature. Again, a non-sugar soluble solid would be required to reduce or eliminate sugars in ice-cream.

The consumption of fresh milk (whole, low-fat, and skim) shows a decreasing trend, primarily caused by the removal of subsidies. Particularly, the consumption of whole milk has been negatively affected, whereas the consumption of low-fat milk is increasing. The price of milk is correlated to the fat content, and with the removal of subsidies, the consumers have, on the one hand, not increased their expenditure on milk and, on the other hand, changed to a cheaper product, low-fat milk. The consumption of skim milk has hardly been affected by the removal of subsidies, showing a steady but very small increase in consumption. Undoubtedly, skim milk is not a competitive product compared to whole or low-fat milk, because it is too different in taste and appearance.

At low shear rates (200–600 s^{-1}) and at high shear rates (1300–2700 s^{-1}) low-fat and skim milk show identical viscosities; 3·36 cP at low shear rates and 2·85 cP at high shear rates. Whole milk on the other hand shows higher viscosities; 3·84 cP at low shear rates and 3·12 cP at high shear rates. Differences in viscosity are consequently not the primary indicator of differences in mouthfeel. Using our laboratory staff as a taste panel it was indicated that 0·02–0·03% kappa-carrageenan in skim milk from a mouthfeel point of view could pass as low-fat or whole milk, but not with respect to taste and appearance. Thus, further development work is needed.

Processed meat products are often used as outlets for the excess fat removed from fresh cuts, and from an economic point of view this is necessary if all of the animal is to be used for human consumption. However, it does mean that some of these products contain 40% fat and even more. Typically, the high-fat processed meat products marketed in Denmark are pâtés, liver pastes, and various kinds of sausages. In the past many attempts have been made to produce and market low-fat versions of these, but never with any success, either because of an unacceptable texture or because of unwillingness on the part of the consumer to pay the increased price.

It is essential that the producers realise that before the lower-fat concept can be marketed effectively, the product must fulfil the two most important criteria for purchase:

—It must taste nice, and taste includes appearance and consistency.
—The price must be close to its corresponding high-fat product.

All attempts, of which I am aware, to market low-fat meat products in Denmark have employed lean meat as substitute for fat, which in many cases has led to unacceptable consistencies and in all cases to products that became priced at levels which the consumers were not willing to pay.

Fat ensures a sliceable or spreadable texture, whereas lean meat provides a rigid (firm) texture which crumbles when you try to spread it, and increasing the meat consumption is hardly in line with a strategy of improving the dietetic balance. Fat is cheap, with a price of around one-tenth of the price of lean meat. In fact, there are only two raw materials that are effectively able to compete with fat, namely water and air.

In pâtés, liver pastes, and slicing sausages, where the fat level has been reduced from 30% to 10% and substituted with water, carrageenan in combination with locust bean gum and guar gum has proved effective in imparting sliceability and spreadability previously provided by fat and, through adjustments in spicing, products with excellent tastes have been made. The costs of producing these low-fat alternatives are slightly lower than those of the regular ones, but still a number of problems remain. With the increased water content, shelf life must be expected to be shorter, especially if the low-fat concept is widened to include low salt, no nitrite and no preservatives. It is perhaps necessary to market low-fat processed meat products in smaller units, for instance in portion packs.

Food legislation may stipulate minimum fat content, maximum water content or minimum protein content; however, legislation is always related to technological justifications of which there are plenty in low-fat meat products.

Consumer attitudes may be stronger against food additives than against fat. Finally, whether you discuss reduction of sugar, reduction of milk fat, or reduction of meat fat, you will end up with mountains of sugar and fat. Within the EEC we are already blessed with a butter mountain, and since the common agricultural policy in the EEC is to maintain planned economy, low-sugar and low-fat products would create further mountains. In addition to this, farmers and co-ops, traditionally representing a strong political factor in Denmark, would probably not welcome a situation in which major parts of their production could no longer be sold.

Still, if low-calorie products have any bearing whatsoever, the industry cannot avoid looking at the products that truly represent calorie problems, and in Denmark leaders in the agricultural sector all agree that product development is a must, if the sector is to survive. Perhaps it is time for this sector to revise its product strategy to include products with lower sugar and lower fat.

REFERENCES

1. 1984 *FAO Production Yearbook, Vol. 38* (1985). Food and Agriculture Organization of the United Nations, Rome.
2. Danmarks Statistik (The Danish Central Statistical Office) (1981). *Statistisk Tiårsoversigt 1981, Vol. 22*, Danmarks Statistik, Copenhagen.
3. Danmarks Statistik (1986). *Statistisk Tiårsoversigt 1986, Vol. 27*, Danmarks Statistik, Copenhagen.
4. *Nordisk Statistisk Årsbok 1978, Vol. 18 (The Nordic Statistical Office Yearbook)*, edited by Nordiska Statistiska Sekretariatet. Published by Nordiske Rådet (The Nordic Council) and Nordiska Statistiska Sekretariatet.
5. *Nordisk Statistisk Årsbok 1985, Vol. 24*, edited by Nordiska Statistiska Sekretariatet. Published by Nordiska Rådet and Nordiska Statistiska Sekretariatet.
6. Danmarks Statistik (1985). Statistiske Efterretninger (Statistical Intelligence), *Indkomst, Forbrug og Priser 1985:12 (Income, Consumption, and Prices) Vol. 3*.
7. Okholm, Lars (1986). *Fedt Nok!* Stavanger.

4

Technical Problems in the Development of Low-Calorie Dairy Products

R. A. WILBEY

*Department of Food Science and Technology,
University of Reading, UK*

ABSTRACT

Milk and milk products form a significant part of the diet. Greater awareness of the possible effects of diet on health has led to increased demand for low-calorie products. The dairy industry has sought to develop products with similar organoleptic properties to the traditional products, mainly by reducing the fat content and (where possible) increasing the moisture content.

With liquid milk there has been a growing market for semi-skimmed and skimmed milks, which has given rise to some packaging problems. A more radical approach, however, was needed to overcome the problems of producing low-fat dairy spreads where a water-in-oil emulsion was needed using only 40% fat, half that of butter. The processing technology used in the manufacture of these products has broken away from the traditional buttermaking technology.

The demand for low-fat and low-calorie cheeses has been met in a number of ways. The more overt use of high moisture may be seen in the low-fat cottage cheeses. Reduced-fat analogues of the more popular hard cheeses, e.g. Cheddar, Cheshire and Edam, have been produced, based on traditional cheesemaking technology, where the reduction of the fat protein level has led to textural problems.

The higher moisture levels in many of the low-calorie dairy products have led to greater potential susceptibility to microbiological spoilage. This in turn has led to further improvements in processing and packaging standards. The handling of the product in the distribution and retail chain must be complemented by correct storage and use by the consumer.

31

INTRODUCTION

The relatively high cost of milkfat has, for some time, provided the
dairy industry with an incentive to market reduced-fat products. This
sector of the dairy market has increased considerably as a result of
greater consumer demand for low-fat products, following the pub-
licity given to recent reports on the British diet. In the COMA (1984)
report for instance,[4] it was recommended that the contribution of fat
be reduced to 35% of total energy, with saturated fat providing not
more than 15% of total energy. (This corresponds to an average of
43% saturated fatty acids in the dietary fat compared to approximately 60% in milkfat.)

LIQUID MILK

In the UK, most of the liquid milk sold is pasteurised but not homogenised. Standardisation of domestic milk is not permitted, so the fat
content will vary with source and season. The degree of separation of
the cream in the bottle to give a 'cream line' is a traditional though
erroneous consumer measure of quality. This error arises because the
creaming effect is not just a function of fat content but is also
dependent on fat globule size and the thermal history of the milk.
Heat treatment denatures the agglutinins which promote agglomeration of fat globules, so that small increases in pasteurisation temperature can result in a significant decrease in the rate of cream separation
in the bottle.

This traditional view of milk quality is being overtaken by demands
for milks with lower fat contents. Skimmed milk has been available
for some time but, with its very low fat content (max. 0·3%), the taste
has little body and appears to be watery when compared to whole
milk. Semi-skimmed milk with 1·5–1·8% milkfat has offered a compromise that is becoming increasingly popular, as illustrated in
Fig. 1.

Though the sales of low-fat milks are rising rapidly the sales are still
below those of many of our European neighbours, as illustrated in
Fig. 2.

An alternative approach to the formulation of low-fat milks has
been to compensate for the lower fat content by increasing the level
of milk-solids-not-fat (MSNF). This further reduces the proportion

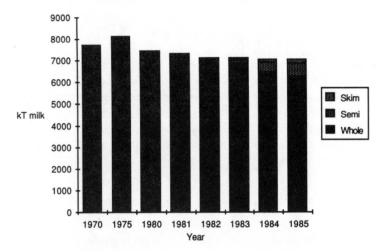

FIG. 1. Liquid milk sales to the UK domestic market.[8,9]

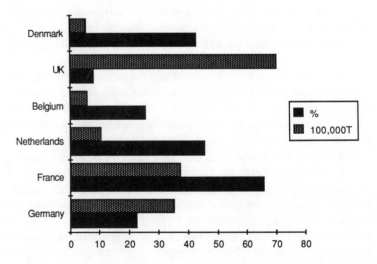

FIG. 2. Sales of liquid milk by dairies to domestic markets, and the percentage of these markets taken by semi-skimmed milk.[9]

TABLE 1
Comparison of Typical Compositions of Milks on the UK Market

Component	% w/w	kJ/ 100 g	kcal/ 100 g	% energy from fat
Whole milk				
Fat	3·8			
Protein	3·4			
Carbohydrate	4·6	272	65	53
Semi-skimmed milk				
Fat	1·6			
Protein	3·4			
Carbohydrate	4·6	189	45	32
Skimmed milk				
Fat	0·1			
Protein	3·4			
Carbohydrate	4·6	132	32	3
St Ivel 'Shape' low-fat milk				
Fat	1			
Protein	3·7			
Carbohydrate	5·3	183	44	21

of energy supplied by the milkfat (see Table 1) and brings the product outside the scope of the current UK regulations.

The effect of the fat on the organoleptic quality may be enhanced by homogenisation. This must be carefully optimised as excessive migration of casein to the fat globules following homogenisation can give rise to dry-tasting milk and reduce the stability in hot acid foods, e.g. coffee.

In assessment of homogenised milk by a trained panel, it was found that an increase in the fat content of 1·5% (i.e. from 3·5% to 5%) was needed before the members could differentiate between the samples two times out of three.[11] For reduced-fat milks the thresholds were lower, 0·3% fat in skimmed milk (with 8·5% MSNF) and 0·8% in fortified skimmed milk (10% MSNF). The comparable threshold for milk-solids-not-fat (MSNF) was 0·5% over a range of fat values. Subsequent investigation[12] indicated that lactose was more important than protein in contributing to the sensory qualities, with threshold values of 0·33% and 2·2% respectively. With untrained panels the sensitivity of discrimination is less developed and results are more variable.[1]

The presence of fat in milk tends to decrease its foaming proper-ties. Reduction of the fat content can lead to foaming problems during the packaging of semi-skimmed and skimmed milks, leading to the use of either vacuum systems or superheated (potable) steam jets to remove the foam. Where possible this should be avoided by careful plant design.

DAIRY SPREADS

Products with primarily a water-in-fat emulsion used for spreading on bread are usually referred to as spreads, irrespective of their spreada-bility. Butter, with over 80% fat (and 99% of its calorific value derived from fat), has been a target for adverse comment. Most butter is now made by continuous churning of cream; mainly sweet cream in the UK and cultured cream in Europe.[17]

In this process the cream is aerated and subjected to shear so that a large proportion of the fat globules are damaged, causing fat to leak out and promote agglomeration of fat globules to form buttergrains. After further agglomeration and drainage, the buttergrains are con-solidated by the action of sugars in the cannon of the buttermaker, and the moisture distribution improved by forcing the butter through orifice plates. Brine may be added to the sweet cream butter during this working to increase the moisture content to the maximum per-mitted and to add salt. The microbiological stability depends on the combination of high salt content in the aqueous phase (approxi-mately 11% w/w, corresponding to an a_w of 0·94;[16] and the small droplet size, ideally $<10\,\mu$m, to inhibit the micro-organisms present. Butters made from ripened cream have a lower pH (typically pH 4·6–5·3) in the aqueous phase.

Reducing the fat below 80% brings the product outside the current legal standards and allows greater scope for product development. Reduction of the fat content will produce a corresponding increase in the aqueous phase. It is not feasible to retain a high salt content in the aqueous phase as the product would taste too salty, though use of a lower pH as in the cultured butters remains an option. The greater quantity of aqueous phase requires a more effective emulsification system, as the probability of coalescence of the droplets is now greater.

Limited reduction of the fat content to approximately 75% by this means has been used in the production of 'Clover' which also has a partial replacement of the milkfat by vegetable fat to improve spreadability and reduce ingredient costs. The emulsification is aided by addition of monoglyceride to the lipid phase, to complement the phospholipid naturally present from the fat globule membrane.

An alternative approach to the addition of emulsifiers to the lipid phase is to reduce the mobility of the aqueous phase. This may be achieved by increasing the viscosity of the aqueous phase or by inducing gelation. Increased levels of milk protein, the addition of stabilisers and gelatin, have been used. Recycling some of the butter-milk protein together with the associated fragments of milkfat globule membrane would improve both the viscosity and surface properties of the aqueous phase. This enriched aqueous phase may then be injected into the butter as it is passed up the buttermaker cannon. This would give a mixture of aqueous phases within the product, varying from the original buttermilk to the added aqueous phase.

An example of this type of product is 'Dane Lite', where the fat has been reduced to 55%, and the protein raised to 4·1%. This protein level corresponds to an average of over 9% in the aqueous phase.

At 55% fat the volume ratio between the lipid phase and the aqueous phase is still favourable to the maintenance of a water-in-oil emulsion, while the calorific value is about two-thirds that of butter, as illustrated in Table 2.

To reach the desired claim of 'half the fat of butter or margarine' the fat level must be reduced to no more than 40%, so that the disperse aqueous phase becomes the largest component. Under these conditions the properties of the aqueous phase become critical in reconciling the organoleptic quality with stability during processing and distribution.

In the simplest system a saline aqueous phase could be dispersed in a lipid phase of fat plus a monoglyceride emulsifier; though these blends have poor taste. Incorporation of milk proteins into the aqueous phase improves the organoleptic characteristics but may give a less stable emulsion since milk proteins, particularly casein, generally favour the formation of oil-in-water emulsions. Micro-biological stability is also decreased.

The destabilising effect of the milk protein addition may be reduced by adding gelatin or other hydrocolloids to the aqueous phase. This addition will ensure that the droplets of aqueous phase are either gelled or have a high viscosity during the final stages of

TABLE 2
Comparison of Compositions of Typical Dairy Spreads

	Component	% w/w	kJ/ 100 g	kcal/ 100 g	% energy from fat
Butter	Fat	81			
	Protein	0·4			
	Carbohydrate	0·7	3 150	753	99
'Clover'	Fat	75			
(Dairy Crest Foods)	Protein	0·8			
	Carbohydrate	1·2	2 853	682	99
'Dane Lite'	Fat	55			
(Butterdane)	Protein	4·1			
	Carbohydrate	1·6	2 160	517	96
'Gold'	Fat	39			
(St Ivel)	Protein	6·5			
	Carbohydrate	2	1 610	385	91

cooling and on chilled storage. This gelation must be readily reversed below body temperature to ensure that a mobile aqueous phase is reformed on the palate since the organoleptic properties of the spread are dependent on breakdown of the emulsion. In this respect the technologist must seek a compromise between emulsion stability, cost and the organoleptic properties. The more stable emulsions with higher levels of gelatin and/or milk protein do run the risk of creating a rather 'tacky' mouthfeel, though this is less of a problem with gelatin where there is a more rapid drop in viscosity on meltdown.

The use of higher protein levels (e.g. 11% in the aqueous phase) has achieved an improved organoleptic quality though at a higher ingredient cost. The first successful dairy low-fat spreads used an aqueous phase based on proteins from fermented buttermilk, the pH was raised from 4·6 to 6·4 and the water binding capacity of the casein increased by the addition of citrate and phosphate. Buttermilk normally contains small quantities of milkfat ($\approx$0·5%) plus fragments of the phospholipid-rich milkfat globule membrane, which would be carried over into the aqueous phase. Byproducts of the fermentation process, e.g. diacetyl, would further contribute to the flavour.

An interesting analogue to this form of aqueous phase was claimed by Wilton *et al.*[18] for an improved product where an oil-in-water emulsion was first formed by dispersing fat and phosphatides in the high viscosity aqueous phase which was then dispersed in the bulk of the fat.

Since the dispersed aqueous phase makes up approximately 57% of the volume of the emulsion, close control of the process is essential to ensure that the final emulsion is substantially water-in-oil. The most common method for preparing the emulsion is by dispersing the aqueous phase in the lipid phase. The emulsion may then be pasteurised, cooled and packed. Scraped surface heat exchangers are preferable for the pasteurisation and essential for the final cooling. The texture of the product may be improved by passing the cooled emulsion through a worker unit.

The high moisture content of low-fat spreads limits the effect of the salt addition. This usually accounts for 2–2·5% of the aqueous phase, corresponding to an a_w of 0·98, and will have a very limited bacteriostatic effect. The relatively coarse emulsion formed in some products can permit some coalescence of the droplets of aqueous phase to take place[2] so that there is less steric hindrance to bacterial growth. Thus much tighter control must be placed on the production, packaging and distribution than for butter and similar high-fat spreads. Mould growth on the surface of the product may occur even at chill distribution temperatures (0–5°C) which are essential for bacteriological stability. This problem may be minimised by a combination of good packing hygiene and the addition of potassium sorbate.

Cost must remain one of the major problems in producing low-fat dairy spreads. Not only is milk a relatively expensive source of ingredients compared to vegetable fats, but the current pricing structure with a subsidy on packet butter introduces a financial penalty for those seeking an 'improvement' on the traditional product. Thus innovation can only be justified financially by a significant replacement of milkfat by vegetable fats as in the case of 'Clover' or by the complete replacement of milkfat in the lipid phase as in the case of 'Gold'.

CHEESE

The main varieties of hard cheese in the UK are made from whole milk and must contain at least 48% fat-in-dry-matter (FDM). The relatively high fat plus low moisture content (less than 39% in the case of Cheddar) provides a rich source of both fat and energy.

Attempts to reduce the calorific value of cheese require a reduction in the fat content and where possible an increase in the moisture. The increase in the moisture content is desirable not just on economic grounds but to avoid excessive protein levels in the aqueous phase.

The FDM content is a major determinant of the organoleptic quality of cheese.[19] For traditional Cheddar cheesemaking a casein: fat ratio of 0·7:1 in the milk is considered optimal.

A semi-skimmed milk (1·6% fat) has been used for some time to give an Edam cheese with 30% FDM. A 'half-fat Edam' with 21% FDM is now in commercial production. Texture remains the major problem, with the cheese being less elastic than the normal Edam and having a drier mouthfeel.

In the manufacture of Edam and similar cheeses the dilution of the whey can aid moisture retention in the curd. Nes[10] reviewed methods of manufacture of low-fat cheeses. Strand[14] concluded that reduction of the FDM below 20% was generally associated with unacceptable deterioration in quality and was considered undesirable. Delbke *et al.*[5] found that for 'low-fat Gouda' a blend of skimmed milk and homogenised cream (giving 0·9% fat) coagulated with rennet and lactic culture at 29°C but without calcium chloride addition, gave the best results. Brining was reduced to 16 hours and the optimum for maturation was 14°C for 2 months.

To produce a cheese with half the fat of Cheddar requires a shift of the FDM from a typical value of 53% to approximately 30%. Reducing the FDM increases the tendency for whey loss from the curd, thus giving a dry-tasting cheese with a crumbly texture. The tendency for whey loss may be reduced by homogenisation of the milk, by reducing the scalding temperature and by introducing a washing stage. This reduced-fat Cheddar was still firmer and more elastic than a full-fat cheese with the same non-fatty milk solids.[6]

Apart from the textural problems with reduced-fat hard cheeses, there may also be poor flavour development. This has been attributed to changes in the pattern of fat and protein breakdown during storage. The enzymes that bring about these beneficial changes are mainly derived from the cheese microflora. Subjecting cultures of *Streptococcus cremoris* to a heat shock of 64°C/15 s is sufficient to kill 96% of the organisms while most of the beneficial enzyme activity survives.[15] The use of shocked culture in addition to the normal culture was found to increase the level of free fatty acids, particularly C_2, C_4 and C_6 acids, giving a mature flavour.[20]

Direct addition of enzymes, both lipases[21] and proteases[13] has also

R. A. Wilbey

been carried out. Low-fat Cheddar containing bacterial protease and incubated at 10°C had an increased flavour intensity though not typical of Cheddar. Electrophoretic patterns suggested similarities between flavour development and proteolysis of gamma-casein, indicating that specific peptides may be involved in the flavour development. Standardisation of ultrafiltered skimmed milk with enzyme-modified cream for low-fat Cheddar was found to be beneficial by Casella and White,[3] though Rank[13] reported that its use had no effect on flavour.

Blends of curds of differing fat contents may be used to produce both hard and soft cheeses with reduced-fat content. Though this method has been used commercially and give a product with a similar flavour to the original cheese, the texture of some reduced-fat hard cheeses tends to be crumbly.

TABLE 3
Comparison of Compositions of Traditional and Reduced-fat Cheeses

	Component	% w/w	kJ/ 100 g	kcal/ 100 g	% energy from fat
Cheddar	Fat	33·5			
	Protein	26			
	Carbohydrate	Tr	1 682	406	74
'Half-fat Cheddar' (Sainsbury's)	Fat	14			
	Protein	29			
	Carbohydrate	Tr	1 050	250	50
Edam	Fat	22·9			
	Protein	24·4			
	Carbohydrate	Tr	1 262	304	68
'Half-fat Edam' (Sainsbury's)	Fat	11			
	Protein	36			
	Carbohydrate	0·2	910	220	45
Cottage Cheese (Sainsbury's)	Fat	4			
	Protein	13·7			
	Carbohydrate	1·6	410	100	36
Cottage cheese (St Ivel 'Shape')	Fat	1·5			
	Protein	14·2			
	Carbohydrate	3·9	355	85	16

Where reduced energy is the main aim then cottage cheese provides an alternative to hard cheeses, with considerable reductions in both fat and calorific values as illustrated in Table 3. (Data for traditional products were derived from McCance and Widdowson, 1960.[7]) The lower energy value of cottage cheese is largely achieved by increasing the moisture content of the product. (The maximum moisture content of low-fat soft cheese is 80%.) The microbiological quality of the cottage cheese thus becomes the prime determinant of shelf life. As with most of the low-fat dairy products, the texture and flavour of cottage cheese is different from that of hard cheese so the product needs to be accepted in its own right.

REFERENCES

1. Bos, K. E. O. (1981). MSc Thesis, Univ. of California, Davis.
2. Brooker, B. (1987). Unpublished data.
3. Casella, A. M. and White, C. H. (1985). *J. Dairy Science*, **68** (Supplement 1), 55.
4. COMA (Committee on Medical Aspects of Food Policy) (1984). *Diet and Cardiovascular Disease, Report on Health and Social Subjects 28*, Department of Health and Social Security, HMSO, London.
5. Delbke, R., Paelinck, H. and Martens, R. (1982). *Revue de l'Agriculture*, **35**, (4), 2717–35.
6. Emmons, D. B., Kalab, M., Larmond, E. and Lowrie, R. J. (1980). *J. Texture Studies*, **11**, 15–34.
7. McCance, R. A. and Widdowson, E. M. (1960). *The Composition of Foods*, HMSO, London.
8. MMB (1984). *EEC Dairy Facts & Figures, 1984*, Milk Marketing Board, Thames Ditton.
9. MMB (1986). *EEC Dairy Facts & Figures, 1986*, Milk Marketing Board, Thames Ditton.
10. Nes, Å. M. (1978). *Meieriposten*, **67** (13), 398–400.
11. Pangborn, R. M. and Dunkley, W. L. (1964). *J. Dairy Science*, **47**, 719–26.
12. Pangborn, R. M. and Dunkley, W. L. (1966). *J. Dairy Science*, **49**, 1–6.
13. Rank, T. C. (1986). *Dissertation Abstracts International, B (Sciences and Engineering)*, **46** (10), 3289.
14. Strand. A. H. (1980). *Meieriposten*, **69** (16), 396–401.
15. Thompson, M. P., Somkuti, G. A.; Flanagan, J. F., Bencivengo, M., Brower, D. P. and Steinberg, D. H. (1979). *J. Dairy Science*, **62** (Supplement 1), 68–9.
16. Troller, J. A. and Christian, J. H. B. (1978). *Water Activity and Food*, Academic Press, London.

17. WILBEY, R. A. (1986). In: *Modern Dairy Technology*, Vol. 1, Ed. Robinson, R. K., Elsevier Applied Science, London, 93–7.
18. WILTON, I. E. M., ENVALL, L. O. G., SUNDSTROEM, K. L. and MORAN, D. P. J. (1978). US Patent 4,071,634.
19. SCOTT, R. (1986). *Cheesemaking Practice (2nd edn)*, Elsevier Applied Science, London.
20. SOMKUTI, G. A., THOMPSON, M. P. and FLANAGAN, J. F. (1979). *Proceedings of the First Biennial Marschall International Cheese Conference*, Miles Laboratories, Madison, Wisconsin.
21. NES, Å. M. (1979). *Meieriposten*, **68** (8), 231–9.

5

CALO Fats, Cholesterol and Calories

M. WOLKSTEIN

Reach Associates Inc., South Orange, New Jersey, USA

ABSTRACT

For at least one billion of today's residents of the US, EEC and other developed countries, problems have arisen connected with their food intake, health and wellbeing. In the US alone, 44 million people are overweight and 65 million Americans, mostly women, are on a diet one time or another during the year. There are over a million heart attacks per year from which 500 000 people die as a result. Today even after 25 years of warnings from doctors and the American Heart Association about lowering the consumption of saturated fats, American men continue to consume an average of about 500 mg of cholesterol a day and women 350 mg a day. This is 60% more than that recommended.

Recent confirmation of the links between fat, calories and cholesterol to obesity, heart disease and cancer is accelerating the use of CALO (Low-calorie) Fats and Oils and the growth of the diet food segment of the food industry.

It is expected that CALO Fats, which are less metabolisable or have less calories than triglyceride fats, will have a tremendous development during the next two decades. CALO Fats have the same functional properties as triglyceride fats but have a caloric value which ranges from about 0–5 cal/gram as compared to 9 for triglycerides.

CALO Fats have already appeared on the market and many technologies are being used for their manufacture. The use of mono- and diglycerides and other emulsions as well as N-Oil, made from tapioca starch, and polydextrose have been widely publicised.

New efforts are being made in the field of chemicals and drugs for suppressing the appetite and reducing cholesterol. Some which have potential include those of Laboratoire Servier, Tryptophan, and Eli Lilly's anti-anxiety drug, which was found to have weight-reducing potential and also Merck's forthcoming new anti-cholesterol drug which has possibilities outside of the drug field and is related to the principle of the CALO Fats.

FATS, CHOLESTEROL AND HEALTH

In January, 1984, the US Federal Government announced the results of the broadest and most expensive research project in medical history. The study which took ten years and cost $150 million will have a profound impact on our diet and health in the future. The subject was cholesterol and its link to heart disease. Among the conclusions were the following:

— Heart disease is directly linked to the level of cholesterol in the blood.
— Lowering cholesterol levels markedly reduces the incidence of fatal heart attacks.

Today, even after 25 years of warnings from doctors and the American Heart Association about lowering the consumption of saturated fats, American men continue to consume an average of about 500 mg of cholesterol a day, and women 350 mg/day. In both cases this is about 60% more than the Heart Association recommends. Figure 1 shows that cholesterol consumption in the US was about 507 milligrams per capita in 1911 and about 484 milligrams in 1981.

About 40% of our daily calories are consumed as fat, this is roughly 30% more than Americans ate 60 years ago, and nearly *three times* the amount consumed by the Japanese and some African and Latin American populations.

The US has one of the highest rates of heart disease in the world. In 1986 more than a million Americans suffered heart attacks and more than half died as a result. The economic and social toll is huge since most of the victims are in their 40s and 50s, let alone the tragic personal loss. According to estimates by the National Heart, Lung and Blood Institute, deaths from heart attacks cost an estimated

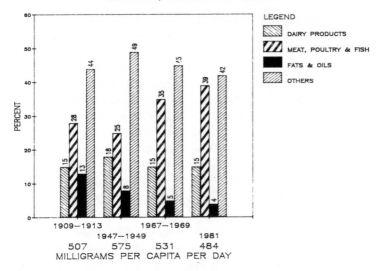

FIG. 1. Cholesterol in the US food supply, by food group.[1]

$60 billion in medical bills, lost wages and productivity. This is more than the total Medicare budget.

The nutrition and clinical studies leave no doubt: fats play a significant role in both heart disease and cancer. The dietary guidelines are also clear: *Cut down on fats!*[1-2]

Apropos of this, *The Wall Street Journal* on February 24, 1987, contained a feature article entitled 'Doctors Widen Cholesterol War, Setting Stricter Patient Guidelines'.[2] According to the article, 'Health Authorities for the first time are setting criteria for desirable cholesterol levels in individuals, and those levels are sharply lower than what heretofore has been considered normal'.

For the first time about one in four adults will be told they have a problem with cholesterol. The criteria will apply to children as well as men and women.

For adults, a probable scenario is as follows:

— If a blood test indicates a cholesterol level higher than 200 milligrams per decilitre of blood serum, the doctor will ask for a second blood test to confirm the first.
— If the test confirms that the level is above 200 but less than 240–250, the doctor will probably urge the patient to go on a

low-fat diet (the first line of defence), one in which eggs, butter, prime roasts and steaks and other animal fats are replaced by vegetable oils, fish and lean meats or CALO Fat modified foods.

— If the level is above 240, the doctor will ask the testing laboratory to provide a detailed breakdown of the types of cholesterol and triglycerides circulating in the blood stream. A strict low-fat diet will be urged for these patients. However, depending on the test results, the doctor may also prescribe one of a growing number of cholesterol-reducing drugs. (Some of these are briefly reviewed later.)

This programme will speed up the further development of CALO (low-calorie and low-cholesterol) foods.

The new attack on cholesterol is aimed at lowering the toll of heart disease, which in 1987 is expected to kill 540 000 Americans. One projection says that by lowering the average cholesterol level by 10% the deaths should be reduced by 100 000.

Until recently, cholesterol levels of 250 or even 300 were often shrugged off. A 1983 survey found that 40% of doctors did not prescribe low-fat diets unless their levels approached the 300 mark.

In the Orient, where heart attacks are rare, average levels are below 150. In the US, where heart attacks are the leading cause of death, the average level among middle-aged men, the most studied population group, is 215 to 220.

Statisticians have determined that the risk of a heart attack begins to rise when cholesterol levels exceed 150 and the risk climbs sharply at levels above 200.

TABLE 1
Cholesterol Levels and Risk of Heart Disease

Age	Risk (mg/dl)		
	Average	*Moderate*	*High*
20–29	Below 200	200–220	Above 220
30–39	Below 220	220–240	Above 240
40+	Below 240	240–260	Above 260

Source: National Institutes of Health Consensus Development Conference, December 1984.

Under the proposed criteria, doctors and testing laboratories would abandon the concept of normal cholesterol levels and would use risk categories for different age groups. *Average risk* would be cholesterol levels found in about 75% of the population with the lowest cholesterol levels while *high risk* would be the levels found in the 5% of the population with the highest cholesterol (see Table 1).

FATS, OBESITY AND HEALTH

Closely related to fat and cholesterol is obesity. For psychological or physical reasons 65 million Americans are currently on a diet. Many more have tried and given up the effort to lose weight.

A concern of scientists is the determination of overweight versus obesity in order to assess the risk to health. A widely used measurement is the Body Mass Index (BMI) which is determined by dividing the weight of a person in kilograms by the square of the person's height in metres. According to Dr George A. Bray of the University of Southern California School of Medicine, if a person's BMI is between 25 and 30, regardless of sex, the person is overweight, a condition of about 25% of the American population. If the BMI is over 30, the person is obese and this category applies to about 12% of Americans. The ideal BMI for any individual is between 23 and 25.[3]

Obesity can affect not only one's quality of life, but also one's longevity. In numerous studies, excessive overweight has been proved to be a reliable predictor for the onset of heart disease, hypertension, certain cancers, diabetes, and diseases of the digestive tract. In fact it is a better predictor for coronary artery disease than smoking. The statistics are such that in 1985 the National Institutes of Health classified obesity as a disease.

Further to this, the American Cancer Society recently estimated that 35% of *cancers* were related to diet and obesity and recommended a decrease in the consumption of fats. Confirming what was stated before, the dietary guidelines are clear: *cut down on fats!*

The logical response for the food industry is to trim food products. Consumer trends towards lighter, healthier foods are well documented with 85% of all shoppers looking for the caloric content of food products on the label. One way to 'lighten' foods without sacrificing the product's appeal would be to substitute CALO Fats for the fat normally present in the product.

CALO FATS AND OILS

The term CALO Fats was proposed as a generic name in a paper given at the 75th Annual Meeting of the American Oil Chemists' Society[23] and widely adopted since.[24]

CALO and CAL Fats and Oils may be divided into categories depending on their formulas, properties and uses. A compendium may involve thousands of products but a broad classification would be as follows:

CALO Fats—CALO Fats and Oils would be either not metabolised by the body or if metabolised would have less caloric content and result in less caloric uptake when compared to the usual food fats and oils. These would include non-metabolised pseudo-fats such as sucrose polyesters (SPEs) and polyesters of other sugars, polyhydric alcohols, and many fatty acids which are partially metabolisable, low-caloric fat substitutes.

In addition this would cover other low-calorie non-ester-type fat and oil replacers such as Pfizer's polydextrose, National Starch's N-Oil, FMC's avicel and others.

CAL Fats—These products such as sugar esters are absorbable, metabolised and caloric and have been under development by many companies for many years particularly the UK sugar company, Tate and Lyle, the State of Nebraska, which offers licences on its process and several Japanese companies.

Requirements for CALO Fats

The fat diet includes the consumption of both visible and invisible fats with invisible fats (natural products including meat, cheese, milk, nuts, eggs, etc.) supplying about two-thirds and visible fats (butter, margarine, shortening, cooking oils, salad oils) making up the other one-third. About 42% of the present US diet of 3200 calories per day is provided by fats which amounts to 1340 calories. To achieve the low-calorie fat diet recommended by nutritionists, i.e. 30% of the calories to be provided by fat with a total caloric intake of 2600 calories, equates to a total fat consumption of 780 calories. This means that fat consumption, on a caloric basis, must be reduced by 42%.

This is most difficult for the average American since we have been trying to do this for some time with very little success. In fact, the quantity of fat consumed has not decreased but has indeed steadily

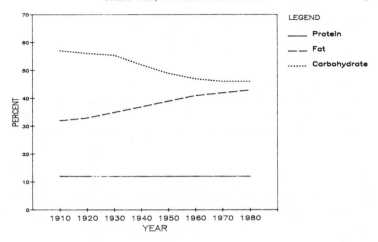

FIG. 2. Percentage of calories from protein, fat and carbohydrate in the US food supply during the past 70 years.[1] (From Rizek, R. L., Welsh, S. O. and Marston, R. M., Paper presented at AOCS short course, Lake Geneva, WI., May 4, 1983.)

increased from about 32% of calories in 1910 to about 42/43% today as shown in Fig. 2.

What is required to realise this reduction is a change in our eating habits to a diet which consists of more complex carbohydrates and the use of foods prepared with CALO Fats, i.e. with less calories per gram. With CALO Fats, the consumption of fat food will need to be reduced by only about 30% if a CALO Fat is used which has an effective energy content (metabolisable energy content realised by the body) of about 4·5 calories per gram and by only 18% with an effective energy content of about 1 calorie per gram.[1]

Further to this, a CALO Fat should be similar to the natural fat it replaces. It must taste like, feel like, look like and smell like natural fats. It must be non-toxic, and its metabolites, if not identical with those which are produced in the body, must be completely excreted, without causing body discomfort and without causing other problems such as anal leakage or diarrhoea.

The factors which determine the energy value of a fat product ingested include its coefficient of digestion, degree of utilisation in the body and heat of combustion (caloric content).

In general terms, the heat of combustion is influenced by the ratio of hydrogen to oxygen. A low ratio results in a lower heat of combustion. Therefore glycerides of shorter chain fatty acids have a lower caloric value than glycerides of long-chain fatty acids.

Low-Caloric Formulations

Since many people are seeking ways to reduce their caloric intake for medical or health reasons, food technologists continue to explore ways to produce food substances that provide the same benefits and taste as the food imitated but not the calories. Many reduced-calorie products already exist including calorie-controlled meals, salad dressings, packaged meats, margarines, canned fruits, diet beverages, frozen desserts and others. In fact, the diet segment represents a major growth field in the American Food Industry. Statistics indicate that the food industry in the US is growing at an average of about 1% per year which is just about the same as the population growth. The diet food segment, however, is growing at about 6% per year and this is being paced by aspartame-containing foods which grew in 1985 at about 30% per year and light frozen entrées, 24% per year. The recent confirmation of the links between fat and cholesterol to heart disease and cancer should help to accelerate the use of CALO Fats and Oils and the growth of the diet food segment to over 10% per year.[1]

CALO and Cal Fat Technology

Numerous types of CALO Fats and Oils have been suggested and tested with some now being used in food. Various processing techniques are also being used to achieve reduced fat intake and thereby reduce caloric intake and weight gain. These include:

1. Good kitchen practices:
   Simple trimming and fat removal and skimming of separated oil during food preparation.
   Broiling and roasting instead of frying.
2. Selection and breeding methods:
   The control of the selection, breeding, feeding and preparation of meat from domesticated animals to produce lean low-fat content meat products.
3. Preparation of prepared foods using cooking methods other than frying or deep frying. Examples include:
   The preparation of potato chips using infra-red heat and by baking.

The use of defatted roasted peanuts instead of deep-fried peanuts and dry-roasted peanuts.

4. The reduction of fat in milk products:
   Low-fat milk has established itself along with homogenised milk. The 1% and 2% fat milk satisfies the nutrition and milk drinking needs while it reduces the fat and caloric intake.

5. The reduction of fat in visible fat products:
   The reduction in fat content in diet margarines from 80% to 40% and below is a reality.
   Diet mayonnaise and salad dressings are gaining good acceptance.

6. Low-fat dessert:
   Imitation ice-creams with lower fat content, and some without any fat are gaining good acceptance.

7. Low-fat formulated foods:
   The food industry and particularly the fats and oils segment, have bowed to consumer and medical demands in the production of foods with higher polyunsaturated fat content in shortenings, margarine, salad oil, dressings and others. In addition, in processed foods, where the composition is subject to control, the fat content is being considerably reduced. For example, the preparation of some formulated foods with beef, ham and chicken flavour have much lower fat contents than the natural meats and still are palatable and appetising.

8. The use of CALO Fats and Oils:
   The use of tailor-made CALO Fats and Oils in place of natural fats and oils in food products to produce foods which have the taste, smell, mouthfeel and appetite-satisfying effect as natural foods but without the calories, i.e. 'Having your cake and eating it too'.

Lean Invisible Fat Produce

Progress is being made in the reduction of fat content in invisible fats. Considerable agricultural and animal drug research is being conducted to produce leaner animals. In addition to reducing the fat content, the growers will save on feed costs. In a recent article in *Chemical Week*[4] it was stated that about 4 billion pounds of excess fat are produced annually on US pigs, cattle, sheep and poultry. The amount of feed, the biggest cost in meat production, consumed to produce the waste fat, is even more monumental. It represents a waste of resources and, to combat this, researchers are developing compounds that stimulate muscle production while limiting fat synthesis. While growth hormones have recently captured most attention a group of compounds that are known as beta-agonists and are analogues of adrenaline could prove more effective.

Companies, actively involved in developing the compounds include Cyanamid, Eli Lilly and Merck Sharp & Dohme in the US and Beecham, Glaxo, Hoechst and Boehringer Ingelheim in Europe. Cyanamid expects to have its beta-agonist, cimaterol, on the market by the early 1990s. Cyanamid hypothesises[4] that the beta-agonists that act as growth promoters bind to not-as-yet identified beta receptors in skeletal muscle. These beta-agonists known as repartitioning agents, repartition nutrients away from fat tissue towards skeletal muscle. The compounds are believed to increase fatty acid mobilisation from fat deposits and to divert the energy in those acids into skeletal muscle production. The compounds also are thought to decrease the rate of muscle protein degradation, and while protein deposition increases in muscle, it does not change in such proteinaceous organs as liver, kidneys, heart and skin.

Repartitioning agents also improve the efficiency of an animal's conversion of feed into weight gain. Such improvement results from the energy spared when an animal deposits muscle instead of fat since the energy required to synthesise fat and protein is about the same and muscle contains 60–75% water, while an equal weight of fat contains less than 20% water.

The compounds have been tested on chicken, pigs, cattle and sheep. In pigs, Cyanamid found that cimaterol feed levels of 0·05–1 ppm reduced back fat up to 11·7% and increased longissimus muscle area up to 14% with significant reduction in feed intake. Cattle fed another beta-agonist, clenbuterol, showed increases of up to 17% in longissimus muscle area and reduction in subcutaneous fat of 40% and kidney and pelvic fat of 35%.

Sheep that were fed clenbuterol showed a 40% rise in longissimus muscle area and a 36% drop in subcutaneous and internal fat. Other work on sheep is in progress at Cornell University (Ithaca, NY).[4] Donald H. Beermann, an associate professor of animal science, has fed sheep cimaterol at a dose of 10 ppm, resulting in an increase in carcass muscle of up to 30%. Carcass fat decreased by as much as 66% in castrated lambs and 38% in ram lambs.

CALO Food Agents

Calories have been reduced in some salad dressing formulations by eliminating oil and employing a gum system to suspend flavourings and spices and to provide emulsion stability. While gums are not used to replace all the fat in formulations, they do provide some of the functions of oils in lower-caloric salad dressings in which the oil phase has been reduced. Xanthan gum, a high-molecular-weight polysaccharide, is used as a suspension stabiliser in pourable salad dressings. Algins from seaweed can also be used to act as emulsifiers and emulsion stabilisers. Formulations may be varied, with oil content varying from zero to 50%, xanthan gum content from 0·20 to 0·50% and algins from zero to 0·50%.

N-Oil, a tapioca dextrin, marketed by National Starch and Chemical Corp., USA, is being used to partially or totally replace fat in food products as well as enhance the fat properties of foods. Food manufacturers can replace 30% to 50% of the oil in a salad oil or frozen dessert by using N-Oil.

Maltodextrin made from corn syrup is a carbohydrate that can partially replace the oil in salad dressings. It can be used to provide formulations with one-half the calories and one-quarter the oil level of a standard salad dressing while still providing a creamy smooth, fat-like texture. Some maltodextrins can be used in oil and flavour encapsulation, pan coatings, and soup and gravy mixes and to produce margarine-type spreads with significant reduced fat content.

Mono- and diglycerides are being used to a considerable extent in the formulation of foods with decreased fat content. Hannigan[5] reported on the use of mono- and diglycerides with 17–20% monoglyceride content and 67–72 iodine value, which could be used as a sole source for the shortening component in cake formulations. In one case, 133 grams of shortening was replaced with 100 grams of mono- and diglyceride, a reduction of about 25%. In another example about 200 grams of emulsifier was used to replace 900 grams (the entire amount) of standard shortening, a fat reduction of 78%. The resulting cakes were considered to be comparable to the controlled cakes baked with the normal amount of shortening. Formulations were developed for both dry mixes and cakes baked from scratch. Deaton and Andres[6] also described an emulsifier system consisting of a blend of mono- and diglycerides, polysorbate 60 and sodium stearoil lactylate, which allows a 30–60% reduction in shortening in cake formulations. In this case the shortening is a liquid oil, which is lower in cost than hydrogenated oils and also can be metered into the batter mix for a more efficient operation.

Companies including Durkee (USA), and others are using mono- and diglycerides to reduce the fat content of many products including low-calorie ice-creams. A major advantage is that these are GRAS (generally regarded as safe).

Engineered CALO Fats and Oils

Research on the formulation of food products with specially engineered 'fat' ingredients or CALO Fats has been in the works for over three decades. During the 1960s the USDA Western and Southern Regional Research Laboratories conducted research on the use of amylose esters, succinostearin and adipostearin.[7-10] In 1960, Arthur Minich was granted a patent for dietetic food compositions prepared by the esterification of neopentyl polyhydric alcohols with fatty acids.[11]

In 1971, F. H. Mattson and R. A. Volpenheim of Procter & Gamble Co. were granted their patent on sucrose polyesters.[12] Sucrose polyester, defined as a mixture of hexa-, hepta- and octa-fatty acid esters of sucrose, may be many different compounds depending on the fatty acid used and the degree of esterification. The Mattson, Volpenheim patent was for low-calorie food compositions produced by replacing at least a portion of the fat content of conventional foods with a sugar fatty acid ester or sugar alcohol fatty ester having at least four fatty acid ester groups with each fatty acid having from 8 to 22 carbon atoms. These compounds were found to have the physical properties of ordinary triglyceride fat but were not digested or absorbed to the same extent when eaten and therefore less caloric. The inventors also found that the properties of the sugar or sugar alcohol fatty acid esters could be tailor-made depending on whether an oil substitute or a fat substitute was desired by using either unsaturated fatty acid ester groups and/or shorter chain fatty acid groups, or saturated fatty acid groups. Various food products were made in which the sugar polyesters were substituted for other fats and oils and in most cases no difference in colour, texture or flavour could be detected.

Problems in the use of sucrose polyesters as replacement for part of the fat or oil in food were the occurrence of anal leakage and the removal of the fat-soluble vitamins A, D, E and K. However, Jandacek[25] solved this problem with the addition of sufficient fat-soluble vitamins to prevent abnormally low levels of the vitamins, and the addition of an anti-anal leakage agent such as hydrogenated palm oil.

Much research and development work is going on with sucrose polyesters. Alex Wei,[26] at Washington State University, conducted metabolic studies using one-day-old chicks since results could be obtained within two weeks. Chickens were used rather than rats because metabolism in chickens was stated to be more similar to human metabolism. Sucrose polyesters were prepared using lard and tallow to produce a semi-solid product with melting characteristics between margarine and butter. The SPE was not metabolised and it was reported that there was no anal leakage problem. The synthesised SPE, when used experimentally as a replacement for milk fat in making ice-cream, produced an ice-cream with very good texture and body.

Mieth and other associates[27] have done recent work on sucrose polyesters and have developed an efficient manufacturing process in which 80–90% SPE yields are obtained. In the process, sucrose octaacetate and fatty acid methyl esters are reacted in the presence of sodium or potassium metal at a temperature of 110–120°C.

Sucrose polyesters are considered GRAS as food additives in Japan although they are being used for their functional characteristics, such as lubricating agents in pharmaceutical tablets and anti-caking agents in powdered products, and not for low-calorie applications.

It is not known, at this time, whether Procter & Gamble Co. will seek approvals for the use of SPE as a drug or food ingredient in the US. It may be both.

Again in 1971, D. D. Whyte obtained a patent, also assigned to the Procter & Gamble Co., for the use of glycerol esters of alpha branched carboxylic acids as substitutes for ordinary glyceride fats in food compositions.[13]

In 1972, Dr V. K. Babayan and H. Lehman obtained their patent on the preparation of polyglycerol and polyglycerol esters.[14] Prior to this patent, the polyglycerol esters of fatty acids were used principally as industrial emulsifying agents. They were unsuitable for direct use in edible products as the colour was relatively dark and the composition of the polyglycerols indefinite; the product had an unpleasant odour and undesirable taste and the usual bleaching procedures were not effective.

The polyglycerol esters may be partial or completely esterified esters and, depending on the chain length of the polyglycerol molecule and fatty acid used, may be solid or liquid. The polyglycerol esters are being used for many different food applications as well as for non-food use. They are unique as tailored fats and dietetic agents and are capable of eliminating or minimising the use of fat in many food compositions.

There is presently some uncertainty as to whether the entire polyglycerol ester is metabolised or not. Babayan assumed that the entire molecule, including the polyglycerol backbone, is metabolised while others have concluded that the polyglycerol backbone is not metabolised and does not contribute to the metabolisable calories.[15] Recent studies by Weiss and Mieth (East Germany) indicated that the lipolyses rates of polyglycerol esters decreased considerably with an increasing degree of condensation and that triglycerol pentapalmitate was not hydrolysed.[16] If complete metabolism does occur the caloric value will vary from about 1·7 kcal/g for decaglycerol monoester to about 7·5 kcal/g for the triglycerol triester. For calorie reduction, the partial esters, i.e. mono- and diesters of the polyglycerols, should be considered for CALO Fat use since these esters have caloric values which range from about 6·5 to about 8 (or 1·7 to 4·5 if not metabolised). These partial esters are also good emulsifiers in that the use of a small amount in an aqueous emulsion provides the mouthfeel satisfaction of eating rich creamy foods. Polyglycerol esters of fatty acids, up to and including the decaglycerol esters, are approved by the US FDA for use in food as additives.

Vernon Trost in 1984 was issued a patent, assigned to Swift & Company, USA, for the use of glycerol dialkyl ethers and glycerol monoester diethers for use in foods in partial or total replacement for fats.[17] According to the patent, while single dialkyl ethers or glycerol monoester diethers may not exhibit all structural similarities and functionalities of conventional fats, blends could be made to provide a wide range of fat-like characteristics and functionalities such as broad melting curves (no sharp melting point) for use in margarine, or sharp melting curve to simulate fats used as frying fats and confectionery fats. Prepared blends used in many different food applications could not be distinguished from that made with the usual triglyceride fats.

Most recently, in April 1985, Donald Hamm of CPC International Inc. was given a patent on low-calorie edible substitutes based on thermally stable polycarboxylic acids esterified with saturated or unsaturated alcohols.[18]

In addition to the above, research is being pursued in the development of CALO Fats and Oils using microbiologically derived products, non-absorbable synthetic polymers with properties similar to edible oils, low-metabolised natural fats and oils, biopolymers, branched polysaccharides, jojoba oil, as well as others.[1]

CHOLESTEROL-REDUCING AGENTS

Food fat can be modified not only to control fat intake but also to reduce cholesterol levels.

Besides being exemplary CALO Fats, sucrose polyesters (SPEs) were found to be powerful cholesterol-lowering agents effective in eliminating both cholesterol manufactured normally by the body and from the diet. In studies conducted by Dr Charles J. Glueck and others at the University of Cincinnati Medical Center, SPE was found to provide food satisfaction with accompanying 10% lowering of plasma cholesterol and 14% lowering of low-density lipoprotein (LDL) in normocholesterolaemic obese subjects when covertly used as a replacement for dietary fats.[19]

In a later study, Dr Glueck et al., reported on the use of SPE as a substitute for dietary fats in hypocaloric diets in the treatment of familial hypercholesterolaemia. It was concluded that clinically significant reductions in total cholesterol and low density lipoprotein cholesterol (20% and 23% respectively), are achieved by the use of SPE as a substitute for conventional dietary fat, allowing the removal of fat and calories from the diet in a palatable manner.[20]

Medium chain triglycerides (MCT) have also been shown to have a very low tendency to deposit as depot fat in contrast to conventional fats. Furthermore, the total cholesterol level in animals (mice, rats, and monkeys) fed MCT were 40–50% lower than that in animals fed lard or corn oil. These unique characteristics of MCT provide a dietary means of controlling body fat and cholesterol.[21]

Drug makers also realise the potential for anti-cholesterol drugs is as great if not greater than the estimated $5 billion per year worldwide market for high-pressure drugs. The 1986 US market for cholesterol drugs was about $100 million, with sales projected by some who peg cholesterol agents as a potential billion-dollar market in the US by the early 1990s.

As indicated previously, if diet alone does not cut the cholesterol level close to the 200 mark, then doctors would prescribe drugs and this would be for many patients. Some drugs now being used and in development are discussed below.

Bile-Acid Sequestrants

These are flavoured powders (ion-exchange resins) that most patients take dissolved in fruit juice. The two products on the market are Mead Johnson's Questran (cholestyramine) and Upjohn's Colestid (colestipol) which absorb bile acids in the intestine. Normally, bile acids are returned to the liver, but when picked up by Questran or Colestid they form a resin-bile complex that is then excreted. While these ion-exchange drugs are safe they do have drawbacks. The drugs are expensive and patient compliance is low because large amounts of the drug must be taken before each meal and patients often compare this to eating sand. Further side effects can include constipation, flatulence and nausea.

Upjohn is working on a tablet form for the drug while Warner Lambert Co. is currently developing a more palatable cholestyramine formulation in a bar form that will come in various flavours including raspberry which is expected to make the drug more acceptable.

Fibric Acids

These drugs increase the activity of an enzyme that breaks down LDL thus lowering triglyceride levels. One of these drugs is Warner Lambert's gemfibrozil which is sold as Lopid. The 1986 worldwide sales of Lopid, which is marketed in 36 countries, totalled $58 million, a 76% increase from 1985.

Lopid has been the subject of considerable study. A five-year trial of Lopid in Finland on middle-aged, high-risk men showed an improvement in 90% of participants. Lopid reduced total cholesterol by an average of 16% and LDL by 21%, while increasing HDL by 23%. Only five heart attacks occurred among the group, 70% fewer than expected.[21]

The results were encouraging enough to lead to a five-year Helsinki Heart Study, the objective of which was to evaluate Lopid as a preventive for heart attacks. The study, which was completed in June 1987, involved 4,000 men with elevated cholesterol levels and 600 men who had already had heart attacks.

A related compound, clofibrate, is sold as Atromid-S by the Ayerst division of America Home Products Corp. This drug has been found to produce side effects such as gallstones and liver problems, limiting its use.

A new fibric-acid derivative, fenofibrate recently licensed by Mead Johnson from a French company showed promising US trials.

Enzyme Inhibitors

This covers the newest type of cholesterol-lowering drugs which are creating the most excitement. Merck is spearheading development of enzyme inhibitors. It has filed a new drug application (NDA) with the Food and Drug Administration on its drug Lovastatin, and expects to market the compound in 1988. Lovastatin inhibits the key enzyme in cholesterol synthesis, 3-hydroxy-3-methylglutaryl-CoA reductase (HMG-CoA reductase). This reduces cellular synthesis of cholesterol, causing cells to increase uptake of blood cholesterol to meet their needs. Such uptake, in turn, reduces the level of blood cholesterol. A study of Lovastatin showed average total cholesterol and LDL reductions of 32% and 39%, respectively. In addition, high-density lipoprotein (HDL) levels in the test group tended to rise slightly.

Squibb is also developing an inhibitor of HMG-CoA reductase. The compound, eptastatin, is currently in clinical trials, and Squibb hopes to file an NDA in 1988.

CONTROL OF OBESITY

New alleys have opened recently which give us encouragement in the battle against obesity.

It seems that the body has fat storage codes which decide where the body will store its fat. Rockefeller University scientists have started to decipher these codes and may be able to predict where individuals might be able to lose weight. They believe they will eventually be able to 'rewrite' the codes to help individuals lose fat from particular areas.

At Roche, a division of Hoffman–LaRoche, researchers are testing a drug that induces the body to burn off fat. The drug is claimed to imitate the metabolism caused by exercise and thereby induce the body gradually to lose weight.

Researchers at Cornell Medical College are studying the source of satiety signals to find out what causes us to stop eating. A peptide being looked at is cholecystokinin-8 which when given to humans during a meal caused a decrease in food intake.

In a recent symposium on obesity[3] papers were presented on carbohydrate cravers. These people often increase their daily caloric intake by 25–50% in the form of carbohydrates. Because Americans often tend to obtain carbohydrates from foods like ice-cream these snacks usually also contain fat. Studies showed that in craving these foods the depressed patients may not be seeking to satisfy hunger but to medicate themselves for depression. The studies also showed that carbohydrate intake increases brain levels of tryptophan, the amino acid which is the precursor for the synthesis of serotonin, a neurotransmitter implicated in mood states. When subjects were given the drug, d-fenfluramine, which increases the amount of serotonin in the brain, their consumption of carbohydrate snacks decreased by as much as 40%. Protein intake was not affected. Tests on monkeys given a proserotonin by Virbac S.A. showed that they all lost weight.[22]

Fenfluramine compounds are now being prescribed in some European countries for treatment of obesity and depression. Laboratoire Servier, a French firm in Neuilly, France, has developed a flenfluramine drug which was described in *Lancet*.

Virbac S.A., a French private company, has filed a patent application on its proserotonin and is working extensively in the field.[22]

Eli Lilly, in the US, is also working hard on its drug fluoxetine which, originally developed as a tranquilliser, was found to be weight-reducing.[22]

Mention should also be given to the use of Schering Plough's Fibre-Trim, a Danish product already used in Australia, Canada and Italy, and two similar products particularly Thompson's Fiber Fill to reduce the appetite.

Reach Associates expects that the food industry will become more drug-orientated and expects to see the blending of food and drugs in the fight against obesity and cholesterol.[22]

REFERENCES

1. WOLKSTEIN, M. *et al.*(1985). In: *Low Caloric Edible Fats and Oils (CALO Fats) and Other Modified Fats and Oils (CAL Fats)*, Reach Associates Inc., South Orange, New Jersey, USA, **1A**, 9-111 to 9-139.
2. BISHOP, J. E. (1987). *The Wall Street Journal*, February 24, p. 33.
3. NEW YORK ACADEMY OF SCIENCE. *Symposium on Obesity*, New York, October 1986.

4. SPALDING, B. J. (1987). Adrenaline Analogues Beef Up Farm Animals, *Chemical Week*, January 28, 44–7.
5. HANNIGAN, K. J. (1980). Fat Reduced Cakes, *Food Engineering*, **52** (3), 32.
6. DEATON and ANDRES (1980). Emulsifier System Reduces Shortening Usage up to 60%, *Food Processing*, **41** (8), 50.
7. FEUGE, R. O and WARD, T. L. (1958). *JAOCS*, **35**, 6338–41.
8. FEUGE, R. O. and WARD, T. L. (1960). *JAOCS*, **37**, 291–4.
9. GROS, A. T. and FEUGE R. O. (1962). *JAOCS*, **39**, 19–24.
10. BOOTH, A. N. and GROS A. T. (1963). *JAOCS*, **40**, 551–3.
11. MINICH, A. (1960). US Patent 2 962 419.
12. MATTSON, F. H. and VOLPENHEIM, R. A. (1971). US Patent 3 600 186.
13. WHYTE, D. D. (1971). US Patent 3 579 548.
14. BABAYAN, V. K. and LEHMAN, H. (1972). US Patent 3 637 774.
15. BABAYAN, V. K., KAUNITZ, H. and SLANETZ, C. A. (1964). *JAOCS*, **41**, 434.
16. WEISS, A. and MIETH, G. (1983). *Die Nahrung*, **27** (3), K13–K14.
17. TROST, V. (1984). US Patent 4 106 681.
18. HAMM, D. (1985). US Patent 4 508 746.
19. GLUECK, C. J. *et al.* (1982). *Journal of the American Medical Association*, **248**, 22.
20. GLUECK, C. J. *et al.* (1983). *American Journal of Clinical Nutrition*, **37**, 347–54.
21. ANON. (1987). Getting to the Heart of Cholesterol, *Chemical Week*, February 11, 72–4.
22. WOLKSTEIN, M. *et al.* (1987). *CALO and CAL Fat Report Up-Date*, Reach Associates Inc., South Orange, New Jersey, USA (in progress).
23. WOLKSTEIN, M. (1984). In: *New Developments in Non Caloric (CALO) Oils and Fats*, a paper presented at the AOCS, Annual Meeting in Dallas, Texas on May 2, 1984.
24. DE LA TULLAYE, J. and DARBON, P. (1986). *Biofutur*, **45**, 19–32.
25. JANDACEK, R. J. (1977). US Patent 4 005 195.
26. WEI, A. and SWANSON, B. G. (1981). PhD Thesis, Washington State University, Microfilms, Ann Arbor, Michigan.
27. MIETH, G., EISNER, A. and WEISS, A. (1983). *Die Nahrung*, **27**, 747–51.

6

Palatinit® (Isomalt), an Energy-Reduced Bulk Sweetener Derived from Saccharose

P. J. STRÄTER

Palatinit® Süssungsmittel GmbH, Obrigheim/Pfalz, Federal Republic of Germany

ABSTRACT

Palatinit® is an energy-reduced bulk sweetener that is produced in two essential steps from saccharose. In a first step the easily hydrolysable 1,2-glycosidic linkage between the glucose and fructose moieties of saccharose is catalysed by immobilised enzymes, rearranged into a 1,6 linkage that is more stable. In a second step the fructose moiety of the molecule is catalysed by Raney–Nickel, hydrogenated to either sorbitol or mannitol. The result is an equimolar mixture of glucose–sorbitol (GPS) and glucose–mannitol (GPM), i.e. Palatinit®.

The physical and chemical characteristics are, apart from the following exceptions, much like saccharose. The major differences are:

— less than half as soluble at 20°C;
— 35–55% lower sweetness (dependent on concentration);
— 10–15 times as resistant to acid and enzymatic hydrolysis;
— the GPM-half of Palatinit® crystallises with two molecules of water of crystallisation.

Palatinit® differs from the better-known sugar alcohols essentially in the following characteristics:

— much higher tendency to crystallisation;
— much lower hygroscopicity;
— virtually no cooling effect.

Metabolically Palatinit® differs from most other disaccharides and disaccharide alcohols in its stability against microbial fermentation and enzymatic breakdown. In comparison to the monosaccharides and monosaccharide alcohols it has (weight for weight) only half the osmotic action. The result is, in comparison to the mono- and disaccharides, poor acid-forming characteristics by oral bacteria, partial and slow resorption in the small intestine and, as a consequence thereof, very small changes in serum glucose and insulin. In comparison to most other mono- and disaccharide alcohols, Palatinit® supplies less available energy for the living organism (animal and man).

Due to its physical characteristics Palatinit® can be very well processed for the manufacture of sweet and not-so-sweet confections like hard-boiled candies, compressed goods, pan-coated goods, baked goods and chewing gum. In many of these applications the low hygroscopicity of Palatinit® is highly appreciated.

In food systems with a relatively high water content like chewable candies, ice-cream, jam and jellies, the low solubility of Palatinit® makes it advisable to combine Palatinit® with other sugar alcohols like maltitol. The low hygroscopicity of Palatinit® combined with the high solubility of maltitol yields better products than could be achieved with sugar alcohol by itself.

In chocolate, water of crystallisation in Palatinit® can lead to a certain sandiness under classical manufacturing conditions. Under careful processing, with temperatures below 47°C, Palatinit® chocolate, combined with some intense sweetener, has a taste and texture that most consumers cannot differentiate from sucrose-made chocolate.

The regulatory situation of Palatinit® is quite well cleared. Joint Expert Committee for Food Additives (JECFA) gave Palatinit®, in its 1985 meeting, an 'acceptable daily intake (ADI) non specified' (no upper limit of use). The EEC Scientific Committee on Food cleared it, together with the other better-known sugar alcohols. Switzerland (2 kcal/g) and the UK cleared Palatinit® for general use in 1983 and in 1987 France also cleared Palatinit® for general use and Sweden cleared Palatinit® for use in confections and chocolate. Clearances for individual Palatinit®-containing food products have been given in Denmark and Germany. In many other European countries the basic safety and usefulness of Palatinit® have been recognised. The authorisation process follows the procedures of these countries. In the US a petition for GRAS-affirmation is pending.

INTRODUCTION

Palatinit®* is a hydrogenated isomer of sucrose which provides the bulk, texture, bland taste and most of the sweetness which sucrose normally supplies to foodstuffs.

Palatinit® is an equimolar mixture of two isomers; the chemical formulas of these are given below.

α-D-Glucopyranosyl-(1→6)-mannitol   α-D-Glucopyranosyl-(1→6)-sorbitol

It has important advantages over both sucrose and sorbitol, which is the major bulk substitute for sucrose in dietary and non-cariogenic foods. Compared with sucrose:

— it is more stable against microbial fermentation and enzymatic and acid hydrolysis (e.g. by food acids);
— it is non-cariogenic;
— it is less glucogenic and utilised more slowly;
— it has a lower caloric value.

Compared with most other sugar alcohols:

— it permits use of standard processes and equipment in manufacture of boiled hard candy, and other applications;
— it has better compression characteristics in pressed mint manufacture;
— it has better taste and organoleptic qualities;
— it permits better fixation of flavour and essential oils;

* Isomalt is the generic name as approved by the British Pharmacopoeia and Codex Alimentarius.

— coating, glazing and panning operations are much easier and more economic;
— chocolate and fondant textures are greatly improved;
— it has a better shelf-life in baked goods and semi-finished products for the baking industry.

Additionally, the non-hygroscopic nature of Palatinit® is very beneficial in protecting moisture-sensitive ingredients against decomposition during processing or on storage. This permits applications outside the candy technology area as well. It has been noted that pastry structure, such as in pie crusts, is much improved with Palatinit® utilisation.

Extensive development work by the food industry in Europe and in the USA has shown that Palatinit® can be substituted on a gram-per-gram basis for sucrose, glucose, mannitol and sorbitol in a wide variety of foodstuffs to produce high-quality products of considerable consumer benefit. An increasing number of products containing Palatinit® are marketed to final consumers in Europe.

PRODUCTION PROCESS

The production process involves two essential steps. In the first step the 1,2-glycosidic linkage between glucose and fructose moieties of sucrose ($C_{12}H_{22}O_{11}$) is rearranged by an immobilised enzyme system to a 1,6-glycosidic linkage. The result is the disaccharide isomaltulose ($C_{12}H_{22}O_{11}$).

In the second step the rearranged sucrose molecule is hydrogenated to the polyol form. The result is an equimolar mixture of glucose–sorbitol and glucose–mannitol, i.e. Palatinit®.

The manufacture of Palatinit® is a safe process and follows good manufacturing practices. Methods of analysis of Palatinit®, as such and in food products, have been established and are made available upon request. (For a more detailed description of the production process see Ref. 1.)

PHYSICAL CHARACTERISTICS

The sweetening power of Palatinit® is approximately 0·5 to 0·6 in comparison with saccharose (=1) in a 10% solution. As is the case

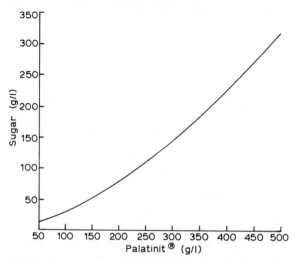

FIG. 1. Aqueous isosweet solution of Palatinit® at 20°C in comparison to sucrose in g/litre.

with other sweeteners, the sweetening power of Palatinit® is dependent on the concentration (see Fig. 1).

The taste profile of Palatinit® is purely sweet, with no aftertaste, comparable to saccharose. In aromatised foodstuffs, Palatinit® intensifies the aroma effect (flavour transfer).

Synergistic effects appear when Palatinit® is mixed with other sugar alcohols, for example xylitol, sorbitol, or Lycasin, or when Palatinit® is used with intense sweeteners (saccharin, cyclamate, aspartame, acesulfame K).

Many polyols have a *negative heat of solution*; i.e. they cause (in the mouth) a more or less pronounced cooling effect. This effect is desirable in products with a peppermint or menthol flavour, but is considered atypical in many other products. Palatinit® has a low negative heat of solution of 39·4 kJ/kg (see Table 1).

The boiling temperature of highly concentrated Palatinit® solutions was ascertained experimentally. To obtain the same final water content in comparison to sucrose solutions, a Palatinit® solution must be maintained at a higher boiling temperature (see Fig. 2).

An important characteristic of Palatinit® is the limited *solubility* in comparison to saccharose and fructose. The maximal concentration is 25% (20°C). This solubility suffices for many applications. In the manufacture of fruit products (marmalades, preserves), the content

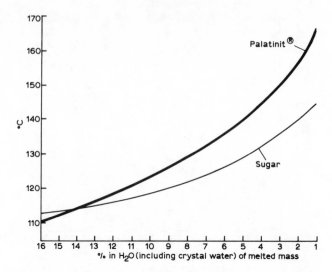

FIG. 2. Temperature and solubility of Palatinit® and sugar solutions.

TABLE 1
Dissolving Heat of Solutions of Sugar and Sugar-Alcohols

	Dissolving heat	
Bulking agents	*kJ/mol*	*kJ/kg*
Saccharose	− 6·21	− 18·16
Sorbitol	−20·2	−110·99
Mannitol	−22·0	−120·88
Xylitol	−23·27	−153·07
Palatinit®	−14·6	− 39·4

of dry substance in the product should not exceed 26% to avoid recrystallisation of Palatinit® (see Fig. 3).

The *viscosity and density* of aqueous Palatinit® solutions differ only minimally from the corresponding saccharose solution and do not require any special consideration regarding production techniques (see Fig. 4).

The *hygroscopicity* of Palatinit® is very low. Palatinit® does not take up water at a temperature of 25°C and a relative humidity (RH) up to 85%. At environmental temperatures of 60°C and 80°C, the

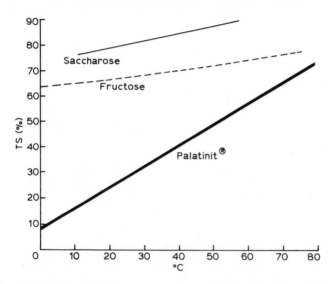

FIG. 3. Solubility of fructose, sucrose and Palatinit® dependent on temperature.

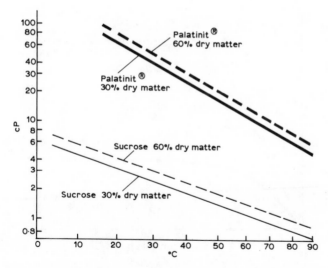

FIG. 4. Viscosity of Palatinit® and sucrose at different concentrations against temperature.

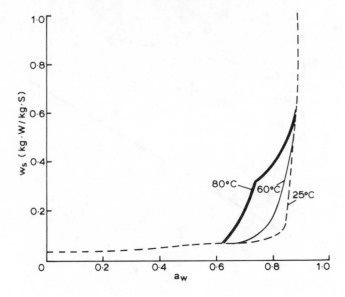

FIG. 5. Sorption isotherms of Palatinit®.

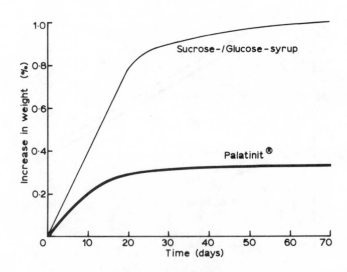

FIG. 6. Hygroscopicity of Palatinit® hard caramels in comparison to saccharose/glucose syrup hard caramels at a relative humidity of 45%, and 20°C room temperature.

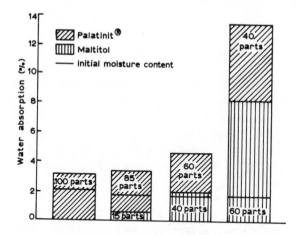

FIG. 7. Water absorption of high boilings (candies) of various composition after storage (8 days) at 72% relative humidity.

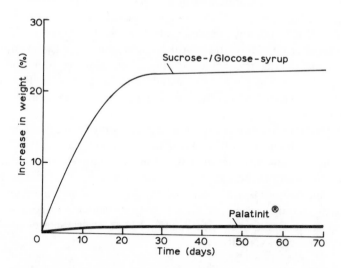

FIG. 8. Hygroscopicity of Palatinit® hard caramels in comparison to saccharose/ glucose syrup hard caramels at a relative humidity of 76%, and 20°C room temperature.

point of water absorption is reached at 75% RH and 65% RH, respectively (see Figs 5–8).

CHEMICAL CHARACTERISTICS

Palatinit® is extremely resistant to chemical alterations. When the crystalline substance is heated above the sintering point or the aqueous solution above the boiling point, it does not result in any changes in the molecular structure, e.g. no dehydration or caramelisation. Palatinit® also does not react with other ingredients in the recipe, e.g. with amino acids to produce Maillard reactions (melanoidins).

It is well known that the H^+-activated or enzymatic hydrolysis of disaccharides is all the more easy, the higher the energy gain during hydrolysis. The energy gain is highest when the two monosaccharides, as is the case in saccharose, are bound at their glycosidic hydroxyl group; it is lowest in (1–6) bonds, as is the case in Palatinit®. Thus, saccharose is completely hydrolysed in 0·01 N HCl at 100°C in less than one-half hour, while the complete hydrolysis of Palatinit® in 1 N HCl at 100°C is only completed after two hours. In 0·1 N HCl at 100°C, after ten hours, the hydrolysis of Palatinit® is only two-thirds complete. Under the worst conditions that might be found in the production of foods (pH level < 2, duration of heating at 100°C for one hour), a 10% hydrolysis of Palatinit® is the maximum that occurs.

Enzymatic hydrolysis can be practically left out of consideration for the production of foods. Due to the minor hydrolysis of Palatinit® into its components glucose, sorbitol and mannitol, the precondition for all further microbiological processes is lacking. That means that Palatinit® cannot be utilised as a substrate by most of the organisms (yeasts, moulds, bacteria) found in foods and beverages. Thus, products manufactured with Palatinit® have a very high degree of microbiological stability.

METABOLISM

It has been demonstrated *in vitro* that Palatinit® is cleaved by the human intestinal disaccharidase enzyme complex more slowly than sucrose by a factor of about 11 versus a factor of 8 in the rat.[2] This results in delayed and incomplete hydrolysis in the small intestine. In man[3-5] as well as in the rat,[6] it has been demonstrated that serum insulin levels and blood glucose levels after ingestion of isomalt increase at a much slower rate than after ingestion of sucrose.

Studies to quantify the absorption of Palatinit® from the small intestine have shown that *ca.* 60% of the Palatinit® ingested by man[7] as well as by the pig[8, 9] appears in the terminal ileum in the form of uncleaved Palatinit® and the cleavage products sorbitol, mannitol and glucose. On the basis of the ingested gross energy of Palatinit®, the retrieval rate of the Palatinit® energy from the small intestine is about 85% of the gross energy of the administered Palatinit®. In the pig, this amount did not depend on the dose (5% or 10% of the rations) or on the form of administration (Palatinit® administered separately or as an ingredient of the ration). In adapted humans, it has also been demonstrated that the extent of fermentation in the large intestine is proportional to the amount of Palatinit® ingested at dose levels of 20–50 g per day.[10]

Substantial amounts of Palatinit® cannot be detected in the faeces of adapted humans[2] or adapted rats[2,11] and pigs[8] after ingestion of this disaccharide alcohol, so the Palatinit® that enters the large intestine must be subject to complete bacterial fermentation. *In vitro*, it was also demonstrated that Palatinit® is completely degraded by the chymes of the terminal ileum of pigs to form volatile fatty acids, CO_2, CH_4 and H_2.[12]

According to studies in rats[13] and pigs,[8, 13] the apparent digestibility of the energy of Palatinit® is in the range of 85–90%, whereas the corresponding value for sucrose is 98%.

ENERGY UTILISATION OF PALATINIT® FOR FOOD-LABELLING PURPOSES*

Studies in Rats and Pigs

By means of comparative slaughter experiments, the retained energy was determined after ingestion of rations containing Palatinit® by rats and pigs over long periods of time. In young growing rats in the weight range of 40–145 g, administration of rations containing 30% Palatinit®, added to supplement a basic diet, yielded 19% less

---

* The author is especially grateful for the contribution of F. Berschauer to this section.

retained energy than an isocaloric amount of sucrose. Under the hypothesis that the basal part of the diet in experimental groups and control supplied the same available energy, the contribution of Palatinit® to energy retention was 76% lower than of sucrose in the control group.[14]

In a comparable experimental setup with heavy rats (200–250 g) energy retention was reduced by 31% in the Palatinit® group. Under the same hypothesis Palatinit® caused a slightly negative contribution to energy retention in comparison with sucrose.[15]

In a comparative slaughter experiment on pigs, rations containing 20% Palatinit® (percentage by weight) yielded a 13% lower energy retention than the comparative diet in which Palatinit® was replaced by 20% sucrose. The contribution of Palatinit® to energy retention was 63% reduced in this study in comparison with sucrose.[16]

In a respiration experiment on adult pigs, it was found that the energy retained by the animals was 18% lower after administering rations that contained 30% Palatinit® (percentage by weight) than in the comparative animals that received sucrose instead of Palatinit®. Calculation of the contribution of Palatinit® to energy retention in this experiment yielded a 78% lower value in comparison with sucrose.[13]

All experiments performed on rats and pigs regarding the energy utilisation of Palatinit® have thus definitely documented the fact that this sugar substitute is utilised to a much lower extent than glucose or sucrose.

The type of calculation described above yields a correct result for a specific experiment with regard to the contribution of Palatinit® to energy retention, but is unsatisfactory because different values are obtained depending on the growth and the energy intake of the animals. On the basis of these experimental findings, the utilisation coefficients of the energy available for energy retention were calculated for Palatinit®. Average values were assumed for the energy maintenance requirement and for the energy utilisation coefficients for protein and fat retention. Those values have been determined in numerous scientific experiments of energy utilisation of various feeds for laboratory animals and farm animals.[17–19] Under the assumption that the maintenance requirement is covered only by the basic diet and is the same in the control group and in the experimental group the utilisation of the energy available for energy retention of Palatinit® is, on average, 58% lower in rats and 40% lower in pigs than in sucrose.

Studies in Man

Using the indirect calorimetry method, the production of CO_2 and the respiratory quotient were measured in human volunteers over a period of four hours after ingestion of 60 g sucrose or 60 g Palatinit®. During the test period, the energy utilisation of Palatinit® calculated on this basis was found to be 65% lower in comparison with that of sucrose.[2]

Results of a comparable magnitude were obtained in a controlled cross-over study on humans. Carbohydrate oxidation after ingestion of 30 g sucrose or 31·6 g Palatinit® was determined over a period of six hours. Within this period of time, carbohydrate oxidation had returned to its initial value. The energy utilisation of Palatinit® calculated from carbohydrate oxidation was only 43% in comparison with that of sucrose, or only 41% if the fact that the Palatinit® dose was 5% higher is taken into account.[3]

In a three-month controlled tolerance study, either 24 g sucrose (at 4 kcal/g) or 48 g Palatinit® (at 2 kcal/g) were administered for three weeks to volunteers receiving a total daily caloric intake of 1500 kcal. In both groups the weight loss in the trial period was 1·3 kg.[20] Thus 24 g sucrose are the energy equivalent of 48 g Palatinit®, and it must be concluded that Palatinit® provided 2 kcal per gram.

Conclusion

The utilisation of partially absorbable carbohydrates like Palatinit® results from the utilisation of the monosaccharides absorbed in the small intestine as well as from utilisation of the volatile fatty acids originating from fermentation in the large intestine.[21-27]

The numerous comparative nutritional studies on monogastric animals (rat/pig) as well as on humans have shown that with regard to digestion, absorption and energy utilisation, there are no fundamental qualitative differences between these different foods.

Regarding energy utilisation of Palatinit®, greater significance should be accorded to the studies performed on humans than to the animal experiments for two reasons.[2,3] First this is because energy utilisation for maintenance requirements, which is more important for man, was measured and second because the studies were performed in the relevant species, man, thus eliminating problems in transferring data from animal experiments to man.

If all the experiments in energy utilisation of Palatinit® on animals are taken into account, it is found that the contribution of Palatinit® to energy retention is at least 50% lower than that of sucrose or glucose. The animal experiments have shown, for Palatinit® in comparison with sucrose, a 50% reduced efficiency in metabolising energy available for energy retention. Studies on man have shown a 50–65% lower utilisation for maintenance of this sugar substitute. It thus seems justified to establish a physiological caloric value of 2 kcal/g for the food labelling of Palatinit®.

OTHER METABOLIC ASPECTS

Serum glucose and serum insulin responses in diabetics and in healthy people are much slower and lower than after intake of sucrose. Therefore Palatinit® can be well incorporated in diets for diabetics.[2–5,28–32]

Oral bacteria are virtually unable to ferment Palatinit®. Acid production and glucan synthesis are inhibited. In animal experiments Palatinit® causes almost no caries. In telemetry tests with humans the pH-curves stay clearly above 5·7.[33–42]

Tolerance of the gastrointestinal tract to Palatinit® has been explicitly monitored in numerous animal studies and in humans in a wide dose and age range.[3,4,5,8,10,16,20,29–32,35,43–46] Intestinal intolerance due to osmotic effects does occur occasionally.

Tolerance is, however, a multi-dimensional phenomenon with interpersonal, intrapersonal and environmental differences: no simple dose–symptom relationship can be found. As a general result it can be said that continued daily doses of at least 50 grams are very well tolerated. The same holds for acute doses of at least 35 grams.

REGULATORY SITUATION

In advance of the regulatory processes, extensive safety testing of Palatinit® was done. These studies have fulfilled the requirements of good laboratory practice (GLP) and comprise a classical set of subchronic, chronic, cancerogenic and reproduction studies of toxicity in four species.

The data have been reviewed by a great number of experts, with positive comments. Among these we note:

— JECFA, 1981; ADI not specified, 1985.
— EEC Scientific Committee on Food, 1985.

— Swiss Eidgenössische Ernährungs-Kommission, 1983.
— British Ministry of Agriculture, Fisheries and Food, 1982.
— Dutch Toezicht op de Volksgezondheid, 1985.
— French Conseil Supérieur de l'Hygiène, 1985.
— German Bundesgesundheitsamt und deutsche Forschungs-gemeinschaft, 1985.

Clearances have been given in a number of countries, as indicated hereunder:

— Switzerland, 1983.
— United Kingdom, 1983.
— France, 1987; Hong Kong, 1987; Sweden, 1987 (confections and chocolate).
— The actual Dutch law does not request clearance (negative list system). The Dutch system will change for sweeteners from a negative list to a positive list. Palatinit® is on the new positive list (proposed legislation).
— In the Federal Republic of Germany the first provisional clearances, e.g. for test marketing, were given in 1981. In 1986 final product clearance was given. Many more are pending.
— In Denmark a first final product clearance was issued in 1986.

PROCESSABILITY

The processability of Palatinit® can be very well compared with sucrose but with a few, important exceptions. These are determined by three characteristics:

1. Palatinit® has a low hygroscopicity.
2. Palatinit® has a low solubility.
3. The mannitol part of Palatinit® crystallises with two mols of water of crystallisation.

The first characteristic makes it extremely well suited for all kinds of hard candy (filled and unfilled) (Figs 6, 8 and 9).

The second characteristic means that Palatinit®, in solid products with a high water content, tends to recrystallise quickly: e.g. jams, jelly beans, sugared fruits, toffees. Therefore mixtures of Palatinit® with other sugar alcohols, e.g. maltitol, hydrogenated glucose syrups, have to be used. In these mixtures Palatinit® compensates

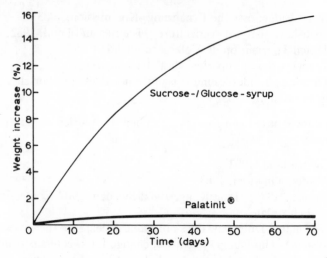

FIG. 9. Hygroscopicity of Palatinit® hard caramels in comparison to saccharose/glucose syrup hard caramels at a relative humidity of 63%, and 20°C room temperature.

TABLE 2
Sugar-Free Palatinit® Coating Scheme for the Open System

Processing parameters	Hard-panned goods with sucrose	Hard-panned goods with Palatinit®	Soft-panned goods with Palatinit®
Tablets	40 kg	40 kg	40 kg
Dry matter content of the solution	70%	starting with 69% after 5 cycles 72%	starting with 69% after 5 cycles 72%
Temperature of the solution	80°C	not less than 75°C	—
Components in the solution dry matter content	100% sucrose	100% Palatinit®	—
Dosage per cycle	approx. 1·2 kg	approx. 1·1 kg	
Number of cycles	14	14	12
Drying time (min)	15	15	5
Total coating-time (min)	225	225	98

A softer coating for the hard-panned goods may be achieved by adding 3% gum arabic into the Palatinit®-solution.

TABLE 3
Palatinit® Table Top. (How Complicated should a Label be?)

Ingredients	Brand A	Brand B	Palatinit® development product
Intense sweetener	Brand X	Brand Y	Brand X or Y
Number of processing aids	6	3	1 (Palatinit®)

very well the hygroscopic characteristics of these bulk sweeteners (Fig. 7). The same characteristics make Palatinit® extremely well suited for pan-coating where better processing times are obtained than with sucrose. Combined with its low hygroscopicity, Palatinit® coatings give an ideal protection for confections that are sensitive to staling and drying out (Table 2).

The low solubility, low hygroscopicity and high chemical stability make Palatinit® very well suited as a carrier for sensitive ingredients like pharmaceuticals, intense sweeteners and flavours (Table 3).

The third characteristic plays a role especially in chocolate manufacture. From 60°C onwards the water of crystallisation comes off causing problems in chocolate products. In conches and their related equipment Palatinit® tends to condense on the moving parts when the temperature is above 60°C. However, with careful processing some of the best-tasting sugar-free chocolates in the world have been made with Palatinit®.

In all other applications, e.g. baked goods, ice-cream, pressed mints, marzipans, desserts, classical recipes can be used with minor adaptations.

REFERENCES

1. SCHIWECK, H. (1980). Palatinit®-Herstellung, technologische Eigenschaften und Analytik palatinithaltiger Lebensmittel, *Alimenta*, **19**, 5–16.
2. GRUPP, U. and SIEBERT, G. (1978). Metabolism of Hydrogenated Palatinose, an Equimolar Mixture of α-D-Glucopyranosido-1,6-sorbitol and α-D-Glucopyranosido-1, 6-mannitol, *Res. Exp. Med.*, **173**, 261–78.

3. THIEBAUD, D., JACOT, E., SCHMITZ, H., SPENGLER, M. and FELBER, J. P. (1984). Comparative Study of Isomalt and Sucrose by Means of Continuous Indirect Calorimetry, *Metabolism*, **33**, 808–31.
4. SIEBERT, G., GRUPP, U. and HEINKEL, K. (1975). Studies on Isomaltitol, *Nutr. Metabol.*, **18** (Supp. 1), 191–6.
5. BACHMANN, W., HASLBECK, M., SPENGLER, M., SCHMITZ, H. and MEHNERT, H. (1984). Untersuchungen zur Stoffwechselbeeinflussung durch akute Palatinit®-Gaben, *Akt. Ernähr.*, **9**, 65–70.
6. KIRCHGESSNER, M., ZINNER, P. M. and ROTH, H.-P. (1983). Energiestoffwechsel und Insulinaktivität bei Ratten nach Palatinit-Fütterung, *Intern. J. Vit. Nutr. Res.*, **53**, 86–93.
7. KRONENBERG, H.-G., SPENGLER, M. and STROHMEYER, G. (1983). Zur Resorption von Palatinit®, dem äquimolekularen Gemisch von α-D-Glucopyranosido-1,6-Sorbit (GPS) und α-D-Glucopyranosido-1,6-Mannit (GPM) im Dünndarm von colectomierten Patienten. (Persönliche Mitteilung.)
8. VAN WEERDEN, E. J., HUISMAN, J. and VAN LEEUWEN, P. (1984). *The Digestion Process of Palatinit® in the Intestinal Tract of the Pig (Report Nr. 528a vom 6.1.1984).* ILOB-Institut voor landouwkundig Onderzoek van biochemische Producten, Wageningen.
9. VAN WEERDEN, E. J., HUISMAN, J. and VAN LEEUWEN, P. (1984). *Further Studies on the Digestive Process of Palatinit® in the Pig (Report Nr. 530 vom 15.2.1984).* ILOB-Institut voor landouwkundig Onderzoek van biochemische Producten, Wageningen.
10. FRITZ, M., SIEBERT, G. and KASPER, H. (1985). Dose Dependence of Breath Hydrogen and Methane in Healthy Volunteers after Ingestion of a Commercial Disaccharide Mixture, Palatinit®, *Brit. J. Nutr.*, **54**, 389–400.
11. ZINNER, P. M., KIRCHGESSNER, M., ASCHERL, R. and ERHARDT, W. (1985). Zur präcäcalen Absorption von Palatinit® beim ausgewachsenen Schwein, *Z. Tierphysiol., Tierernährg. u. Futtermittelkd*, **53**, 79–83.
12. BOL, J. and KNOL, W. (1982). In Vitro *Fermentation of Palatinit®, Report No. A 82.302/220828.* Civo Institutes TNO, Zeist, Netherlands.
13. KIRCHGESSNER, M. and MÜLLER, H. L. (1983). Palatinit®-Verdaulichkeit, Umsetzbarkeit und Verwertung der Energie im Modellversuch an Sauen, *Z. Ernährungswiss.*, **22**, 234–40.
14. STAUDACHER, W. and KIRCHGESSNER, M. (1984). Protein- und Fettansatz sowie Energieverwertung bei Verfütterung von Palatinit® an wachsenden Ratten, *Z. Tierphysiol., Tierernährg. u. Futtermittelkd.*, **52**, 272–83.
15. ZINNER, P. M. and KIRCHGESSNER, M. (1982). Zur energetischen Verwertung von Palatinit®, *Z. Ernährungswiss.*, **21**, 272–8.
16. FEVRIER, C. and PASCAL, G. (1986). *Utilisation énergétique du Palatinit® et du saccharose chez le porc en finition*, INRA, Station de Recherches sur l'Elevage des Porcs.
17. MENKE, K.-H. and HUSS, W. (1980). *Tierernährung und Futtermittelkunde*, Verlag Eugen Ulmer, Stuttgart.

18. SCHIMANN, R., NEHRING, K., HOFFMANN, L., JENTSCH, W. and CHUDY, A. (1971). *Energetische Futterbewertung und Energienormen*, VEB Deutscher Landwirtschaftsverlag, Berlin.
19. MOUNT, L. E. (1980). *Energy Metabolism*, Butterworth, London.
20. SPENGLER, M., SOMOGYI, J. C., PLETCHER, E. and BOEHME, K. (1987). Tolerability, acceptance and energetic conversion of isomalt (Palatinit®) in comparison with sucrose. *Aktuelle Ernährungsmedizin*, **6** (12), 210–14.
21. GROSSKLAUS, R. (1983). Energy Gaps?, *Nutr. Res.*, **3**, 595–604.
22. WIGGINS, H. S. (1984). Nutritional Value of Sugars and Related Compounds Undigested in the Small Gut, *Proc. Nutr. Soc.*, **43**, 69–75.
23. RUPPIN, H., BAR-MEIR, S., SOERGEL, K. H., WOOD, C. M. and SCHMITT Jr, M. G. (1980). Absorption of Short-Chain Fatty Acids by the Colon, *Gastroenterology*, **78**, 1500–7.
24. UMESAKI, Y., YAJIMA, T., YOKOKURA, T. and MUTAI, M. (1979). Effect of Organic Acid Absorption on Bicarbonate Transport in Rat Colon, *Pflügers Arch.*, **379**, 43–7.
25. CUMMINGS, J. H. (1984). Microbial Digestion of Complex Carbohydrates in Man, *Proc. Nutr. Soc.*, **43**, 35–44.
26. UMESAKI, Y., YAJIMA, T., TOHYMA, K. and KUTAI, M. (1980). Characterization of Acetate Uptake by the Colonic Epithelial Cells of the Rat, *Pflügers Arch.*, **388**, 205–9.
27. ARGENZIA, R. A. and SOUTHWORTH, M. (1974). Sites of Organic Acid Production and Absorption in Gastrointestinal Tracts of the Pig, *Am. J. Physiol.*, **228**, 454–60.
28. KEUP, U. and PÜTTER, J. (1974). Serumglucose- and insulinverlauf bei gesunden Probanden nach einmaliger oraler Palatinit- bzw. Saccharosebelastung, *Pharma-Bericht Nr. 4781 vom 01.07.1974*, Bayer AG.
29. DROST, H., GIERLICH, P., SPENGLER, M. and JAHNKE, K. (1980). Blutglucose und Seruminsulin nach oraler Applikation von Palatinit im Vergleich zu Glucose bei Diabetikern vom Erwachsenentyp, *Verh. dtsch. Ges. Inn. Med.*, **86**, 978–81.
30. PETZOLDT, R., LAUER, P., SPENGLER, M. and SCHÖFFLING, K. (1982). Palatinit bei Typ-II-Diabetikern: Wirkung auf Blutglucose, Seruminsulin, C-Peptid und freie Fettsäuren im Vergleich zu Glucose, *Deutsche Medizinische Wochenschrift*, **107** (No. 50), 1910–13.
31. KASPAR, L. and SPENGLER, M. (1984). Wirkung oraler Gaben von Palatinit® auf den Insulin-Verbrauch bei Typ-I-Diabetikern, *Akt. Ernähr.*, **9**, 60–4.
32. POMETTA, D. and TRABICHET, C. (1985). Rapport concernant l'utilisation du Palatinit chez les diabetiques de type II traités par le regime seul. Hôpital Cantonal Universitaire de Génève, 12.09.1983, *Akt. Ernähr.*, **10**, 174–7.
33. BRAMSTEDT, F., GEHRING, F. and KARLE, E. J. (1976). Prüfung der Kariogenität von Palatinit im Vergleich zu Xylit und Saccharose im Tierexperiment, *Bericht vom 07.12.1976*.
34. KARLE, E. J. and GEHRING, F. (1979). Kariogenitätsuntersuchungen von Zukeraustauschstoffen an xerostomierten Ratten, *Dtsch. zahnärztl. Z.*, **34**, 551–4.

35. KARLE, E. J. and GEHRING, F. (1978). Palatinit®, ein neuer Zucker-austauschstoff und seine karies-prophylaktische Beurteilung, *Dtsch. zahnärtzl. Z.*, **31**, 189–91.

36. VAN DER HOEVEN, J. S. (1980). The Cariogenicity of Disaccharide Alcohols in Rats, *Caries Res.*, **14**, 61–6.

37. MÜHLEMANN, H. R. (1978). Effects of Topical Application of Sugar Substitutes on Bacterial Agglomerate Formation, Caries Incidence and Solution Rates of Molars in the Rat, *Bericht vom 16.02.1978.*

38. GEHRING, F. and KARLE, E. J. (1981). Der Saccharoseaustauschstoff Palatinit® unter besonderer Berücksichtigung mikrobiologischer und kariesprophylaktischer Aspekte, *Z. Ernährungswiss.*, **20**, 96–106.

39. CIARDI, J., BOWEN, W. H., ROLLA, G. and NAGORSKI, K. (1983). Effect of Sugar Substitutes on Bacterial Growth, Acid Production and Glucansynthesis, *J. dent. Res.*, **62**, 182.

40. IMFELD, T. N., HIRSCH, R. S. and MÜHLEMANN, H. R. (1978). Telemetric Recordings of Interdental Plaque pH during Different Meal Patterns, *Brit. dent. J.*, **144**, 40–5.

41. IMFELD, T. N. (1983). Identification of Low Caries Risk Dietary Components, *Karger*, Basel, 117–41.

42. GEHRING, F. and HUFNAGEL, H.-D. (1983). Intra- und extraorale pH-Messungen an Zahnplaques des Menschen nach Spülungen mit einigen Zucker- und Saccharoseaustauschstofflösungen, *Oralprophylaxe*, **5**, 13–19.

43. MUSCH, K., SIEBERT, G., SCHIWECK, H. and STEINLE, G. (1973). Ernährungsphysiologische Untersuchungen mit Isomaltit an der Ratte, *Z. Ernährungswiss. (Suppl.)*, **15**, 3–16.

44. PÜTTER, J. and SPENGLER, M. (1975). Zur Verträglichkeit von Palatinit® (BAY i 3930) als Einzeldosis, *Pharma-Bericht Nr. 5475*, Bayer AG.

45. SPENGLER, M. and SCHMITZ, H. (1984). Gastrointestinale Toleranz älterer Menschen gegenüber oraler Gaben von Palatinit® (Generic Name: Isomalt) bei Gabe von Tagesdosen à 24 g über 10 Wochen, *Pharma-Bericht Nr. 13218*, Bayer AG.

46. PAIGE, D. M., BAYLESS, T. M. and DAVIS, L. R. (1986). *The Evaluation of Palatinit Digestibility*, Johns Hopkins University, Baltimore, Maryland, Revised Report II, May 1986.

7

Polydextrose

P. R. MURRAY

Pfizer Chemicals, Sandwich, Kent, UK

ABSTRACT

Consumer interest in reduced- and low-calorie food and beverage products is growing, and as a result these markets are now beginning to show very exciting expansion. However, for this trend to continue, new products entering the market must have good consumer acceptance and taste. Many of the previous problems experienced in creating these types of foods can now be overcome with polydextrose.

Polydextrose is a unique, low-calorie (1 kcal/g) bulking agent made from glucose, which allows the creation of reduced- and low-calorie foods by replacing all or part of the sugars and some of the fats, without sacrificing mouthfeel, texture, bulk or palatability.

Applications with calorie reductions of 25–90% include: ice-cream, baked goods, jams, yoghurts, soft drinks, frozen dairy desserts, puddings, confectionery, cereal bars and snack products.

Polydextrose is not sweet, so sweetness levels can be adjusted over a wide range to meet consumer demands for reduced sugar products.

Polydextrose is only partially digested in a similar way to dietary fibre, therefore most of it is metabolically unavailable to man. Furthermore, it does not affect the utilisation of vitamins, minerals or essential amino acids and will cause fewer problems than the other sugar replacers currently used in foods.

In dental tests polydextrose was shown not to promote tooth decay or plaque formation; therefore it can be used to develop reduced-cariogenic foods and confectionery.

Polydextrose is approved for food use in the USA and many European countries, with approval pending in several others. Its use in special reduced-energy foods is also formally endorsed by an increasing number of Diabetic Associations.

Polydextrose foods can, therefore, be used as part of a balanced, reduced-energy diet to make it more interesting, enjoyable and satisfying, with the added benefits of reduced fat and sugar consumption.

INTRODUCTION

In many countries, the reduced- and low-calorie food and beverage markets are now showing very exciting growth. This development offers exceptional marketing opportunities to many food companies, first because they are new markets, and second because people are indicating a strong interest in healthy eating, dieting and weight control. More than 78 million Americans now regularly consume low-calorie products.[1] The beverage industry is meeting these new demands with better-tasting diet soft drinks and 'light' beers, and their efforts have been rewarded by considerable expansion of market demand for their products.

Exciting new markets, for better-tasting reduced-calorie foods, can now be shared by many other food companies, as many of the previous problems in creating these food products may now be overcome with polydextrose, a low-calorie bulking agent made from glucose.

Food products with a third fewer calories can readily be made by replacing part of the sugar and fat in the food with polydextrose. When all of the sugars and part of the fat are replaced and a good

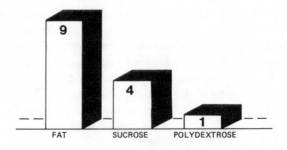

FIG. 1. Caloric utilisation values (kcal/g).

intense sweetener is used, calorie reductions of 50% or more are possible. These large caloric reductions are possible because polydextrose is only partially metabolised in man, resulting in an energy value of only 1 kcal/g. Compare this with fat which has approximately 9 kcal/g and most sugars which have about 4 kcal/g (Fig. 1). This inherent low-calorie property allows the development of good-quality, reduced-energy foods.

POLYDEXTROSE—PRODUCT DESCRIPTION, COMPOSITION AND STRUCTURE

Polydextrose was discovered at Pfizer Central Research Laboratories by Dr H. H. Rennhard, who explored a series of polysaccharides for their potential as non-caloric or reduced-calorie replacements for sugar and as partial replacements for fat, flour and starch.[2] The polysaccharides were prepared by the thermal polymerisation of glucose in the presence of an acid that functions as catalyst and a relatively small amount of polyol that functions as a plasticiser. Many polymers of glucose were prepared and evaluated, but polydextrose, which uses citric acid as the catalyst and sorbitol as the polyol, was eventually chosen as it exhibited optimum functional properties.

Polydextrose is a water-soluble, randomly bonded condensation polymer of glucose, containing minor amounts of bound sorbitol and citric acid. As shown, polydextrose is composed almost entirely of randomly cross-linked glucose polymers with all types of glucosidic bonds, the 1–6 bond predominating, and it contains some sorbitol end-groups and monoester bonds with citric acid (Fig. 2). Along with the polymer itself, there are small amounts of the residual starting materials, glucose, sorbitol and citric acid. In addition, small amounts of levoglucosan and hydroxymethyl-furfural are produced as a result of caramelisation of glucose (Table 1). Both of these substances occur widely in foods since they are formed whenever sugar is heated or starch is acid-degraded. Sorbitol plays an important role in the polymerisation by helping to control the upper molecular weight limit and preventing the formation of water-insoluble materials. The approximate percentage molecular weight distribution is shown in Table 2. Note that there is little or no polymer with molecular weight over 15 000.

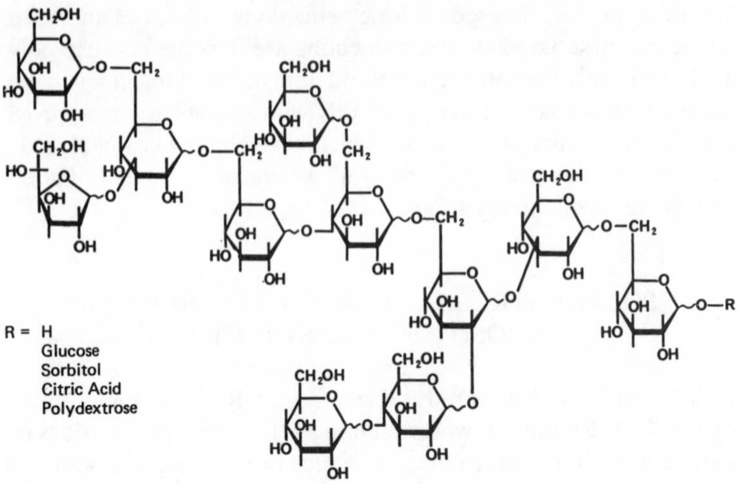

FIG. 2. Illustration of chemical bonds present in polydextrose.

TABLE 1
Polydextrose Composition

	%
Polymer	> 90[a]
Glucose	< 4[a]
Sorbitol	< 2[a]
Levoglucosan	< 4[a]
Water	< 4
Sulphated ash	< 0·3

[a] Anhydrous, ash-free basis.

TABLE 2
Approximate Molecular Weight Distribution of
Polydextrose (by Sephadex Chromatography)

Molecular weight range	%
162– 5 000	88·7
5 000–10 000	10·0
10 000–16 000	1·2
16 000–18 000	0·1

Polydextrose is currently available in three forms: polydextrose (powder), polydextrose Type N (70% solution) and polydextrose Type K (powder).

Polydextrose is an amorphous, white to light tan, water-soluble powder and can be used for most applications. It contains residual acidity and, therefore, has a pH range of 2·5 to 3·5.

Polydextrose Type N is a clear, colourless to yellow, 70% solution made by partially neutralising polydextrose with potassium hydroxide. It has a pH range of 5 to 6.

Polydextrose Type K is a dry blend, formulated with potassium bicarbonate so as to provide the same pH as polydextrose Type N solution when dissolved in water.

PROPERTIES

Some of the properties of polydextrose and Types N and K are listed in Table 3. Other properties are as follows:

TABLE 3
Properties of Polydextroses

	Polydextrose	*Polydextrose Type N*	*Polydextrose Type K*
Form	Powder	70% solution	Powder
Appearance	White to tan powder	Clear, colourless to yellow	White to tan powder
pH (in solution)	2·5 to 3·5	5·0 to 6·0	5·0 to 6·0
Neutralising agent	—	Potassium hydroxide	Potassium bicarbonate

Solubility

Polydextrose is very soluble in water, and solutions with concentrations as high as 80% can be prepared. It is insoluble in ethanol, but is partially soluble in glycerin and propylene glycol. Aqueous solutions can easily be prepared from polydextrose powder, but the rate of solution depends on the speed and shear of the mixing equipment and the manner in which the powder is added to the water. In preparing concentrated solutions, difficulties in dissolving polydextrose in water can be overcome by the slow addition and efficient mechanical dispersion of the polydextrose in hot water. The blending of a second soluble material with the polydextrose as a dispersing agent will also facilitate solution.

Stability

Polydextrose and polydextrose Types N and K both were stable over a 90-day investigative period at 25°C, 45°C, and 60°C. The only significant change was observed at elevated temperatures where the polydextrose Type N exhibited a darkening in colour. The higher the temperature, the greater the rate of change. For this reason storage of the Type N in a cool place is recommended.

Viscosity

Like sucrose, solutions of polydextrose behave as typical Newtonian liquids. Brookfield viscosity-temperature relationships for a 70% solution of polydextrose and a 70% solution of sucrose are shown in Fig. 3. The polydextrose solution is slightly more viscous than the sucrose solution under the same conditions. At 20°C, the difference in viscosity between the two solutions is approximately 1000 cp. The viscosity–concentration relationships for polydextrose and sucrose at 25°C are shown in Fig. 4.

Humectancy

Polydextrose can function as a humectant to prevent or slow undesirable changes (either an increase or a decrease) in the moisture content of food. Figure 5 shows how polydextrose powder absorbs moisture under controlled atmospheric conditions until an equilibrium, which is characteristic of the relative humidity, is reached. Figure 6 demonstrates how polydextrose Type N (70% solution) loses water to attain the same equilibrium. In hard confectionery and baked goods, polydextrose can help control the rate of moisture gain or loss during prolonged periods and, therefore, can serve as an important additive in extending shelf life. The rate of change (gain or loss) of moisture will be affected by several factors such as the nature of the food, the recipe used, and the packaging and conditions under which it is stored or used.

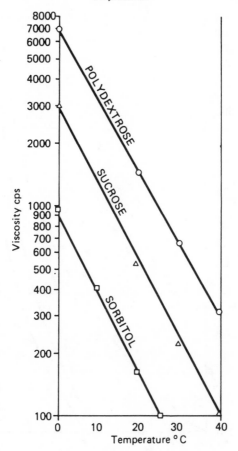

FIG. 3. Temperature/viscosity relationships for 70% solutions.

Equilibrium Relative Humidity

The ERH values of solutions of polydextrose, glucose, sorbitol and sucrose are shown in Table 4.

Melting Properties

Polydextrose is amorphous and melts above 130°C. After cooling, it produces a clear glass with a brittle texture similar to hard confectionery. Unlike sugar, though, polydextrose will not crystallise.

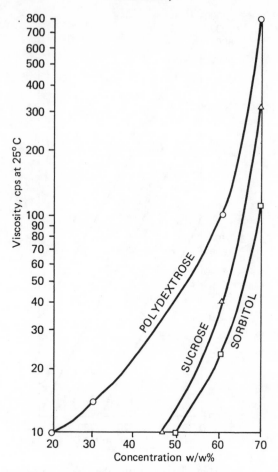

FIG. 4. Concentration/viscosity relationship.

Sweetness

Polydextrose has no sweetness. Consequently, it can provide improved mouthfeel and textural qualities in food without adding excess sweetness.

FUNCTIONALITY

Polydextrose can perform a number of useful functions when replacing sugars and fats. They are as follows:

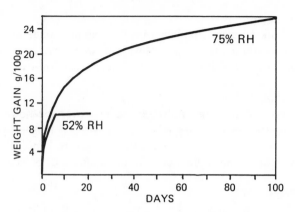

FIG. 5. Hygroscopicity of polydextrose at 25°C.

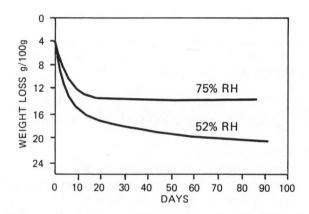

FIG. 6. Loss of water from polydextrose Type N solution at 25°C.

TABLE 4
Equilibrium Relative Humidity (ERH)
at Different Solution Concentrations (% w/w)

Product	40%	50%	60%	70%	80%
Polydextrose	—	> 95%	92%	89%	73%
Sucrose	—	> 95%	91%	—	—
Glucose	92%	89%	86%	—	—
Sorbitol	93%	90%	85%	76%	71%

Bulking Agent

As a bulking agent, polydextrose contributes solids to maintain palatability and textural qualities without sweetness. Its one calorie per gram aids in the development of reduced- and low-calorie foods.

Formulation Aid

As a formulation aid, polydextrose improves the flowability of other ingredients in a dry mix. In preparing a finished product, uniform dispersion and the prevention of severe lumping of other solid ingredients are benefited with the addition of polydextrose.

Humectant

The humectant aspect of polydextrose controls moisture and can thereby provide tenderness and softness in such products as baked goods and confectionery.

Texturiser

As a texturiser, polydextrose provides improved mouthfeel and viscosity qualities. It can be used to control, modify, and improve texture in formulated food products.

METABOLISM AND CALORIC VALUE

Caloric Value

Studies using polydextrose prepared from uniformly radiolabelled ^{14}C-glucose and sorbitol have demonstrated that the maximum utilisation of polydextrose in animal and man is about 25%.[3,4] Therefore, the actual caloric value of polydextrose is 1 kcal/g, compared to 4 kcal/g for most carbohydrates and 9 kcal/g for fats. The low caloric content (1 kcal/g) of polydextrose is due to its poor gastrointestinal absorption and its high resistance to microbial degradation in the colon.[4] After oral administration of polydextrose, the major portion of it (approximately 60%) is excreted unchanged in the faeces (Fig. 7). A fraction of the remaining administered material is utilised by gut microflora and converted into volatile fatty acids (VFA) and carbon dioxide. The latter by-product is of no nutritional value, most of it being expelled as flatus or transported to the lungs and exhaled. The VFAs are absorbed, are caloric to the host, and then eventually expelled as CO_2 in the breath. These microbial metabolites are

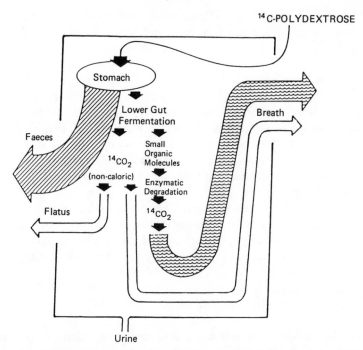

FIG. 7. Summary of the metabolism and disposition of [^{14}C] polydextrose in man and rat.

produced whenever ingested food containing an assimilative carbon source reaches the lower intestine. Essentially, polydextrose is digested like dietary fibre. Clinical studies have shown that the absorption and utilisation of vitamins, minerals and essential amino acids are unaffected.[5]

Toleration

Polydextrose is well tolerated in amounts likely to be ingested in foods, and will cause considerably fewer gastrointestinal problems than sorbitol[6] and other polyols, e.g. maltitol, lactitol, isomalt, etc. which are currently being used in a number of new products. This has been confirmed in practice by a number of major food companies and Diabetic Associations.

In adults, the average polydextrose laxative threshold dosage was found to be 90 g/day (ranging from 50 to 130 g).[7] Children on polydextrose dosages of up to 1 g/kg of body weight/day (the maximum dosage studied) exhibited increased flatulence as the only significant side effect.[8]

Diabetic Suitability

Polydextrose has been formally endorsed by a number of Diabetic Associations. Tests in Type II Diabetics have shown that poly-dextrose does not significantly affect blood glucose or insulin (Figs 8 and 9) levels.[9,10] Secondly, it fits in well with the new dietary recommendations as it can be used to replace some fats and sugars in the various diabetic products so leading to a useful reduction in energy load for the diabetic.

It is considered that between 50 and 70% of all diabetics would benefit from a reduction in energy intake. In the UK polydextrose is not subject to the 25 g maximum daily intake which now applies to all the bulk sweeteners, e.g. sorbitol, fructose, maltitol, lactitol, etc.

REDUCED CARIOGENICITY

In-vitro studies have shown that neutralised polydextrose is not utilised by oral *Streptococcus mutans*, the bacterium responsible for fermenting sugars and producing dental plaque and the acids that lead to carious lesions.[11] Polydextrose does not significantly lower the pH of interdental plaque in humans (Fig. 10). In rats, polydextrose in the diet resulted in less plaque formation, and fewer smooth surface and fissure caries than sucrose.[11] In essence, neutralised polydextrose does not promote tooth decay.

REGULATORY APPROVAL AND LABELLING

Polydextrose and its 1 kcal/g calorie value have been approved in the United Kingdom, United States of America, Canada, Ireland, Switzerland, Sweden, Japan, Austria, Norway, Netherlands, Australasia and Finland. Submissions have been made in West Germany, Belgium, Denmark, France, Spain and Italy. Furthermore, the American, British, Swedish and Norwegian Diabetic Associations have endorsed the use of polydextrose in foods suitable for the diabetic.

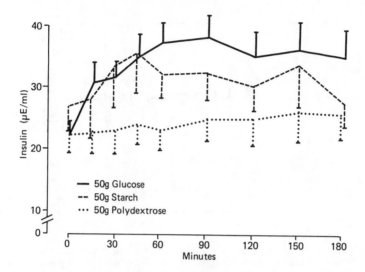

FIG. 8. Serum insulin levels of Type II Diabetics after oral administration of 50 g glucose (——), 50 g starch (----) and 50 g polydextrose (....) ($\bar{x} \pm$ SEM).

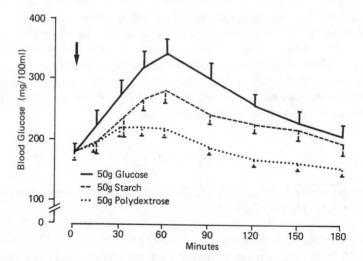

FIG. 9. Capillary blood glucose levels of Type II Diabetics after oral tolerance tests with 50 g glucose (——), 50 g starch (----), and 50 g polydextrose (....) ($\bar{x} \pm$ SEM).

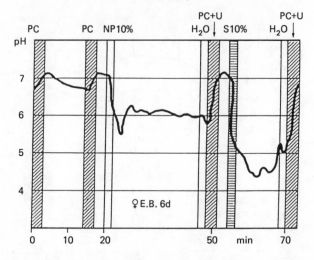

FIG. 10. Telemetric measurement of the pH of interdental plaque. First wash with 10% polydextrose solution followed by 10% sucrose solution. PC = paraffin chew. PC+U = chew with carbamide containing paraffin; NP = polydextrose type N; S = sucrose; H_2O = mouth rinse with water; d = age of plaque in days.

In the UK, polydextrose is approved as a miscellaneous additive (SI 1982 No. 14). Polydextrose should not be used in food products specially prepared for babies or young children. The Association of Public Analysts has approved the 1 kcal/g calorie value and stated that polydextrose should be included in the list of ingredients according to concentration and that the caloric value be included in any nutritional statement. Polydextrose is not a carbohydrate as defined in the 1984 Food Labelling Regulations.

APPLICATIONS

Polydextrose has been successfully evaluated in a number of food products. They include:

Ice-Cream/Dairy Desserts

Polydextrose can be used as a total or partial replacement for sugar, as well as a partial replacement for fat. Very good-quality ice-cream and frozen desserts, with caloric reductions as high as 50%,

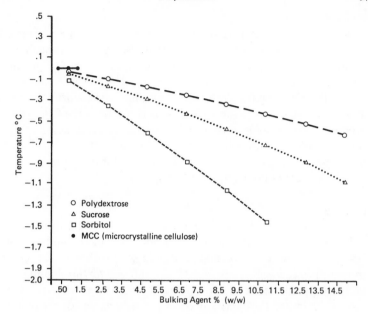

FIG. 11. Freezing points of various concentrations of aqueous solutions of bulking agents or sucrose.

have been made using polydextrose in combination with a bulk sweetener, e.g. fructose, or appropriate intense sweetener, e.g. aspartame. The high viscosity of polydextrose at 0°C gives ice-cream the texture and creaminess of a much higher fat product. Addition levels of 8–15% w/w have been evaluated, with 12% polydextrose giving very good results.[12] Polydextrose solutions show a slightly higher freezing point when compared to equivalent sucrose solutions (Fig. 11); however, sorbitol or fructose can be used to adjust this.[13] Melting rate and overrun are comparable to the standard product.[14,15] Most flavours need to be re-balanced for the aspartame-sweetened products and a number of flavour manufacturers have developed a good range of suitable flavours. It is recommended that the aspartame is added in solution form after pasteurisation to prevent off-flavours developing.

An excellent reduced-calorie ice-cream can be made using fructose in combination with polydextrose.

Baked Goods

Polydextrose functions extremely well in the preparation of baked goods with 33% calorie reduction, such as biscuits, cakes, doughnuts, wafers, pastries and pies. In such products it acts as a bulking and tenderising agent, and may be used as a total or partial replacement for sugar, and as a partial replacement for fat. No significant changes in volume, structure or flavour are observed compared to normal products. The weak acidity of polydextrose is overcome by using a small quantity of sodium bicarbonate in the formulation or, alternatively, polydextrose Type K can be used in the formulation. Dry cake mixes have also demonstrated good shelf life.

Desserts

In combination with a good intense sweetener, e.g. aspartame, polydextrose can be used to make instant and cooked puddings with 50–70% calorie reduction and gelatin desserts with 90% reduction. In these products, polydextrose gives improved texture, mouthfeel, set and appearance, and can also assist dispersion of solids and so reduce lumping. Products stored in foil packaging for six months under accelerated storage conditions remained free flowing and stable.

In instant desserts, levels of 8–9% w/v (as served) (i.e. about 50% w/w of polydextrose in the formulation) were considered optimum for providing the best qualities. A combination of pre-gelatinised tapioca starches and the fine milling of the aspartame gave good flavour and sweetness appreciation. In some formulations the addition of low salt levels helped in increasing viscosity and improving the flavour profile.

Confectionery

Good products with one-third fewer calories and not promoting tooth decay can now be made. Applications include high boilings, chocolate, caramels, toffee, gum drops, marshmallows, fondants and Turkish delight.[16] These can be made on existing equipment with minimal changes in the manufacturing process. Polydextrose can be used to replace part of the sucrose, corn syrup and some fats. It melts above 130°C and after cooling produces a clear glassy product with a brittle texture. Boiling temperatures of polydextrose solutions tend to be slightly higher than equivalent sucrose solutions. Polydextrose prevents the cold flow and storage problems of hydrogenated glucose syrup confectionery and also provides a true calorie reduction for these reduced-cariogenic products.

Low-Calorie Yoghurts

The texture and mouthfeel of artificially sweetened low-fat yoghurts can be improved by the addition of 5–14% polydextrose Type N solution. Reduced sugar fruit conserves can also be made for use in 'Swiss Style' fruit yoghurts.

Jams

Polydextrose can be used in reduced-sugar and diabetic jams to provide solids, improve fruit flavours and reduce calories. Tests have shown that 10–25% w/w polydextrose in these types of product provide the best properties.

Extruded Snacks

New products low in fat, high in fibre and with a calorie reduction are of growing interest. A crisper wholewheat snack, with improved texture and eating qualities, can be obtained by replacing up to 20% of the wheat starch with polydextrose.

Low-Calorie Soft Drinks

Quite often low-calorie soft drinks lack the mouthfeel of the all-sugar counterpart. Polydextrose used at 3–5% w/v replaces this lost mouthfeel and can also help to make the sweetness of the intense sweeteners more rounded and less bitter.

Other Products

Polydextrose has also been successfully evaluated in instant drinks, jellies, milk drinks and powders, cereal bars and sauces.

THE DEVELOPING MARKET

Products in many of these applications are already on the market either in the UK, in Europe or in the USA. By making use of polydextrose's unique combination of properties, good-tasting, reduced-calorie food products can, and are being made. These products are designed to meet the need of the following market groups:

— People who want to keep slim.
— People wanting to control their weight.
— Diabetics.

Polydextrose provides many new exciting opportunities. It helps to create and develop these new markets by providing the following benefits:

— substantial calorie reduction;
— sugar and fat reduction;
— diabetic suitability;
— reduced cariogenicity;
— improved taste;
— more satisfying to eat.

Polydextrose foods can, therefore, be used as part of a balanced, reduced-energy diet to make it more interesting, enjoyable and satisfying, with the added benefits of reduced fat and sugar consumption.

REFERENCES

1. THE CALORIE CONTROL COUNCIL, USA (1986).
2. RENNHARD, H. H. (to Pfizer Inc.), US Patent 3 766 165 (Oct. 16, 1973).
   RENNHARD, H. H. (to Pfizer Inc.), US Patent 3 876 794 (Apr. 8, 1975).
3. FIGDOR, S. K. and RENNHARD, H. H. (1981). *J. Agric. Fd Chem.*, **29**, 1181.
4. FIGDOR, S. K. and BIANCHINE, J. R. (1983). *J. Agric. Fd Chem.*, **31** (2), 389.
5. SCRIMSHAW, N. S. and YOUNG, V. R. (1977). *Pfizer.*
6. RAPHAN, H. (1975). (IV) *Pfizer.*
7. RAPHAN, H. (1975). (V) *Pfizer.* ALTER, S. (1974). *Pfizer.*
8. BUNDE, C. A. (1975). *Pfizer.*
9. BACHMANN, W., HASLBECK, M. and MEHNERT, H. (1982). *Akt Endokr. Stoffw.* **3**, 124–5.
10. MCMAHON, F. G. (1974). *Pfizer.*
11. MUHLEMANN, H. R. (1980). *Swiss Dent.*, **2** (3), 29.
12. GOFF, D. H. and JORDAN, W. K. (1984). *J. Fd Sci.*, **49** (1), 306–7.
13. BAER, J. B. and BALDWIN, K. A. (1985). *Dairy Field*, Feb., 68–70.
14. GOFF, D. H. and JORDAN, W. K. (1985). *Dairy Field*, Sept., 98–100.
15. ROTHWELL, J. (1985). *Ice Cream & Frozen Confectionery*, June, p. 442.
16. BARNETT, C. D. (1986). *Candy Industry*, Feb.

8

Acesulfame K: Properties, Physiology and Applications in Calorie-Reduced and Low-Calorie Products

G.-W. VON RYMON LIPINSKI

Hoecshst AG, Frankfurt/Main, Federal Republic of Germany

ABSTRACT

Acesulfame K gained international acceptance after having been issued an acceptable daily intake value (ADI) by the World Health Organization and Food and Agriculture Organization in 1983. In the European Community the Scientific Committee for Foods listed Acesulfame K among the acceptable sweeteners. A total of approximately 20 countries have now approved the use of Acesulfame K in at least some products.

Acesulfame K is a white, crystalline material which has good stability both in the solid state and in the aqueous solution. It is easily soluble in water.

Acesulfame K is approximately 200 times sweeter than sucrose. The sweet taste is perceived quickly and does not linger. Taste characteristics in normal concentrations are good, and aftertastes may become perceptible only at elevated concentrations. Acesulfame K shows good synergism with aspartame and cyclamate.

Acesulfame K has been thoroughly tested for its safety. It is neither carcinogenic nor mutagenic. As Acesulfame K is not metabolised by the human body, it is completely calorie-free. No pharmacological activity has been observed and Acesulfame K does not interact with the normal functions of the body. Most microorganisms do not degrade Acesulfame K.

Due to its good stability, taste characteristics and safety, Acesulfame K can be used as a single sweetener or in combination with other intense or bulk sweeteners in a variety of foods and beverages. In soft drinks, mixtures of Acesulfame K and aspartame compete well against sucrose and offer acceptable stability. In cocoa beverages Acesulfame K gives very good results as a single sweetener and withstands heat treatment. Combinations of Acesulfame K and bulk sweeteners or fillers can be used in products requiring heat treatment, for example baked goods or sweets. The number of available products of these categories containing Acesulfame K is steadily increasing.

INTRODUCTION

Acesulfame K gained international acceptance after having been issued an acceptable daily intake value (ADI) by the World Health Organization and Food and Agriculture Organization in 1983.[1] Its use has been permitted under the 'Sweeteners in Food Regulations 1983' in the United Kingdom.[2] A total of approximately 20 countries have now approved use of Acesulfame K in at least some products.

PHYSICAL AND CHEMICAL PROPERTIES

Acesulfame K is a white, crystalline material. The stability in the solid state appears to be virtually unlimited. It does not have a defined melting point and, instead of melting, it starts to decompose at temperatures around 225°C, i.e. above the levels normally found in foods even during high-temperature processing.

Acesulfame K can easily be dissolved in water. Solubility is high, even at room temperature, and rises sharply with increased temperature (Fig. 1). Even at 20°C more than 20% (w/w) solutions can be

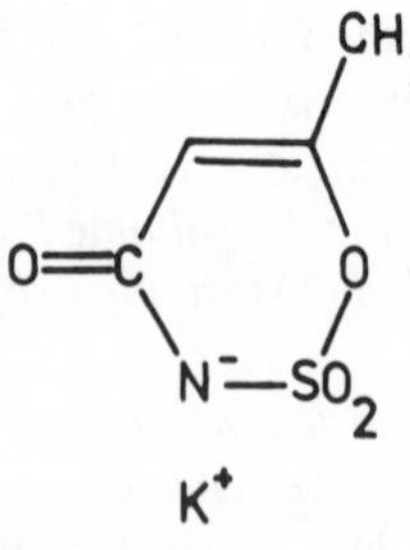

FIG. 1. Acesulfame K.

g Acesulfame K /100ml

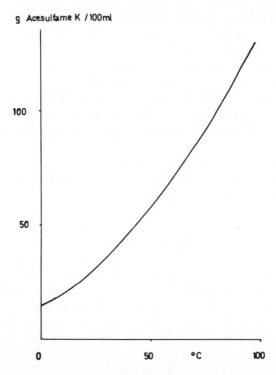

Fig. 2. Solubility of Acesulfame K in water.

prepared; the respective value at 100°C is more than 50% (w/w).[3] Therefore, solubility is not only greatly higher than required for food applications, but even satisfactory enough for preparation of stock solutions (Fig. 2).

Stability of Acesulfame K in aqueous media is very good and meets the requirements for food processing and storage. Decomposition of Acesulfame K in solution depends on the pH value, but is not noticeable in the normal pH range of foods and beverages, i.e. pH 3 to almost neutral. Even below pH 3, a level encountered only in a few products, no serious stability problems arise, provided temperature exposure and storage time do not exceed customary values.

Losses of Acesulfame K after storage at 20°C for one year will hardly be recognisable at pH 2·5 and hardly be analytically detectable at pH values above 3. Even after continuous exposure to 30°C no recognisable losses are anticipated for pH levels above 3. Even after ten years' storage at room temperature, a solution buffered to pH 7 was found to have no significant loss.

When diluted fruit juices and non-carbonated beverages were compared to buffered aqueous solutions, no important differences in stability were detected. Therefore, Acesulfame K meets the stability requirements for the food and beverage-producing industries.

No interferences and interactions of Acesulfame K with food constituents or other food additives have been detected so far. In model studies, using single food constituents or substances modelling food constituents, no reactions or interactions of Acesulfame K and these products could be detected.

SENSORY PROPERTIES

Acesulfame K is approximately 200 times sweeter than sucrose in diluted aqueous solutions. This value seems applicable for the use of Acesulfame K in low concentration, although higher sweetness intensities have been reported from some studies.[4] Sweetness intensity decreases with increasing concentration to values around 100 times (Table 1).

Taste characteristics of Acesulfame K are distinguished by a fast onset of sweetness without a noticeable delay. The sweetness does not linger and, as a rule, fades quickly. When used in appropriate concentrations, taste characteristics of Acesulfame K are considered

TABLE 1
Isosweet Concentrations of Acesulfame K and Sucrose
according to Hoppe and Gassmann[4]

Acesulfame K (mg/litre)	Sucrose (g/litre)	Sweetness intensity of Acesulfame K
43·3	9·9	229
86·9	18·8	216
144	28·8	200
225	40·1	178
322	49·7	154
530	60·6	114

to be good. In elevated concentrations, however, aftertastes may become perceptible.

According to the East German researchers Hoppe and Gassmann,[4] maximum sweetness levels exist for the different sweeteners which cannot be exceeded by increasing the concentration. Levels of maximum sweetness determined by Hoppe and Gassmann are so low, that use of sweetener mixtures seems advisable whenever medium to strong sweetness levels have to be achieved. Certain mixtures of intense sweeteners or intense and bulk sweeteners show synergistic taste enhancements. These effects may be due to independent perception of single sweeteners by different receptor types. Synergism is obvious when equal volumes of isosweet solutions of appropriate sweeteners are mixed and compared to solutions of the single sweeteners. Whenever synergism occurs, the resulting mixture tastes much sweeter.

Acesulfame K shows good synergism with aspartame and cyclamate, whereas no intensification of sweetness occurs in mixtures with saccharin.[5]

From sweetness intensity curves a synergistic sweetness enhancement of 25–40% would seem to be possible. Studies in our laboratory sometimes demonstrated even higher synergistic ratios.

In addition, a change in the taste profile is encountered in sweetener mixtures in comparison to single sweeteners. As time-intensity perception seems important for the assessment of taste characteristics in addition to taste intensity, this additional effect may also be important for application of sweetener mixtures.

TOXICOLOGY AND PHYSIOLOGY

Acesulfame K has been thoroughly tested for its safety. No negative results have been reported, as demonstrated by the allocation of an acceptable daily intake value (ADI) by the Joint Expert Committee on Food Additives of WHO and FAO[1] and of the Scientific Committee for Food of the EEC.[6]

Acesulfame K is readily and virtually completely absorbed by the intestine. In a human study using ^{14}C-marked Acesulfame K, over 99% of the dose was excreted in urine and less than 1% in faeces. The blood concentration increased quickly reaching its maximum after 1 to 1·5 h. Elimination occurred quickly with 98% of the ingested activity being eliminated in the first 24 h. From pharmacokinetic calculations it was concluded that no accumulation of Acesulfame K in the body seems possible even after repeated ingestion within short periods.

In a comprehensive pharmacological test programme Acesulfame K did not interfere with the normal functions of the body. Effects were observed only in test systems in which potassium may have an influence, as Acesulfame K contains approximately 20% potassium. Acesulfame K was fed to diabetic rats for a prolonged period in order to study its influence on a diabetic organism. In this study no negative effects were observed.

Metabolic investigations were combined with pharmacokinetic investigations. It was demonstrated that several animal species and man do not metabolise Acesulfame K. It is excreted completely unchanged. Therefore, it is 'calorie-free' and does not contribute to the energy content of the diet at all.

As cyclamates are known to be metabolised by intestinal bacteria, effects of Acesulfame K on bacteria were studied in combination with investigations on the metabolism. Not only was the absence of metabolism after short-term exposure demonstrated, but also no metabolism could be detected when ^{14}C-marked Acesulfame K was administered to animals which had been fed an Acesulfame K-containing diet for several weeks previously.

At elevated concentration (above normal use level), Acesulfame K may inhibit at least certain bacteria; e.g. with concentrations five to ten times higher than normal inhibition of *Streptococcus mutans* (the bacterium causing dental lesion) was demonstrated.[7]

In combination with physiological considerations the actual possibility of replacing nutritive carbohydrates or bulk sweeteners may be contemplated from an acceptability point of view. The acceptable daily intake for Acesulfame K is 0–9 mg/kg body weight. For many applications a sweetness intensity factor of 200 times seems appropriate. Therefore the ADI allocated for Acesulfame K corresponds to an acceptable daily sucrose equivalent of 1·8 g/kg body weight. This value corresponds to 126 g sucrose for a 70 kg adult and 90 g for a 50 kg adult. Since for technical reasons complete substitution of all nutritive carbohydrates and bulk sweeteners in the normal diet is not possible, the present acceptability level should enable the food industry to develop and market a whole range of products containing Acesulfame K. This view is confirmed by a number of intake studies and calculations.

APPLICATIONS IN LOW-CALORIE AND CALORIE-REDUCED FOODS AND BEVERAGES

Good stability, simple application, and acceptable taste characteristics and profile make Acesulfame K suitable for use in virtually all applications in which intense sweeteners may be used. In a number of applications Acesulfame K may be used as the single sweetener. Whenever functional properties imparted by sucrose are important for a product, combination with suitable bulk sweeteners is necessary, for example sorbitol, isomalt, maltitol or lactitol or fillers such as polydextrose. In products requiring fairly strong sweetness, mixtures of Acesulfame K and other intense sweeteners will be an attractive alternative to the use of single Acesulfame K or single other intense sweeteners. Strong economic advantages may result from use of these mixtures, as, due to synergism, remarkably lower quantities of sweeteners will be required.

The following description of applications in low-calorie and calorie-reduced foods will be accompanied by some indications of products (Table 2). Several products developed in our laboratory have been tested with a limited number of panellists either by scaling methods or in direct comparison to standard or sucrose-containing products. Some data will show that use of Acesulfame K enables the

TABLE 2
Applications and Intended Uses of Acesulfame K

Soft drinks and fruit juices
Squashes and dilutables
Powdered beverages
Table-top sweeteners
Dairy products
Chocolate
Sweets
Marzipan
Bakery products
Desserts
Jams
Pickles
Chewing-gum
Chewing-tobacco
Toothpaste
Pharmaceuticals

food industry to develop products which have a good taste and an acceptable shelf life for dietary purposes.

Soft Drinks

Soft drinks are an important field of application for intense sweeteners, as sucrose or high fructose corn syrups are used as taste compounds and not for functional reasons. Depending on the type of product, sucrose concentrations between 7 and more than 10% are frequently encountered. Several hundred mg/litre of intense sweeteners are required to achieve the same sweetness level. Therefore synergism seems of particular interest for soft drinks. In mixtures of Acesulfame K and aspartame for example at least 30% less of total intense sweeteners are required when appropriate mixtures are used.

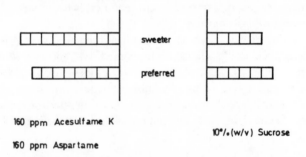

160 ppm Acesulfame K

160 ppm Aspartame

10°/.(w/v) Sucrose

FIG. 3. Comparison of lemon-flavoured carbonated beverages containing sucrose or Acesulfame K and aspartame.

In addition, the mixtures impart a well-balanced and round sweetness to beverages.

A carbonated lemonade prepared in our laboratory competed well against a sucrose-containing product. Compared to pure Acesulfame K, taste improvement is achieved; compared to pure aspartame there was less lingering sweetness and improved stability (Fig. 3). Whenever stability problems may be encountered due to long shelf life of beverages, the ratio between two sweeteners may be changed, although quantity savings are lower than for mixtures in which both sweeteners make the same contribution to the total sweetness.

Results demonstrated for the lemonade have basically also been obtained for other flavours, although concentrations of sweeteners vary slightly depending on the flavours of beverages.

Calorie reduction seems interesting as an alternative to the production of low-calorie products. Using the same flavour as in the preceding example, the results for a beverage containing 50% of the usual sucrose level, were again favourable.

In powdered beverages sometimes a high synergism of approximately 50% was observed in mixtures of Acesulfame K and aspartame.

In milk-based beverages, such as cocoa-flavoured products, stability of sweeteners against hydrolytic decomposition is important. These products may be exposed to elevated temperatures during pasteurisation or UHT treatment and kept on the shelf for certain

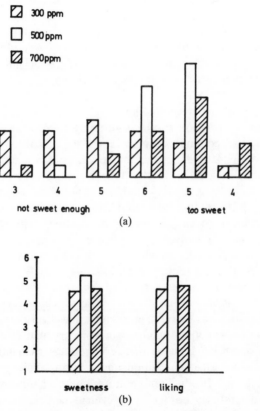

FIG. 4. Sweetness intensity, sweetness preference and overall liking assessments for cocoa beverages containing different concentrations of Acesulfame K.

periods. Acesulfame K gives good results in these beverages as demonstrated by a scaling assessment of a beverage on a 1 to 6 scale for sweetness intensity and overall liking (Fig. 4).

Table-Top Products

Another important field for the applications of intense sweeteners is table-top products, as no functional properties are required in this application. Table-top products such as non-effervescent or effervescent tablets, granular table-top products, low-density 'spoon by spoon' products and solutions can be manufactured using Acesulfame K. For table-top applications, as a single sweetener, good results have been obtained. Although synergistic enhancement occurs in this application, mixtures with other intense sweeteners have not become important yet, although even ternary mixtures of three intense sweeteners have been under consideration. In addition to completely calorie-free tablets consisting of Acesulfame K and carboxymethyl cellulose as binder, a calorie-free sprinkle sweet has been developed using cellulose as an excipient.

Products Requiring Heat Stability

In a variety of food products prolonged exposure to elevated temperatures is common. Therefore, the ingredients of these products have to withstand elevated temperatures for some time, even if the addition of sweeteners at the end of heating processes is possible. In these foods, e.g. bakery and confectionery products, intense sweeteners have seldom been used because sucrose or other carbohydrates fulfil important technological functions. Therefore simple replacement of the carbohydrate products by intense sweeteners is not possible without thorough change of the products' characteristics. These products require combined use of bulk sweeteners or fillers and intense sweeteners. The sweetness level provided by sucrose is considered as the standard sweetness by many consumers. Therefore, mixtures of bulk sweeteners and Acesulfame K which have a similar sweetness intensity are of particular interest.

Acesulfame K can be used in bakery products, as in model studies no indications of decomposition under normal baking conditions have been found. Product temperatures not much higher than 100°C are normal within the products, and even in the outer parts of bakery products a level of 180°C is not normally exceeded. These values are below the decomposition limit of Acesulfame K, and due to the pH level of bakery products no hydrolytic decomposition occurs in the humid inner parts. In bakery products calorie-reduction is possible if fillers or disaccharide alcohols are used instead of sucrose. For diabetics, however, replacement of sucrose is necessary. Acesulfame K has been tested in bakery products with favourable results. Compared to standard products containing sugar, good results were obtained when sugar was completely replaced by sorbitol or by a mixture of sorbitol and polydextrose. In additional studies a more limited number of panellists indicated that isomalt is at least as suitable for replacement of sucrose in combination with Acesulfame K.

By combined use of bulk sweeteners with Acesulfame K higher variations in the individual perception of the sweetness intensity were noted. Products having a similar sweetness level as sucrose-containing standard recipes, however, registered similar to only slightly inferior preference ratings compared to the standard.

Jams and marmalades should also contain a water-soluble bulking ingredient. Sorbitol, polydextrose and reduced sugar concentrations in combination with polydextrose were tested in our laboratory. In particular, the mixture of Acesulfame K and sorbitol was found to bring about a more fresh and fruity taste.

Sugar-free sweets will probably become more popular as they are less cariogenic than standard products containing sucrose or starch syrups. Sweetness intensity of sugar-free products (except xylitol-containing products) is lower compared to standard products. Therefore, small quantities of heat-stable intense sweeteners may bring the sweetness level to the higher standard. Acesulfame K has been tested in a number of recipes, for example, in sorbitol-based products. In comparison to the pure sorbitol product better ratings were registered. Due to the good performance of Acesulfame K in sugar-free products and due to its good stability, sugar-free candies and sugar-free marzipan containing Acesulfame K are available in Switzerland. Isomalt is used as the bulk sweetener in these products.

CONCLUSION

The few examples given demonstrate the good performance of Acesulfame K in low-calorie and calorie-reduced products. Acesulfame K rounds the sweetness of sugar alcohols in products requiring fillers. It is suitable for bakery products, sweets, and fruit-based products due to its good stability. In low-calorie applications such as soft drinks, Acesulfame K combines well with other intense sweeteners, for example aspartame and cyclamate. Due to synergism, a well-balanced taste at a reasonable cost can be achieved by using mixtures of Acesulfame K and these sweeteners.

The number of products containing Acesulfame K has been low for some time. With the improved availability the number of products has increased recently and will increase further with planned and expected product launches.

REFERENCES

1. JOINT FAO/WHO EXPERT COMMITTEE ON FOOD ADDITIVES (1983). *Evaluation of Certain Food Additives and Contaminants*, WHO Technical Report Series, 696, 21–2.
2. *The Sweeteners in Food Regulations* (1983). HMSO, London.
3. RYMON LIPINSKI, G.-W. VON (1985). *Food Chem.*, 16, 259–69.
4. HOPPE, K. and GASSMANN, B. (1985). *Lebensmittelindustrie*, 32, 227–31.
5. RYMON LIPINSKI, G.-W. VON and LÜCK, E. (1976). Ger. Pat. 26 28 294.
6. SCIENTIFIC COMMITTEE FOR FOOD (1985). *Sweeteners*, Office for Official Publications of the European Communities, Luxembourg.
7. SIEBERT, G., ZIESENITZ, S. C. and HOFMEISTER, M. (1985). *Caries Res.*, 19, 188–9.

9

NutraSweet® Brand Sweetener: A Look Beyond the Taste

B. HOMLER

The NutraSweet® Company, Mount Prospect, Illinois, USA

ABSTRACT

The categories that will be discussed in the following paper—both approved and pending approval—are just an indication of the many existing and potential applications for NutraSweet® brand sweetener. As our research and development continues, additional applications, previously considered impossible, will be shown to be quite feasible. Heat will become less and less of a concern as parameters for use are defined and new stabilising technologies are introduced to the food industry by the NutraSweet® Company.

NutraSweet® has dramatically changed the rules of the product development game by taking low-calorie foods off the back shelves in the supermarket and placing them in the mainstream of consumers' daily diets.

INTRODUCTION

NutraSweet® is the brand name for the high-potency sweetener marketed by The NutraSweet® Company, and is generically known as aspartame (APM).

Sweetness has always been one of man's most desired pleasures. The sweet taste is by far the most pleasing of our basic 'tastes' (sour, salt, bitter and sweet) that we experience daily. But, until recently, people's search for sweetness meant undesirable calories, tooth decay or a less-than-perfect taste.

Yet low-calorie foods are now such a part of our lives that it is difficult to remember that less than 25 years ago they were found only in the back shelves of supermarkets in sections designated as dietary foods. In the '60s low-calorie foods and beverages were special items marketed to a limited group of consumers—diabetics and a few others—who had to modify their diets for medical reasons.

Today, low-calorie foods are abundant, accepted products that are marketed towards *all* consumers. Their positioning as having a role in maintaining a healthy lifestyle has virtually displaced the old image of 'low-calorie' food for medical modification of the diet.

NutraSweet® brand sweetener has extended the choice of sweetening agents available to food and beverage manufacturers of low-calorie foods. The future of new line extensions looks even brighter.

Today, NutraSweet® brand sweetener is still one of the newest sweeteners on the market, but after five years it has already surpassed the potential we saw for it. As an example of the future growth, one need only look at the growing list of approved categories in which NutraSweet® can now be used in the United States, and at the 50 countries around the world where aspartame is approved for many categories where US approval is still pending. Consequently, NutraSweet® is feasible for a wide variety of product applications, because technical, marketing and consumer issues have been examined and proven viable in a market situation in many parts of the world.

Categories presently approved in the US are as follows: carbonated soft drinks, ready-to-eat cold cereals, powdered soft drinks, chewing-gums, table-top sweeteners, instant presweetened coffee and teas, dairy analogue topping mixes, multiple chewable vitamins, dry mix puddings and gelatins. Aspartame can also be used in drug formulations.

Added to this list of uses are four new categories approved by the FDA in November, 1986. These include:

— refrigerated or frozen drinks—with or without juice;
— frozen novelties on a stick;
— ready-to-drink tea beverages and concentrates;
— breath mints—compressed and candy-like mints formulated as breath fresheners.

FUTURE APPROVALS

Petitions still pending approval at FDA are the following food categories:

— refrigerated ready-to-eat desserts;
— spoon-for-spoon table-top sweeteners;
— aseptic juice drinks;
— frozen dairy/non-dairy desserts (non-standardised ice-cream, frozen yogurts, sherbets, puddings);
— refrigerated flavoured milk beverages;
— yogurt-type products;
— fruit spreads and toppings;
— frozen ready-to-serve no-bake cheesecake and fruit toppings;
— cookie wafer fillings;
— carbonated alcoholic beverages (7% alcohol), i.e. wine coolers.

As stated earlier, many of these product categories are available outside the US. Canada has yogurts and dairy desserts, spoon-for-spoon table-top sweeteners, aseptic drinks and dessert products, including a frozen pie product. Europe has a variety of confection products, yogurts, frozen dairy products, fruit spreads (jams/jellies).

WHAT IS NUTRASWEET® BRAND SWEETENER/ASPARTAME?

Aspartame is a dipeptide of two amino acids, L-phenylalanine as the methylester and L-aspartic acid. It possesses intense sweetness—180–200 times that of sugar—and uniquely intensifies and enhances many flavours. In fact, in the United States, aspartame is classified as 'a nutritive substance with intense sweetness and flavour-enhancing properties'.

Studies have shown that aspartame is digested and metabolised just like any other protein food and yields its basic components, and 4 kcal/g, just as any other protein or carbohydrate. Essentially, NutraSweet® has no caloric impact due to its intense sweetening power, resulting in only small quantities being used to produce the desired sweetness in a finished food product.

Choice of a sweetener, both caloric and non-caloric, depends on a variety of factors, including the quality of the product formulated and the need for bulking agents. NutraSweet® brand sweetener is only a sweetener and flavour enhancer. Sugar imparts properties other than sweetness—such as bulk, structure, tenderness, viscosity, moisture retention, caramelisation, ability to form a glaze, and preservative effect. Thus, in some applications, a bulking agent will have to be used along with NutraSweet®. Examples of bulking agents that can be used are maltodextrins, polydextrose, hydrogenated starch hydrolysates, polyhydric alcohols and products available in Europe, such as maltitol, lactitol, Palatinit® and others.

TASTE QUALITY

The prime advantage or benefit derived from NutraSweet® brand sweetener is its sweet, clean, sugar-like taste without bitterness. This has been confirmed in many studies, including a quantitative descriptive analysis test (QDA) conducted with a standard reference of 10% sugar versus 530 ppm of aspartame. Panellists were trained to describe sweet and bitter attributes and then score them. As can be seen in Fig. 1, the overlay of NutraSweet® follows, very closely, the descriptive analysis of sugar. By the same testing procedure, it can be seen, in Fig. 2, that a saccharin solution deviates significantly from sugar in terms of initial bitterness and aftertaste bitterness.

FLAVOUR ENHANCEMENT

In addition to its use as a sweetener, NutraSweet® also enhances and extends food and beverage flavours. This enhancement is especially true for fruit flavours. This unique property improves the quality and value of newly approved products such as juice drinks, fruit drinks, stick novelties (fruit bars, water ices) and breath mints. In general, the use levels of aspartame will vary from 0·01% for flavour modification to 0·6% for sweetening and flavour enhancement.

IMPROVED NUTRIENT DENSITY

NutraSweet® brand sweetener can make possible an increase in nutrient density by permitting the increase of the amount of other

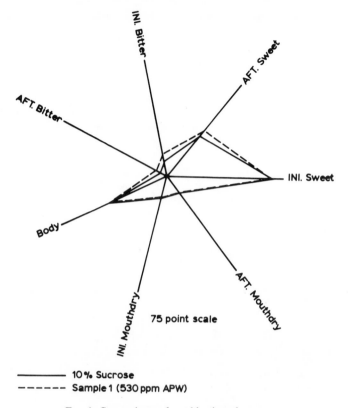

FIG. 1. Comparisons of test blends and sucrose.

beneficial ingredients. For example, if some or all of the sugar or other sweetener is replaced in a cereal, then grain and fibre in those products can be increased. In a fruit bar, more fruit can be added with the sweetness provided by NutraSweet®. Sugars also can be replaced by milk solids, grains, nuts and other items to improve nutritional quality and allow products to have new textural qualities—generating new product concepts.

STABILITY

Food and beverage processors are often surprised by the advances made in understanding and controlling NutraSweet® stability. Not-

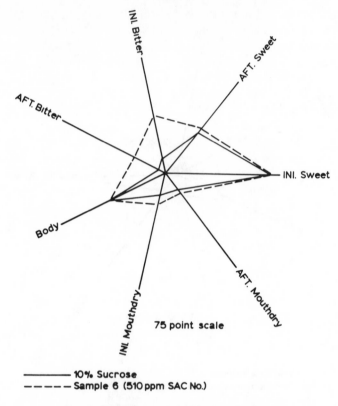

FIG. 2. Comparisons of test blends and sucrose.

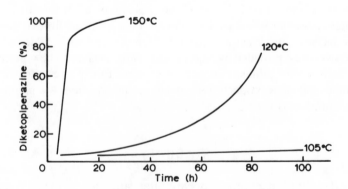

FIG. 3. Dry decomposition of NutraSweet® by heat.

withstanding, questions regarding stability are often the first ones asked. The overview presented below should resolve those concerns, especially knowing that many products that were thought to be impractical with aspartame are already successes in the market in many areas of the world.

Dry stability of aspartame is quite good even under very adverse conditions (Fig. 3). Temperatures well over 150°C (302°F) are needed for breakdown to become substantial in the dry form.

Aspartame contains an ester linkage that, under certain conditions of moisture, temperature and pH can hydrolyse to the dipeptide or

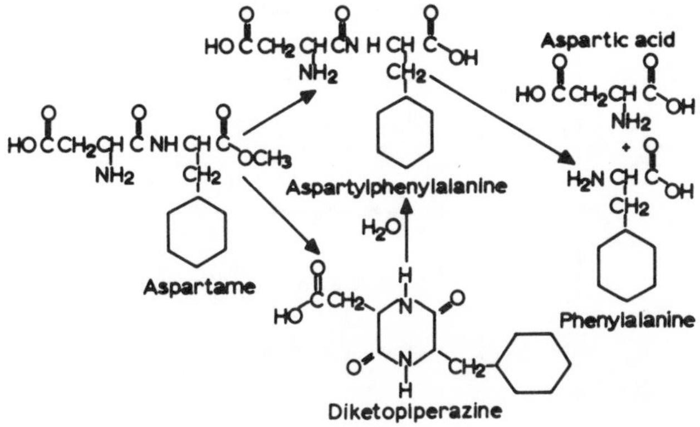

FIG. 4. Aspartame conversion products.

cyclohydrolyse to its diketopiperazine (DKP). The pathway (Fig. 4) shows that, ultimately, the products of conversion are the individual amino acids making up aspartame. What must be remembered is that none of the conversion products are sweet, none have an off-taste and no colours are produced.

When NutraSweet® brand sweetener was introduced, the misconception existed that the product would not be used where processing required a heat step. As with most reactions, higher temperatures do increase the rate of loss. This may limit the use of aspartame where processes call for high temperatures *over extended times*. Aspartame can, however, be used *now* in many heat applications if a few simple rules are followed.

FACTORS AFFECTING STABILITY

Stability is affected, in solution, by three interrelated factors; these
are time, temperature, and pH of the product. As shown in Fig. 5, as
the time at any given temperature increases, the percentage of
aspartame remaining decreases. As the temperature increases for a
given process time, the amount of aspartame remaining decreases.
pH will produce different effects over a range.

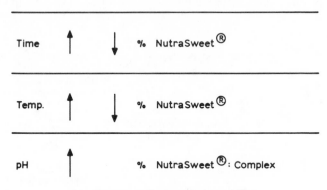

FIG. 5. Factors affecting solution stability.

Control and adjustment of any or all of these three factors (time,
temperature and pH) will allow you to optimise aspartame stability
for a wide range of products and process conditions.

INFLUENCE OF pH AND TEMPERATURE

pH is especially important as aspartame is most stable in the pH range
2·5 to 5·5, where most foods exist (i.e. carbonated beverages,
powdered drinks, juices, novelties, yogurts, spreads, etc.). As shown
in Fig. 6, the optimum pH is 4·2, about that of a root beer beverage.
Outside this range, stability decreases more rapidly but, by adjusting
temperature and/or distribution time, stability—even at a pH that
one might consider adverse—becomes quite acceptable.
   A dairy frozen dessert may have a pH ranging from 6·5 to over
7—according to Fig. 6—outside the range where aspartame might be

considered stable. But due to temperature—0°F or lower—the rate of reaction is dramatically reduced; and, because moisture is tied up as ice, stability for 6–8 months is achieved. That is quite good for this type of application.

A refrigerated chocolate milk at pH 7 exhibits a minimal loss of aspartame because it is refrigerated throughout distribution, sale and home storage. In addition, the product is open-dated for use within 21 days. Thus, whereas the high pH level might at first appear as an inappropriate application for aspartame, a very acceptable product can be produced. With short shelf life, constant refrigeration and

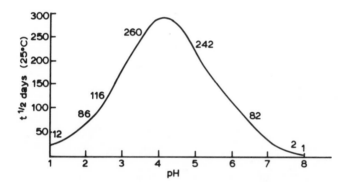

FIG. 6. NutraSweet® stability profile at 25°C.

compensation for pH level, loss of aspartame is minimised. A chocolate milk has been sold in Canada since 1986.

Some food processors have questioned the viability of aspartame use in foods where pasteurisation or other heat processing steps are necessary. A juice drink product can be pasteurised by High Temperature Short Time (HTST) systems, cooled, packaged, and distributed refrigerated. Open-dating of the product is 6–8 weeks. Processing generally involves heating at 185–210°F for 15–30 s with rapid cooling. Loss in processing is generally 2–5% of the starting material.

Aspartame will also find use in aseptic drinks where the time/ temperature relationship is very short (276°F for 3–15 s) with rapid cooling. Recovery of aspartame is over 95%. Aseptic products are currently sold in Canada.

HEAT PROCESSING

Understanding the relationships presented above—the influence of time, temperature, and pH—will aid in minimising loss of aspartame. As shown in Fig. 7, stability with high-temperature processing at any pH is quite good—if the time is kept short. This 80°C (176°F) condition is representative of High Temperature, Short Time pasteurisation. Note at the time point of up to several minutes there is essentially full recovery of aspartame.

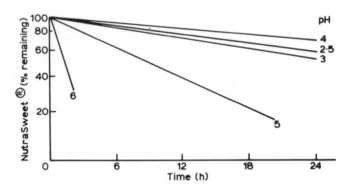

FIG. 7. Stability of NutraSweet® in aqueous buffer at 80°C (176°F).

Adverse effects of high temperature during processing or cooking can be reduced considerably by:

— adjustment of pH to a value closer to optimum;
— reducing the time of exposure to high temperature by adding aspartame during the last stages of cooking to minimise exposure;
— rapid cooling following cooking.

NEW APPLICATIONS

Chilled/Frozen Drinks

The use of NutraSweet® brand sweetener in chilled and frozen juice products and drinks opens a new and important area of product applications. Juice blends and aseptic packaging are the fastest-

TABLE 1
Chilled/Frozen Juices

Refrigerated	6–8-week shelf life	
pH	3·3–3·6	
Frozen	Shelf life over one year	
APM use	350–450 ppm (depends on juice level)	
Refrigerated loss	10–15%	6 weeks
Frozen loss	25–30%	One-plus years
Heat treatment–refrigerated		
185–210°F (84–95°C)	15–30 seconds—cool immediately	
None	Frozen	

growing areas of the juice category. With aspartame's ability to enhance flavour, quality low-calorie juice-type products will be available to the consumer. Products of lighter, more refreshing taste (without added sugar), will move products from primarily morning consumption to all-day, all-family usage. Products with 0–60% juice sold refrigerated or frozen are the primary category application (Table 1). Shelf life, as previously stated, is over 8 weeks refrigerated and over one year frozen. Frozen products can be produced with dilution concentrations of 3:1 to over 15:1, permitting flexibility of container size, reconstitution volume, and balancing of freeze point with the removal of sugar or other carbohydrate sweeteners. The pH of these products is in the range of 3·3–3·6—near the optimum for aspartame. Use level will depend on the sweetness profile desired, the juice level of the product and degree of synergy and flavour enhancement achieved with the juice added to the product. A probable range of 350–450 ppm will be generally acceptable.

Processing is HTST, aseptic or UHT. No stability concerns with recovery of aspartame will exist with proper post-heating cooling.

Frozen Novelties on a Stick

NutraSweet® brand sweetener in frozen novelties is another new category of use. Approval is for any single service novelty product on a stick. This includes items such as pudding pops, gelatin novelties, dairy bars (non-standard ice-cream), fruit juice pops, ice pops, etc.

TABLE 2
Chocolate 'Fudge-Bar' Formula

Component	%
Milk solids non-fat	11
Butterfat	1–2
Polydextrose Type K	7·5
20 DE Maltodextrin	7·5
Cocoa	3·0
Star stabiliser	0·35
Polysorbate 80	0·10
NutraSweet®	0·07

Approx. calories 55 per 2·5 fl. oz

Parameters that must be considered include freezing point depression, proper ice crystal formation and bulk replacement with the removal of carbohydrate sweetener.

Among the list of bulking agents that can be used are polydextrose (in dairy-based products only), maltodextrins under 20 DE (dextrose equivalent) sugar alcohols—including (outside the US) lactitol, Palatinit®, maltitol. In practice, a combination of bulking agents will optimise freeze point, taste quality, and texture of the final novelty. Additions of gelatins, microcrystalline cellulose, stabilisers, and emulsifiers, such as currently used in the industry, will also improve product texture and allow incorporation of overview for control of ice crystals and eating quality. A typical formulation is shown in Table 2. Products have been available outside the US since 1984.

Breath Mints

With the approval of the breath mint category, we have the first confection product with NutraSweet®, aside from chewing-gum, in the United States. Products are already available in Canada, Switzerland, and South America (Colombia).

Process temperatures in confections can get quite high but, as explained earlier, the time of addition of aspartame becomes important. In this application, the aspartame is added after the boiling step when the product has been cooled for the addition of flavours and colours. The product is then handled in the normal processing fashion. Sugar and other carbohydrate sweeteners are replaced with

TABLE 3
Breath Mints

Component	%
Sorbitol	99·30
Magnesium-stearate	0·40
Natural–artificial peppermint flavour	0·10
Natural spearmint flavour	0·10
NutraSweet®	0·10

Processing steps:

1. Blend the flavours with a portion of the sorbitol until homogeneous.
2. Add the above mixture to the rest of the sorbitol and blend well until homogeneous.
3. Add to the above the magnesium-stearate (lubricant) and the Nutra-Sweet® and blend well until homogeneous.
4. Run the blend through the tableting machine.

sorbitol or another approved non-sugar bulking agent. A typical formulation is presented in Table 3.

Stability in confection products is quite good due to the low moisture in the system and the ability to add aspartame after heat exposure.

10

Saccharin and Food Intake

M. G. TORDOFF

Monell Chemical Senses Center, Philadelphia, Pennsylvania, USA

ABSTRACT

There is little scientific support for the general belief that saccharin and other nonnutritive sweeteners aid weight loss. Adding saccharin to food or water for long periods does not usually affect caloric intake or body weight. Work presented here examines an animal model of the short-term effects of saccharin ingestion. Rats given 0·2% saccharin solution to drink for brief periods (30–120 min) eat 10–15% more food than during tests without saccharin. This increased food intake is under multiple controls. A cephalic-phase response is implicated, but not one based on hyperinsulinaemia, as rats with insulin secretion impaired by pancreatic parasympathectomy show normal increases in food intake when drinking saccharin. On the other hand, hepatic parasympathectomy abolishes the increase in food intake, suggesting that a neurally mediated change in liver metabolism may be a primary cause. Hydrational state also plays a role, as intact rats allowed to drink hypotonic but not isotonic saccharin solutions increase short-term food intake. Finally, a component of the increase in feeding is learned. Rats given an arbitrary food flavour while drinking saccharin solution and another food flavour during control tests, eat more when given saccharin than do rats tested with unflavoured food. After several pairings of saccharin with a food flavour, a preference for the flavour develops, and it becomes sufficient to increase food intake. Thus, the consequences of drinking saccharin are to (i) initiate a cephalic-phase activation of hepatic metabolism, (ii) produce a hypo-

tonic internal milieu, and (iii) reinforce food intake and enhance flavour preference. These events act in concert to increase food intake. The short-term effects of drinking saccharin may hamper attempts to restrict food intake and body weight gain.

There are few scientific data to confirm or deny the generally held belief that nonnutritive and low-calorie sweeteners aid calorie reduction and weight loss. This review summarises data from animal experiments that cast light on the interaction between the ingestion of nonnutritive sweeteners and food intake in man. The primary focus is on my own recent work, which has involved an examination of the mechanisms in the rat that control the feeding response produced by drinking saccharin solution. After a description of related studies using rodents, a summary of this work is given. This is followed by a discussion of the relevance of the results of animal studies to man and their possible implications for the long-term use of nonnutritive sweeteners as aids to weight control.

STUDIES OF THE INTERACTION BETWEEN SACCHARIN AND FOOD INTAKE IN ANIMALS

The Taste of Saccharin to Rats

Studies of nonnutritive sweeteners in animals are hampered by the small choice of artificial sweeteners available. Rats and most other nonprimate species do not prefer solutions of aspartame or cyclamates to water,[1-3] suggesting that they do not find them sweet. Although it is difficult to be sure, sodium saccharin is probably perceived by rats as being sweet,[4] but not as sweet as the human perception of this compound. Rats prefer to drink low concentrations of glucose (i.e. 5–10%) than the most preferred concentrations of saccharin solution[5,6] (i.e. 0·15–0·20% in water). They do not sham-drink (i.e. ingested but not absorbed) saccharin solution,[7] and show little or no preference for solid food 'sweetened' with saccharin.[5,8,9] Thus, without extraordinary measures, experiments in rats are limited to the study of saccharin as a prototypical nonnutritive sweetener and, even in favoured concentrations, the taste of saccharin is probably less intense than could be achieved with sugar solutions. This is an important problem when attempting to assess the relevance of animal studies to human soft drink consumption, particularly as it might explain the small or absent effects found in most animal studies.

Previous Work

Long-term studies

Despite the frequent use of saccharin as a 'calorie-free' measure of ingestive behaviour[6,10] or as a substitute for sugar as a reinforcer,[11,12] there has been little attempt to determine whether saccharin consumption influences food intake. Although it was reported recently that rats increased weight after 13 weeks of drinking saccharin,[13] most studies have found that rodents given saccharin to drink for long periods generally do not alter daily food intake or body weight gain.[1,5,8,14–16] This has led to a consensus that saccharin intake and calorie intake are regulated independently[16] (although diet and nutritional status apparently affect the volume of saccharin consumed).[5,9,17] Unfortunately, however, all the studies to date have used insensitive methods, involving animals with genes and diets that are unlikely to produce obesity. Thus, although saccharin has little effect on long-term calorie intake and body weight in the relatively stable situation of the *ad libitum* chow-fed rodent, it is unclear whether this extends to the more human-like conditions of a mixed high-calorie diet and a genetic predisposition to obesity.

A second problem with previous long-term animal studies is that they have used a homogeneous, composite diet, which conceals any influences of nonnutritive sweetener consumption on the source of calories (carbohydrates, fats, or protein). Recent work suggests that rats given a choice of macronutrients from three separate cups, maintained constant daily calorie intake but decreased carbohydrate intake and increased fat intake when given saccharin to drink.[18] Furthermore, rats fed a Ran-1961 'human' diet (based on Dutch population food consumption) increased calorie intake and weight gain when sodium cyclamate was substituted for some of the sucrose in the diet.[19] Although the mechanism of this effect has not been elucidated (particularly as it is unclear whether rats find the taste of sodium cyclamate unpleasant), one explanation could be that animals with limited access to carbohydrate are forced to increase fat consumption, which may be a more potent factor in producing obesity. Whatever the explanation, it raises the possibility that under some conditions, addition of a noncaloric sweetener to the diet can have undesirable effects on body weight.

Short-term studies

Short-term tests of the interaction of saccharin consumption with food intake have found more dramatic results. For example, rats fed a limited daily food ration, which is normally well tolerated, rapidly lose weight and may die if they also drink saccharin or sugar solution.[20–22] The physiological mechanism for this effect has not been studied, although an explanation based on 'reactive hypoglycaemia' has been offered,[22] stemming from the finding that rats die more rapidly if they drink saccharin after injection of lethal doses of insulin.[23,24]

An extensive series of experiments by Mook and students[5,17,25,26] has addressed the question of why rats start and stop drinking saccharin. Some of the results are relevant to the control of food intake. For example, food-deprived rats that drink saccharin to 'satiety', will start to drink again if they are presented with a sweeter but not a less sweet solution.[25] Mook has suggested that 'gustatory adaptation' related to sweetness intensity can account for this phenomenon, although without supporting neurophysiological data it is difficult to know whether the adaptation occurs in the mouth, brain, or periphery.

THE MONELL STUDIES

The phenomenological approach and severe food deprivation schedules of previous studies have proved relatively uninformative, as they neither expose the control mechanisms of feeding behaviour nor provide a realistic model of nonnutritive beverage consumption by man. My work in this area, conducted in collaboration with Dr Mark Friedman at the Monell Chemical Senses Center, has led to a more satisfactory animal model.[27–30] It was based on the observation that free-feeding rats given saccharin to drink during the first 2 h of the dark period (when rats eat their largest meal of the day) increase food intake by about 10%. The increase in feeding was a serendipitous finding of studies designed to examine the influence of sweet solution ingestion on food preference. Rats were given a solution to drink and food containing an arbitrary flavour (usually nonnutritive chocolate or chicken) during some tests, but no solution and a different arbitrary flavour during others. After several (8–10) pairs of training trials (flavoured food and a solution versus the other flavour alone), the two flavoured foods were given together and the rats could choose between them. Figure 1 shows the results of three experiments, with the drinking solution as 1% almond extract flavouring, 10% glucose, or 0·2% saccharin. During training tests, food intake was unaffected by drinking almond, decreased by drinking glucose (in apparent compensation for the calories derived from the solution), and increased by drinking saccharin. Food preference was increased by drinking the two sweet solutions but not by drinking almond.

The changes in food preference produced by drinking saccharin or glucose imply that rats associate the positive effects of drinking the sweet solution with the food flavours (see below). Other implications of this finding are discussed elsewhere.[27] The increase in food intake produced by drinking saccharin was apparently related to its property as a nonnutritive sweetener, because neither an unsweet nonnutritive solution (almond) nor a sweet nutritive solution (glucose) increased food intake. Although the average increase in food intake produced by drinking saccharin was 13·4%, this was somewhat misleading as rats did not increase their food intake when given saccharin to drink on the first few occasions but increased intake on later trials by as much as 35–40%.

This finding led to an analysis of the mechanisms that mediated the increase in feeding produced by saccharin ingestion. Several possible factors were apparent. First, the sweet taste of saccharin solution could initiate neural reflexes that influence metabolism and consequently alter food intake. Second, taste could motivate feeding behaviour directly, either by providing 'hedonic' reinforcement or by altering the perceived palatability of food. Third, as saccharin solution is hypotonic, drinking saccharin could influence food intake by interacting with the regulation of water balance. The contribution of each of these factors to the increase in feeding was investigated separately.

Drinking Saccharin Initiates Cephalic-Phase Reflexes that Increase Feeding

Saccharin is metabolically inert, and the possibility that it may influence feeding by exerting a direct action on metabolism has been negated by the demonstration that intragastric infusions of saccharin

132   M. G. Tordoff

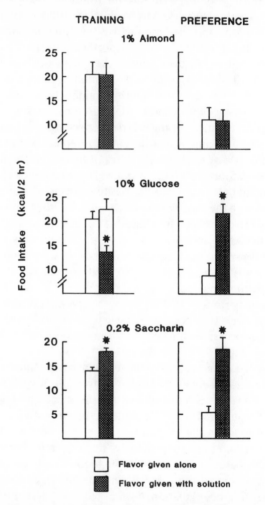

FIG. 1. Effect on food intake and food preference of drinking 1% almond extract, 10% glucose, or 0·2% saccharin solutions. Separate groups of free-feeding rats received 2-h tests, with flavoured food and the solution to drink during some tests and another flavoured food and only water during the others. Mean intakes are shown on the left (the unshaded portion of the right-hand bar for 10% glucose shows the calories derived from the glucose solution). After 8–10 pairs of tests, rats were given a simultaneous choice between the two flavours. Intakes of each are shown on the right. *p<0·05 relative to intake of flavoured food given alone.

do not influence calorie intake.[31] It may alter metabolism indirectly, however, through its effects in the oral cavity. Sweet tastes produce neurally mediated 'cephalic-phase' reflexes which, by enhancing digestion and reallocating endogenous fuels towards energy storage,[32,33] prepare the animal for incoming nutrients.

With respect to the control of food intake, most attention has been paid to cephalic-phase reflex-induced increases in plasma insulin levels. Several forms of obesity are associated with increased insulin levels,[33,34] and it has been hypothesised that (i) exaggerated cephalic-phase reflex insulin release contributes to the hyperphagia and obesity produced by ventromedial hypothalamic lesions,[33] and (ii) obesity results from the consumption of sugar, as this produces in sequence, hyperinsulinaemia, hypoglycaemia, and increased hunger (especially for sugar).[35] Stimulation of the oral cavity with saccharin has been shown to increase plasma insulin levels[36-38] and reduce blood glucose under some conditions.[24,39] It therefore seemed possible that changes in metabolism produced by cephalic-phase reflexes might mediate the increase in food intake produced by drinking saccharin.

Signals produced by saccharin in the oral cavity activate pancreatic insulin release by way of the vagus nerve.[38] Consequently, interruption of this neural link disrupts the cephalic-phase reflex. To test whether the increase in food intake produced by drinking saccharin involved cephalic-phase reflexes related to pancreatic insulin release or to changes in hepatic metabolism, rats were prepared with transections of either the coeliac vagus, which carries parasympathetic innervation to the pancreas, or the hepatic vagus, which innervates primarily the liver. Saccharin ingestion increased subsequent food intake (relative to tests without saccharin) in rats with control surgery or coeliac vagotomy, but not in rats with hepatic vagotomy (Fig. 2). This implies that a neurally mediated increase in insulin is not responsible for the increase in feeding but that a change in the metabolism of the liver may be involved.

Rats with control surgery increased plasma insulin levels during (but not 15 min after) saccharin ingestion but rats with coeliac vagotomy had attenuated insulin responses, confirming that interruption of the cephalic-pancreatic reflex was functionally effective. In other work, intact rats, that drank saccharin 90–120 min before food was given, ate more food than they did during tests without saccharin. The 90-min interval was easily sufficient to allow saccharin-

M. G. Tordoff

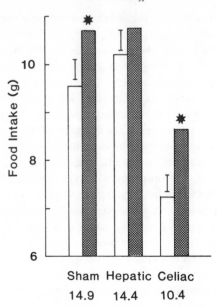

FIG. 2. Effect on food intake of drinking saccharin in rats with selective vagotomies. Transecting the primary parasympathetic innervation of the liver (hepatic vagus) prevented the increase in food intake produced by drinking saccharin that was seen in rats with control (sham) surgery or transection of the parasympathetic innervation of the pancreas (coeliac vagotomy). Numbers under columns give mean intake of saccharin solution (ml). * Food intake on tests with saccharin to drink (shaded bars) significantly ($p < 0.05$) greater than intake on tests without saccharin (unshaded bars). Free-standing vertical lines show standard errors of the difference between means. Food intake was measured during the first 30 min after a 20-h fast. Saccharin was given for 30 min before food access.

induced elevations in plasma insulin to dissipate, yet the rats still increased their food intake, arguing that insulin does not directly control the increase in feeding. This may be similar to work showing that rats given pharmacologic doses of insulin and allowed to return to normoglycaemia with food unavailable, ate more when food was given. The liver was strongly implicated in this feeding response because intake could be blocked by infusions of fructose in intact but not hepatic-vagotomised rats.[40] Considered together with the demonstration that saccharin-induced increases in feeding can be prevented by hepatic vagotomy, the results suggest that the feeding response contains a component mediated by a cephalic reflex that can modulate hepatic metabolism.

Many tastes, including those of nutritive sweeteners, can produce cephalic-phase reflexes but they do not generally increase food intake. Under some test conditions, rabbits will increase food intake after drinking sugar solutions, although the effects are extremely short-lived.[41] In 2-h tests with rats, drinking 10% glucose solution decreased food intake by approximately the calories ingested in the solution (Fig. 1), suggesting that the critical conditions are a preferred taste without postabsorptive or metabolic consequences. To test this possibility directly, I examined whether the increase in feeding could be produced with a nutritive sweetener that was ingested but not absorbed. Rats were fitted with gastric cannulas, which allowed ingested fluids to drain from the stomach without being absorbed. Before receiving food each day, they sham-drank a highly preferred 32% sucrose solution for 15 min or waited for the same period. During five pairs of tests with or without prior sham-ingestion of sucrose, they ingested on average 17.9 ± 3.1 ml of the solution. In the 1st h of a 5-h feeding period (with cannulas closed) they ate 6.64 ± 0.28 g after sham-drinking sucrose compared with 5.62 ± 0.18 g without access to sucrose. This highly significant increase in feeding demonstrates that the effects of drinking saccharin are not the result of some unique property of this nonnutritive sweetener but are most likely related to the ingestion of a preferred solution without post-absorptive effects. The magnitude of the increase, which was much larger than those seen after drinking saccharin, is consistent with the possibility that rats do not respond dramatically to saccharin because they do not find it particularly sweet.

Drinking Saccharin as a Reinforcer of Food Intake

The conditioned stimulus

Rats will press a bar or perform other tasks in order to drink saccharin solution.[12] They also prefer the taste of a neutral flavour that has been mixed with saccharin.[11] These results imply that rats find saccharin ingestion reinforcing. It was possible that these re-inforcing effects might increase food intake, by increasing either the frequency of feeding or the food's perceived palatability (preference). These alternatives represent different forms of learning (instrumental and classical conditioning, respectively) but for saccharin-induced feeding the distinctions are somewhat blurred, as the increase in food intake is an operant in one case and both the conditioned and unconditioned response for the other.

Classical conditioning requires a discriminable conditioned stimulus. In the tests described in the previous section, there were few (if any) stimuli that could be regularly associated with saccharin ingestion. It was predicted that, if learning contributed to the results, an easily identifiable stimulus presented along with saccharin would enhance learning and consequently increase the feeding response. This was examined by comparing rats given no obvious food cues (plain food) to those with saccharin-contingent flavours added to their food (flavoured food). Drinking saccharin increased food intake slightly more if food contained flavours (15·1%) than if it did not (10·4%; Fig. 3). This implies that a proportion of the increase in food intake was learned. A similar conclusion is supported by the development of conditioned taste preferences, and the slow acquisition of the increased feeding response (see above). In addition, when tested without saccharin to drink at the end of the experiment, the group trained with flavoured food showed a typical pattern of behavioural extinction (i.e. they initially ate more of the flavour previously paired with saccharin than the flavour previously given alone, but with repeated tests this difference abated). Taken together, these results argue that food intake is increased by the reinforcing effects of drinking saccharin.

The reinforcer

The above work suggested that food flavours could be cues that can increase food intake when associated with a reinforcer. The most obvious candidate for the reinforcer was saccharin's sweet taste but this proved to be incorrect. Rats on a restricted feeding schedule were given saccharin to drink either before or after eating flavoured food. Only the group that drank saccharin before eating, increased food intake (Fig. 4). This rules out the immediate aspects of saccharin ingestion (including its taste) as the reinforcer, because learning requires that the behaviour to be learned must occur before the reinforcer, but in this case they were in the opposite order. Instead, it seems more likely that an effect of drinking saccharin that lasts beyond its immediate sensory impact was responsible for the reinforcement. When taken together with the results from rats with

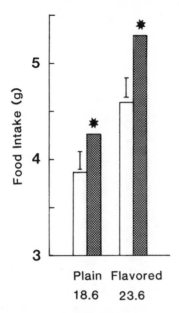

FIG. 3. Effect of adding saccharin-contingent flavours to the food on the increase in feeding produced by drinking saccharin. *Food intake on tests with saccharin to drink (shaded bars) significantly ($p < 0.05$) greater than intake on tests without saccharin (unshaded bars). Numbers under columns give mean intake of saccharin solution (ml). Free-standing vertical lines show standard errors of the difference between means. Rats received 12 pairs of 2-h trials at the start of the dark period, with or without saccharin to drink. During tests of the 'flavoured' group, one food flavour (e.g. nonnutritive chocolate added to Purina rat chow) was always given during tests with saccharin and another flavour (e.g. nonnutritive chicken) was given during tests without saccharin.

hepatic vagotomy (see above) and conditioned taste preferences,[42] the most likely possibility is that rats that have ingested saccharin associate food cues with cephalic-phase changes in liver metabolism, or their consequences.

Role of the Vehicle for Saccharin in Increasing Food Intake

Because saccharin is a high-intensity sweetener, only small quantities are required to produce solutions that rats (and people) prefer, and the solutions are therefore hypotonic. This is unlike preferred concentrations of glucose or other nutritive sweeteners, which are isotonic or hypertonic. Rats frequently drink 30 ml of a 0·2% saccharin solution in a 2-h test, which can induce a considerable

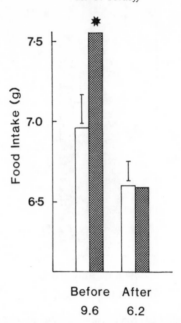

FIG. 4. Effect of drinking saccharin before or after access to flavoured food on food intake. *Food intake on tests with saccharin to drink (shaded bars) significantly ($p < 0.05$) greater than intake on tests without saccharin (unshaded bars). Numbers under columns give mean intake of saccharin solution (ml). Free-standing vertical lines show standard errors of the difference between means. Two groups of rats received ten pairs of tests during successive daily 2-h feeding periods. On some days the rats were given food of an arbitrary flavour; on others they were given another flavour and also saccharin solution to drink, either before or after the feeding period.

imbalance in fluid homeostasis.[43] It is possible that they could counteract this internal dilution by eating more (hypertonic) food. Several tests of this possibility were conducted. In one, separate groups of rats drank solutions of 0·2% saccharin, 0·9% (isotonic) NaCl, or 0·2% saccharin diluted in 0·9% NaCl. Food intake was increased by drinking saccharin dissolved in water but slightly decreased by drinking saccharin dissolved in isotonic saline (Fig. 5). Although there are clear differences in the taste of the solutions, this cannot easily account for the results as, if anything, the rats drank more of the saccharin-salt mixture than of saccharin alone, which implies (but does not prove) they preferred the taste of the mixture. The most obvious remaining difference between the solutions is their tonicity,

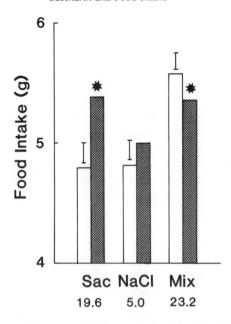

FIG. 5. Effect on food intake of drinking 0·2% saccharin, 0·9% saline, or 0·2% saccharin mixed in 0·9% saline. *Food intake on tests with solution to drink (shaded bars) significantly ($p < 0.05$) different from intake on tests without saccharin (unshaded bars). Numbers under columns give mean intake of saccharin solution (ml). Free-standing vertical lines show standard errors of the difference between means. *Ad libitum*-fed and -watered rats received 12 pairs of tests during the first 2 h of successive dark periods, with a solution to drink during some tests and no solution during others.

suggesting that, indeed, a component of the increased feeding produced by drinking saccharin solution is a behavioural response to overhydration.

Several other findings supported the possibility that overhydration can increase food intake. For example, treating rats with antidiuretic hormone, which prevents the excretion of excess water, prolonged the increase in feeding produced by drinking saccharin. In addition, rats that drank a mildly palatable 0·45% (hypotonic) NaCl solution increased food intake relative to tests without the solution to drink, which in addition to supporting an explanation based on overhydration demonstrates that sweetness is not required for a solution to increase intake. Finally, intragastric infusion of water increased subsequent food intake, although the effects of this manipulation were small and inconsistent.[29]

CAN THE RESULTS IN RATS BE APPLIED TO MAN?

Taken together, the results of the studies conducted at Monell suggest that three factors interact to increase feeding when rats drink saccharin. These are (i) cephalic-phase reflex-induced changes in hepatic metabolism, (ii) reinforcement produced by the consequences of drinking saccharin, and (iii) overhydration produced by ingestion of hypotonic fluid. Each factor is sufficient by itself to increase food intake, but none can completely account for the increase in feeding seen in the normal situation. The question arises of whether the mechanisms found in the rat have a role in determining the behaviour of man, first, by influencing short-term feeding, and second, by influencing the long-term regulation of food intake and body weight. Each of the three factors will be considered in turn.

Cephalic-Phase Reflexes

There is strong evidence to suggest that cephalic-phase reflexes produced by the sight and taste of food exist in man,[44–47] although whether this includes neurally mediated changes in liver metabolism is unknown. Nevertheless, a relationship between the magnitude of cephalic-phase reflexes and subsequent food intake has been demonstrated in man.[44,45] A role for cephalic-phase reflexes in the response to nonnutritive sweeteners is suggested by the work of Brala and Hagen.[48] These investigators measured intake of snack foods eaten by normal-weight undergraduates 90 min after ingestion of a milkshake preload. Before drinking the milkshake, which was sweetened with either aspartame or sucrose, half the subjects were pretreated with gymnemic acid, which blocks the perception of sweetness. Subjects, with sweetness perception blocked, ate significantly fewer snack foods than subjects given the same milkshakes but who had unaltered taste perception. This implies that sweetness increases food intake. The 90-min delay between consuming the milkshake and eating the snack meal precludes a direct effect of cephalic-phase induced changes in insulin secretion because these effects were unlikely to last more than a few minutes.[28,36,37,44,45] However, the results are compatible with cephalic-phase effects on hepatic metabolism similar to those demonstrated in the rat.

Whether cephalic-phase reflexes have any function in controlling long-term food intake or body weight is unknown. The best evidence from work on animals is that rats that show intense cephalic-phase reflexes (using plasma insulin as an index) after drinking saccharin have normal body weights when fed chow but gain weight more rapidly than controls when fed a supermarket diet.[49] Obese humans tend to have more exaggerated cephalic-phase reflexes than their lean counterparts.[46] It is feasible that humans with exaggerated cephalic-phase reflexes who drink nonnutritive sweeteners are more prone to become obese.

Reinforcement

Although there are no direct studies of the interaction between the reinforcing properties of nonnutritive sweeteners and food intake in man, both humans and rats show a preference for arbitrarily flavoured drinks that have been previously mixed with saccharin,[11,50] suggesting that similar associative mechanisms exist in both species. The possible reinforcing effects of nonnutritive sweetener consumption are unlikely to be expressed in laboratory investigations of human feeding, as these have used single or counterbalanced tests, which would eliminate or obscure any available discriminable stimuli. As the dietary habits of many individuals outside the laboratory include relatively regular patterns of food choices (e.g. sodas with hamburgers) and eating locations, in practice, associations between the effects of nonnutritive sweeteners and particular edible or environmental stimuli may be more important.

The sensory and hedonic properties of foods (including nonnutritive sweeteners) are probably unimportant in determining body weight gain, as (despite popular dogma) enhancing food palatability has no reliable influence on long-term feeding or body weight.[51] This implies that the reinforcing effects of nonnutritive sweetener consumption are unlikely to produce long-term changes in calorie intake. They may, however, play a role in determining the source of calories. Rats and college students that have satiated their appetite for one food flavour will eat more of other flavours, an effect that is apparently due to 'hedonic' (rather than psychophysical) adaptation to the taste.[52-54] There is limited evidence that this is effective for prolonged periods in man,[55] which is consistent with the finding in rats that drinking nonnutritive sweeteners may inhibit the consumption of a relatively sweet source of carbohydrates and favour the consumption of fats and protein.[19] It is possible that changes in food choice could contribute to the development of obesity.

Hydration

A 300-g rat can easily drink 30 ml of saccharin solution in a 2-h test. By weight, this would be equivalent to a 155 lb human drinking 8 litres of fluid. However, an increase in feeding can be demonstrated in rats after they drink as little as 2 ml of saccharin[27] or are intubated with 3 ml water,[29] which is roughly equivalent (by proportion of body weight) to the volume of a typical human soft drink. Thus, the volumes involved are not inappropriate for expression of a mechanism based on overhydration in man.

Although there is no work that directly addresses the relationship between positive water balance and food intake in man, a comparison of two studies of aspartame consumption may be illustrative. Subjects in Brala and Hagen's[48] study (described above) who drank milkshake preloads, gave sucrose pleasantness and hunger ratings at various times, but these did not vary in any systematic fashion. Blundell and Hill,[56] on the other hand, found that subjects asked to provide pleasantness and hunger ratings after ingestion of a solution of aspartame decreased perceived pleasantness and increased perceived hunger. This initial study had several limitations (see the highly critical but inaccurate review by Booth[57]). Nevertheless, the results of this and more recent work by Blundell and colleagues (see Chapter 11) suggest that, under some conditions, aspartame can increase the motivation to eat. As aspartame does not influence food intake if given by tablet,[58] and other nonnutritive sweeteners given in solution increase both hunger ratings and food intake (see Paper 11), it is unlikely that the effects of aspartame on appetite are mediated by its neuropharmacological action. In the light of the results in rats, a more plausible explanation would involve a combination of neurally mediated changes in metabolism and increased hydration. If this is true, then the difference between the results of Brala and Hagen,[48] and Blundell and Hill[56] may well be due to the difference in tonicity of the vehicle (milkshake versus solution).

It has recently been shown that adding water to rat foods is a potent method of inducing obesity.[59] The mechanism for this effect is unknown, although changes in diet texture or taste have been ruled out (Ramirez, unpublished data). It is possible that positive water balance induced by periprandial drinking could produce similar effects in man.

DO NONNUTRITIVE SWEETENERS AID WEIGHT REGULATION?

There are obvious problems in applying the results of studies in rats to the behaviour of man, and in using short-term changes in behaviour as indicators of long-term effects. Nevertheless, the factors that control the short-term response to nonnutritive sweeteners in the rat are most likely present and operative in man. Some of the work mentioned above suggests that nonnutritive sweetener consumption can lead to an increase in subsequent appetite and food intake. However, these increases last a few hours at most, and are probably counteracted by other regulatory controls of energy homeostasis. Thus, although it seems fairly clear that nonnutritive sweeteners can enhance appetite under some conditions, it is much less clear whether the short-term controls have any long-term effects, and consequently whether they are significant factors in the regulation of body weight.

The best evidence that nonnutritive sweeteners can lead to a reduction of weight comes from the work of Porikos and colleagues.[60,61] These investigators found that hospitalised subjects decreased calorie intake when aspartame was substituted for sucrose in the diet. However, their work is difficult to interpret for several reasons, such as extremely high food intakes during control periods (>3000 kcal/day), the transience of the decrease in calorie intake produced by aspartame substitution, and the relevance to the normal situation of removing all sucrose from the diet (see Booth[57] for other problems).

Other studies have used correlational approaches, where comparisons were made between groups of nonnutritive sweetener users and nonusers, so it is unclear whether differences in food intake and body weight are the result of the use of nonnutritive sweeteners or other factors that might predispose individuals to consume these products. Most of these studies have observed no effect on body weight,[62,63] and changes in food intake and selection that are most likely due to the nonnutritive sweetener user's desire to lose weight.[63] One exception is the massive epidemiological study of Stellman and

Garfinkel,[64] which found that (i) nonnutritive sweetener users were more likely to be overweight than nonusers, (ii) significantly greater frequencies of nonnutritive sweetener users than nonusers reported gaining weight, although the average increase in weight was only a few ounces, and (iii) users and nonusers ate various food items with different frequencies but there was no discernible change in intake of macronutrients. The cause of these results could be either non-nutritive sweetener use or a related factor, such as the desire to lose weight, which is correlated with both weight gain and nonnutritive sweetener consumption.[63] Nevertheless they suggest that, for whatever reason, the average consumer of nonnutritive sweeteners is unlikely to lose weight.

There is no doubt that drinking beverages made with nonnutritive sweeteners can provide the benefit of a desirable taste without calories. Whether this can be considered a significant battle in the war against excess calorie consumption is unclear. Some studies suggest that nonnutritive sweetener ingestion may antagonise the motivation to lose weight. It therefore seems unlikely that substituting drinks made of nonnutritive sweeteners for those made of sugar will, by itself, aid weight loss; however, this strategy may be effective when used together with vigilant control of calorie intake from other sources.

ACKNOWLEDGEMENTS

The work conducted at the Monell Chemical Senses Center and preparation costs of this paper were supported by National Institute of Arthritis, Diabetes, and Digestive and Kidney Diseases Grant DK-36339 and Monell funds. I thank Dr Mark Friedman for his considerable scientific and technical help.

REFERENCES

1. NAIM, M., ROGATKA, H., YAMAMOTO, T. and ZEHAVI, U. (1982). *Physiol. Behav.*, **28**, 979–86.
2. SCLAFANI, A. and ABRAMS, M. (1986). *Physiol. Behav.*, **37**, 253–6.
3. MURRAY, E. J., WELLS, H., KOHN, M. and MILLER, N. E. (1953). *J. Comp. Physiol. Psychol.*, **46**, 134–7.
4. NOWLIS, G. H., FRANK, M. E. and PFAFFMAN, C. (1980). *J. Comp. Physiol. Psychol.*, **94**, 932–42.

5. MOOK, D. G. (1974). *Psychol. Rev.*, **81**, 475–90.
6. VALENSTEIN, E. S. (1967). *J. Comp. Physiol. Psychol.*, **63**, 429–33.
7. SCLAFANI, A. and NISSENBAUM, J. W. (1985). *Am. J. Physiol.*, **248**, R387–R390.
8. ADOLPH, E. F. (1947). *Am. J. Physiol.*, **151**, 110–25.
9. STROUTHES, A. (1977). *Animal Learning Behav.*, **5**, 42–6.
10. LEIBOWITZ, S. F., HAMMER, N. J. and BROWN, L. L. (1980). *Physiol. Behav.*, **25**, 829–44.
11. HOLMAN, E. W. (1980). *J. Exp. Psychol., Animal Behav. Processes*, **6**, 126–36.
12. SHEFFIELD, F. D. and ROBY, T. B. (1950). *J. Comp. Physiol. Psychol.*, **43**, 471–81.
13. ROLLS, B. J. (1987). In: *Sweetness*, Ed. Dobbing, J., Springer-Verlag, London, 161–72.
14. FRIEDHOFF, R., SIMON, J. A. and FRIEDHOFF, A. J. (1971). *J. Am. Dietetic Assoc.*, **59**, 185–486.
15. HAUSMANN, M. F. (1933). *J. Comp. Psychol.*, **15**, 419–28.
16. KENNEY, J. J. and COLLIER, R. (1976). *J. Nutr.*, **106**, 388–91.
17. MOOK, D. G. and CSEH, C. L. (1981). *Appetite*, **2**, 15–34.
18. TORDOFF, M. G. and TEPPER, B. J. (1987). Unpublished observations.
19. DALDERUP, L. M. and VISSER, W. (1969). *Nature*, **221**, 91–2.
20. STROUTHES, A. (1973). *Physiol. Behav.*, **10**, 781–91.
21. SCLAFANI, A. (1973). *Physiol. Behav.*, **11**, 595–601.
22. HAMILTON, L. W. (1971). *J. Comp. Physiol. Psychol.*, **77**, 59–69.
23. VALENSTEIN, E. S. and WEBER, M. L. (1975). *J. Comp. Physiol. Psychol.*, **60**, 443–6.
24. DEUTSCH, R. (1974). *J. Comp. Physiol. Psychol.*, **86**, 350–8.
25. MOOK, D. G., BRYNER, C. A., RAINEY, L. D. and WALL, C. L. (1980). *Appetite*, **1**, 299–315.
26. MOOK, D. G., KUSHNER, B. D. and KUSHNER, L. R. (1981). *Appetite*, **2**, 267–80.
27. TORDOFF, M. G. and FRIEDMAN, M. I. (1987). Unpublished manuscript I.
28. TORDOFF, M. G. and FRIEDMAN, M. I. (1987). Unpublished manuscript II.
29. TORDOFF, M. G. and FRIEDMAN, M. I. (1987). Unpublished manuscript III.
30. TORDOFF, M. G. (1988). In: *Sweeteners: Health Effects*, Ed. Williams, G., Princeton Scientific, Princeton, NJ.
31. BORER, K. T. (1968). *J. Comp. Physiol. Psychol.*, **65**, 213–21.
32. BRAND, J. G., CAGAN, R. H. and NAIM, M. (1982). *Ann. Rev. Nutr.*, **2**, 249–70.
33. POWLEY, T. L. (1977). *Psychol. Rev.*, **84**, 89–126.
34. BRAY, G. A. and YORK, D. A. (1979). *Physiol. Rev.*, **59**, 719–809.
35. GEISELMAN, P. J. and NOVIN, D. (1982). *Appetite*, **3**, 202–23.
36. BERTHOUD, H.-R., BEREITER, D. A., TRIMBLE, E. R., SIEGEL, E. G. and JEANRENAUD, B. (1981). *Diabetologia*, **20**, 393–401.
37. LOUIS-SYLVESTRE, J. (1976). *Am. J. Physiol.*, **203**, 1043–54.

38. WOODS, S. C. and BERNSTEIN, I. L. (1980). *Physiol. Behav.*, **24**, 485–8.
39. JORGENSEN, H. (1950). *Acta Phys. Scandinav.*, **20**, 33–7.
40. FRIEDMAN, M. I. and GRANNEMAN, J. (1983). *Am. J. Physiol.*, **244**, R374–R382.
41. GEISELMAN, P. J. (1985). *Nutr. Behav.*, **2**, 175–88.
42. TORDOFF, M. G. and FRIEDMAN, M. I. (1986). *Am. J. Physiol.*, **251**, R192–R195.
43. ROLLS, B. J., WOOD, R. J. and STEVENS, R. M. (1978). *Physiol. Behav.*, **20**, 15–19.
44. BELLISLE, F., LOUIS-SYLVESTRE, J., DEMOZAY, F., BLAZY, D. and LEMAGNEN, J. (1983) *Physiol. Behav.*, **31**, 515–21.
45. BELLISLE, F., LOUIS-SYLVESTRE, J., DEMOZAY, F., BLAZY, D. and LEMAGNEN, J. (1985). *Am. J. Physiol.*, **249**, E639–E645.
46. JOHNSON, W. G. and WILDMAN, H. E. (1983). *Behav. Neurosci.*, **97**, 1025–8.
47. SJOSTROM, L., GARELLICK, G., KROTKIEWSKI, M. and LUYCKX, A. (1980). *Metabolism*, **29**, 901–9.
48. BRALA, P. M. and HAGEN, R. L. (1983). *Physiol. Behav.*, **30**, 1–9.
49. POWLEY, T. L. and BERTHOUD, H.-R. (1985). *Am. J. Clin. Nutr.*, **42**, 991–1002.
50. ZELLNER, D. A., ROZIN, P., ARON, M. and KULISH, C. (1983). *Learn. Motiv.*, **14**, 338–50.
51. NAIM, M., BRAND, J. G., KARE, M. R. and CARPENTER, R. G. (1985). *J. Nutr.*, **115**, 1447–58.
52. ROLLS, B. J., VAN DUIJVENVOORDE, P. M. and ROWE, E. A. (1983). *Physiol. Behav.*, **30**, 21–7.
53. ROLLS, B. J. (1986). *Nutr. Rev.*, **44**, 93–101.
54. ROLLS, B. J. (1985). *Am. J. Clin. Nutr.*, **42**, 932–9.
55. ROLLS, E. T. (1985). *Physiol. Behav.*, **34**, 1017–20.
56. BLUNDELL, J. E. and HILL, A. J. (1986). *Lancet*, **1**, 1092–3.
57. BOOTH, D. A. (1987). In: *Developments in Sweeteners—3*, Ed. Grenby, T. H., Elsevier Applied Science, London, 287–316.
58. RYAN-HARSHMAN, M., LEITER, L. A. and ANDERSON, G. H. (1987). *Physiol. Behav.*, **39**, 247–53.
59. RAMIREZ, I. (1987). *Appetite*, **9**, 1–19.
60. PORIKOS, K. P., HESSER, M. F. and VAN ITALLIE, T. E. (1982). *Physiol. Behav.*, **29**, 293–300.
61. PORIKOS, K. P., BOOTH, G. and VAN ITALLIE, T. E. (1977). *Am. J. Clin. Nutr.*, **30**, 1638–44.
62. MCCANN, M. B., TRULSON, M. F. and STULB, S. C. (1956). *J. Am. Dietetic Assoc.*, **32**, 327–30.
63. PARHAM, E. S. and PARHAM, A. R. (1980). *J. Am. Dietetic Assoc.*, **76**, 560–63.
64. STELLMAN, S. D. and GARFINKEL, L. (1986). *Prev. Med.*, **15**, 195–202.

11

Artificial Sweeteners and Appetite in Man

J. E. BLUNDELL, P. J. ROGERS and A. J. HILL

Biopsychology Group, Department of Psychology,
University of Leeds, UK

ABSTRACT

Artificial sweeteners effectively uncouple the sweet taste of a solution or food item from its calorific consequences. In general the sensory stimulation of a sweet taste could influence appetite by triggering cephalic phase reflexes or by disrupting innate or previously learned relationships between taste qualities and nutritional value (cue-consequence associations). In addition some artificial sweeteners may facilitate or suppress appetite through actions upon central or peripheral mechanisms involving neurotransmitters or hormones.

In a series of experiments artificial sweeteners have been compared with either glucose or sucrose in order to determine their effects upon negative gustative alliesthesia, hunger motivation, food preferences and calorie intake. Oral loads of glucose or sucrose solutions produced consistent effects—a suppression of perceived pleasantness of sucrose and a reduction of rated hunger motivation. Equivalent loads of aspartame gave rise to a partial alliesthesia but did not suppress hunger or other rated measures of eating motivation. Further studies have compared the effects of different artificial sweeteners and have monitored the action on calorie consumption. The results of these studies should throw light upon the relative importance of perceived pleasantness of food and perceived hunger in the short-term control of food intake.

INTRODUCTION

Artificial sweeteners constitute an important class of food additives which are being used in progressively increasing quantities. However, intake of these substances is not evenly distributed throughout the population. Owing to the inclusion of artificial sweeteners in particular types of product and to the perceived value of sweeteners in helping to treat obesity or to prevent weight gain, this class of food additive is likely to be consumed in large amounts by certain subgroups of the population and hardly at all by others. Despite the widespread ingestion of artificial sweeteners and the likely effect that sweet substances will exert on eating and appetite, only a handful of studies have investigated the relationship between consumption of artificial sweeteners and mechanisms of hunger and food consumption. The most substantial study has been conducted by Porikos, van Itallie and colleagues,[1-4] but the particular design chosen together with certain other methodological constraints leave the outcome open to question. Oddly, despite the importance of the issue, there has been no series of experiments carried out to investigate the action of artificial sweeteners under varying environmental or physiological circumstances and in different types of subjects. There is also a lack of basic information concerning sweeteners and appetite under standard laboratory conditions. Although considerable attention has been directed to the possible toxicity of artificial sweeteners, effects on appetite are grossly under-researched.

ROLE OF SWEETENERS IN EATING

Sweetness is a powerful psychobiological phenomenon which has physiological significance and exerts strong effects on the pattern of food consumption.[5] A preference for sweet-tasting substances is probably an innate disposition of many animals including man.[6] Sweet-tasting substances are inherently pleasurable to most individuals and can act as potent rewards. Consequently, on the basis of sensory qualities alone the sweetness of a food will tend to promote its ingestion.

There are two particular ways in which the adjustment of sweetness could influence food consumption and appetite. First, in nature the sweet taste is almost invariably linked to high-calorie nutritionally useful commodities. This association between the taste of food and its metabolic value is important in the control of energy intake. One way in which organisms (including man) control episodes of eating is by predicting caloric value on the basis of taste (e.g. ref. 7).

There is good evidence that the biological system is innately programmed to establish links between cues (taste sensations) and consequences (metabolic effects of foods) and this constitutes a part of
the biological wisdom of the body (e.g. ref. 8). The operation of this
system allows organisms to anticipate the effects of food ingestion in
advance of the digestion and absorption of the products. It follows
that the use of artificial sweeteners in foods will effectively uncouple
sweet taste from caloric value. Since normally sweetened foods are
also likely to be consumed along with artificially sweetened items, the
sweet taste of food no longer provides a reliable cue for predicting
metabolic effects. Consequently, one mechanism for regulating
energy intake would be undermined.

Second, the cephalic phase reflex is the term given to anticipatory
responses which prepare the gastro-intestinal system for the arrival of
food. Such responses can be detected at various levels of the system
including salivary secretion, gastric outflow and pancreatic secretion.
In man, the sight and smell of food are sufficiently potent to trigger
cephalic phase insulin responses,[9,10] and the response in obese
subjects is four times that in lean people. In rats the taste of saccharin
can provoke a cephalic phase insulin response.[11] In turn, the size of
the cephalic phase response is related to the degree of hyperphagia
on a good-tasting diet. The stimulus-induced cephalic phase responses are accompanied by a raised tendency to consume food.
Consequently, it may be expected that, in humans, sweet substances
will enhance cephalic phase reflexes and promote ingestion.

ARTIFICIAL SWEETENERS AND MECHANISMS
CONTROLLING EATING

The potent rewarding capacity of the sweet taste means that the
acceptability of foods can be increased by making them sweet.
Palatability is one of the most important dimensions controlling
short-term intake in man, and this is one way in which artificial
sweeteners will influence ingestion. It is also likely that artificial
sweeteners will trigger cephalic phase responses and, owing to the
disengagement of sweet taste and calories, they may disrupt a natural
biological regulatory system. However, not all intense sweeteners
have the same composition. Of the sweeteners currently in use—
saccharin, acesulfame-K, cyclamates and aspartame—one has

attracted special interest because of its dipeptide structure. Aspartame is composed of two amino acids—phenylalanine and aspartic acid. This particular composition means that aspartame may influence feeding control mechanisms in a variety of ways. For example, phenylalanine is known to release cholecystokinin,[12] an anorexigenic hormone released from the duodenum following food consumption. It has been proposed that cholecystokinin is an endogenous satiety agent and it has been demonstrated to inhibit food intake in animals[13] and man.[14] In addition, phenylalanine may trigger amino acid receptors within the alimentary canal which are involved in regulatory processes concerning digestive functions, salivation and food intake.[15] A further effect of ingested phenylalanine could occur via changes in brain synthesis of the catecholamine neurotransmitters dopamine and noradrenaline.[16] In the rat, oral dosing with aspartame leads to dose-related changes in noradrenaline in the hypothalamus,[17] a region where noradrenergic receptors influence the control of feeding patterns and food selection.[18] Although the dynamics of phenylalanine-induced changes in catecholamine synthesis are different in man, similar feeding mechanisms could well be affected.

It follows that artificial sweeteners may influence the expression of appetite and eating by means of a number of mechanisms:

1. Cephalic phase reflexes.
2. Cue-consequence conditioning (uncoupling of sweetness-energy).
3. Triggering of endogenous satiety factors.
4. Action on brain mechanisms of hunger.

It follows, of course, that these mechanisms are independent of each other and that some or all may be brought into play at any particular time. Consequently, following the ingestion of artificial sweeteners a number of possible actions may arise:

1. No effect on hunger-satiation.
2. Leave a residual hunger.
3. Facilitate hunger.
4. Intensify satiation (induce anorexia).
5. Combinations of the above—simultaneous or sequential.

In addition, it should be considered that there may be sizeable individual differences in the sensitivity of particular mechanisms. For example, people who are dieting severely may be particularly vulnerable to the triggering of cephalic phase reflexes—it was noted earlier that the size of the cephalic phase insulin response is four times greater in obese than lean subjects.[9]

On the basis of the comments set out above it seems likely that artificial sweeteners will exert some action on mechanisms controlling appetite and eating. The questions are whether the effects will be sufficiently prominent to be readily measured, whether experimental tests can be conducted so as to reveal the nature of the effects, and whether these actions are likely to be invoked by natural day-to-day ingestion of artificial sweeteners.

EXPERIMENTAL STUDIES ON ARTIFICIAL SWEETENERS AND HUNGER/SATIETY

The above arguments provide a rationale for a systematic investigation of the effects of artificial sweeteners on appetite—as experimental tools which exquisitely disengage the sweet taste from calories, and as components of food products widely consumed. Some possibilities have been tested in a series of experiments in which the effects of aspartame and other artificial sweeteners (saccharin, acesulfame-K) have been compared with the effects produced by energy-rich sweeteners such as glucose or sucrose.

Monitoring Hunger and Satiation

It follows from the possible mechanisms outlined above that, if a number of actions occurred together, even weakly, then artificial sweeteners could generate a rather unusual profile of changes in the processes of hunger and satiation which normally control patterns of eating. Consequently, monitoring techniques are required which permit the disclosure of different types of effects. Figure 1 illustrates the fluctuations which occur in various parameters during the ingestion of a meal or following a preload. Changes occur, for example, in subjectively perceived ratings of hunger and fullness, in the perceived pleasantness of food or taste stimuli, and in expressed choices for foods of various types. These parameters are sensitive to manipulations in the total energy content of food,[19] macronutrient composition,[20] palatability[21] and to pharmacological challenge.[22] The procedures have been described in detail elsewhere.[23, 24] The experiments described below employed various measures of behaviour and

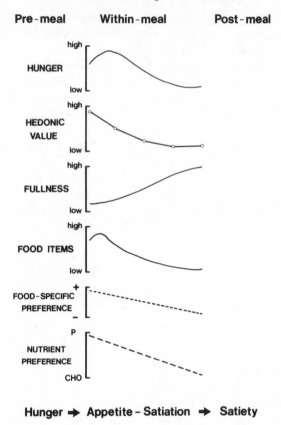

FIG. 1. Fluctuations in motivational parameters which accompany eating during the course of a meal.

perception widely regarded as reflecting the intensity of satiation and satiety, together with certain other techniques traditionally applied to the experimental investigation of sweet substances.[25]

Paradoxical Effects of Aspartame

In the first study, 50 young adults (35 females, 15 males) of normal height for weight were tested. A between-subjects design was used and subjects received one of the following three loads:

A. 50 g glucose dissolved in 200 ml tap water   ($N = 17$)

B. 162 mg aspartame (9 tablets of Canderel) in
200 ml tap water   (*N* = 17)

C. 200 ml tap water   (*N* = 16)

Subjects made ratings of pleasantness and intensity of the sucrose solution on 100 mm visual analogue rating scales (providing a score of 0–100). Two booklets containing sufficient scales for the experiment were provided. One required subjects to rate the pleasantness of the sweet solution (a 20% sucrose solution) on scales which were word-anchored by the phrases 'extremely pleasant' and 'extremely unpleasant'. On the other, subjects judged the intensity of the solution on scales ranging from 'extremely weak' to 'extremely strong'. Ratings of motivation to eat were made on 100 mm visual analogue scales (word anchored at either end) in the following order. They were: (a) 'How strong is your desire to eat?' (Very strong–Very weak); (b) 'How hungry do you feel?' (As hungry as I have ever felt–Not at all hungry); (c) 'How full do you feel?' (Very full–Not at all full) and (d) 'How much food do you think you could eat?' (A large amount–Nothing at all). This last rating is called prospective consumption.

Subjects attended the laboratory immediately after lunch at 2.00 o'clock in the afternoon. They were instructed how to complete each of the assessments and were asked to make their first ratings of motivation to eat. They then collected a small plastic cup containing approximately 10 ml of the standard (20%) sucrose solution. They were told to take all of the tastant into their mouth and to keep it there for a few seconds, tasting it fully before spitting it out into a sink. Subjects immediately made ratings of the pleasantness and intensity of the taste, turning over each scale once completed to prevent future referral. These ratings were the baseline measurements. Subjects were then randomly assigned to one of the three load conditions (A, B or C) and two minutes after making their baseline judgements were required to consume the contents of their beaker within the period of a minute. Ten minutes after the load subjects again rated their motivation to eat and sampled and rated the sucrose solution. Ratings of eating motivation were always completed prior to the rating of taste. This procedure was continued at ten-minute intervals for one hour. During this time subjects were asked not to discuss the experiment and not to smoke or eat until the completion of the study. Subjects were unaware that the tastants sampled at each ten-minute period were identical.

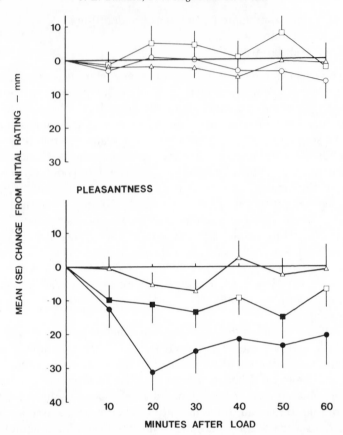

FIG. 2. The effect of consuming glucose (circles), aspartame (squares) or water (triangles) upon the perceived intensity and pleasantness of sucrose at 10-min intervals after the loads. Closed symbols indicate a significant change from baseline ($p<0.05$, 2-tailed test).

The result of consuming loads of glucose, aspartame and water on perceived pleasantness and intensity of a sweet taste is shown in Fig. 2. There was a highly significant effect of the glucose load on ratings of pleasantness ($F(6,96) = 5.952, p<0.01$). On every occasion after the load the pleasantness of sucrose was significantly lower than baseline. Aspartame also significantly reduced the pleasantness of sucrose ($F(6,96)=2.741, p<0.05$), although the extent of this change was about half of that experienced by the subjects in the glucose

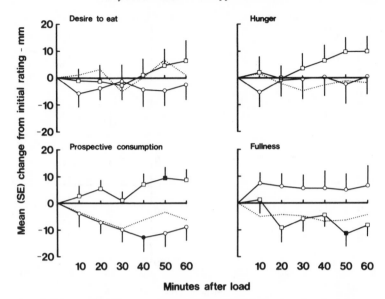

FIG. 3. The effect of consuming glucose (circles), aspartame (squares) or water (dotted line) upon ratings of desire to eat, prospective consumption, hunger and fullness at 10 min intervals after the loads. Statistically significant changes from baseline are indicated by closed symbols ($p < 0.05$).

condition. Consuming an equal volume of water did not alter subjects' perception of pleasantness. Neither were there any effects of load upon ratings of intensity, i.e. altered perception of pleasantness was not due to changes in the perception of intensity.

Regarding the changes in motivation the treatments did not produce massive effects. This is probably because subjects had recently eaten and motivation to eat was relatively low. The data are shown in Fig. 3. It can be seen that the changes produced by aspartame and glucose were invariably in opposite directions. The clearest separation occurred in ratings of prospective consumption, where glucose reduced subjects' estimates of how much food they could eat (significant at 40 minutes), while aspartame increased this rating (significant at 50 minutes). Overall, there was a clear tendency for glucose to reduce ratings of hunger and appetite and to increase fullness, whereas aspartame acted in the opposite direction.

In other words, in this study the oral glucose load, which combined sweet taste with calorific properties, produced a consistent effect

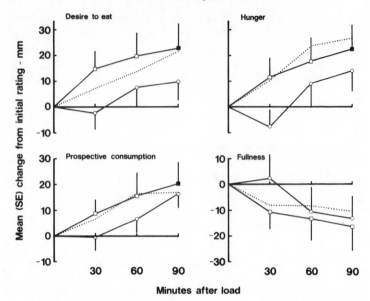

FIG. 4. Effect of glucose (circles), aspartame (squares) or water (dotted line) upon motivational ratings 30, 60 and 90 min after the loads in subjects who had not eaten for 3 h. Closed symbols indicate a significant change from baseline ($p<0.05$).

upon the measures of satiation. Glucose markedly reduced the perceived pleasantness of sweet solutions, decreased measures of hunger and appetite and increased ratings of fullness. In contrast, aspartame gave rise to an ambiguous profile of effects. On one hand the aspartame load produced a moderate negative alliesthesia (decreased perceived pleasantness of sweetness) indicative of mild satiation, whilst on the other hand this agent tended to augment ratings of motivation (indicating a mild stimulation of appetite).

In a further study we have explored the effects of aspartame and glucose on motivational measures in subjects who had been instructed to refrain from eating for three hours. The results set out in Fig. 4 indicate the changes in motivation which occurred at 30, 60 and 90 minutes after consuming the loads. This experiment used a within-subjects design so that the same subjects were tested under all three conditions (glucose, aspartame—concentrations as in the previous study—and water).

Changes in ratings following the water load indicate that subjects became more hungry and less full over the 90-minute experimental period. This was entirely expected since these subjects were fairly hungry at the start of the experiment. Over the first 30 minutes the glucose load reduced ratings of hunger and appetite and slightly increased feelings of fullness. Thereafter the glucose load markedly suppressed the motivation to eat compared with the control treatment (water load). In contrast, aspartame did not suppress appetite or hunger at any interval; on the contrary, aspartame tended to augment the rated motivation to eat and to lessen feelings of fullness.

In this study the non-calorific aspartame load failed to attenuate in any way subjects' ratings of appetite, and at the end of the 90-minute test period subjects were left with a sizeable 'residual hunger'. From other experiments (e.g. ref. 19) it can be deduced that this high level of residual hunger would give rise to increased food consumption.

Effects of Aspartame and Sucrose on Appetite

In a further study in this series we have compared the effects of aspartame with those produced by the natural sweetening agent against which all artificial sweeteners are compared—namely sucrose. The general design of the study was similar to those described above. A within-subjects design was used and all subjects were female. They were tested following a two-hour period of not eating. The four treatment conditions were as follows:

A. 50 g sucrose dissolved in 200 ml tap water
B. 288 mg aspartame (16 tablets of Canderel) in 200 ml tap water, calibrated so as to be of equal sweetness to the sucrose load
C. 200 ml tap water
D. No ingestion

These treatments therefore had the following properties:

	Volume	*Sweetness*	*Energy*
A.	Yes	Yes	Yes (188 kcal)
B.	Yes	Yes	No (5 kcal)
C.	Yes	No	No
D.	No	No	No

The results of this experiment indicate that the sucrose load produced a consistent and synchronised effect on all measures of satiation. As predicted, the sucrose load brought about a consistent decrease in ratings of pleasantness (i.e. moderate negative alliesthesia) together with a marked suppression of hunger and desire to eat and an increase in fullness. The effects for aspartame were quite different. Interestingly, this high dose of aspartame (288 mg—nearly twice the concentration used in our previous experiments) did not produce a stronger decrease in ratings of pleasantness—in fact only a rather weak negative alliesthesia was observed. This may indicate a rather unusual dose-response function for aspartame. (Indeed, in an unpublished study we have noted that this high concentration of aspartame produced more variable responses than the lower strength solution—162 mg in 200 ml.) For measures of motivation the effects of aspartame were similar to those for the water load and control condition. Over the course of the 60-minutes test period aspartame

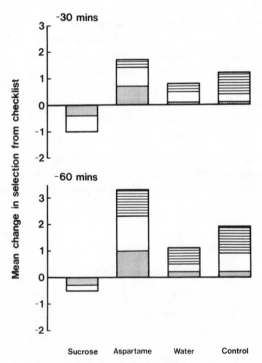

FIG. 5. The effect of treatments on the selection of high-carbohydrate (stippled columns), high-fat (plain columns) and high-protein (graded columns) food items from the food preference checklist at 30 and 60 min after ingestion. The increase in selected items following aspartame is significant at 60 min ($p < 0.05$, 2-tailed test).

gave rise to a significant increase (from baseline) in hunger and a decrease in fullness. An exception was that aspartame produced a significant decrease in ratings of desire to eat at the ten-minute test point. This probably reflects a cognitive effect of consuming the sweet-tasting solution—see below.

An interesting profile of changes emerged from the analysis of food checklist responses (see ref. 23). In keeping with the decrease in ratings of hunger and appetite, the sucrose load gave rise to a small negative shift in the checking of food items (Fig. 5). In contrast, all other treatments gave rise to increases, with the largest effect produced by aspartame. In other studies we have reported strong positive correlations between hunger, actual food consumption and checklist scores. Therefore, these data suggest that this dose of aspartame is producing a mild facilitative effect on appetite.

Taken together the effects of sucrose demonstrated in this experiment are similar to those noted previously for glucose. A sweet and calorific load gave rise to a constellation of effects on measures of satiation which are consistent. In contrast, aspartame, in this experiment, produced an ambiguous profile. Surprisingly, this high concentration of aspartame produced only a weak negative alliesthesia—indicating a very mild satiating effect. The pattern of effects for the motivational ratings showed the opposite effect—a slight facilitation of appetite. The checklist scores indicated a tendency to promote appetite.

Comparison of Artificial Sweeteners

In order to establish whether the effects revealed above were specific to aspartame or were more general features of all artificial sweeteners we have compared the effects of preloads of aspartame, saccharin and acesulfame-K matched for sweetness and volume with a 25% glucose solution. Twelve subjects were tested in a repeated measures design with each subject receiving each treatment. The solutions were administered in counterbalanced order. After ingesting the solutions at 12.00 midday, subjects filled in rating scales periodically during the following 60 minutes in order to track the changes in hunger and other perceived sensations. At the end of this time subjects were given a lunch-time test meal (at 13.00 hrs) comprising sandwiches, cakes, biscuits and yoghurt. The amount of each product consumed together with total calories and intakes of specific macronutrients (protein, carbohydrate and fat) was measured.

HUNGER

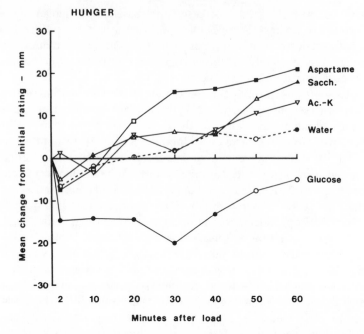

FIG. 6. The effect of consuming glucose (circles), aspartame (squares), saccharin (triangles), acesulfame-K (inverted triangles) and water (dotted line) upon hunger ratings at 10-min intervals after the loads. Closed symbols indicate a significant change from baseline ($p < 0.05$).

The effects of the preloads upon ratings of perceived hunger are shown in Fig. 6. Although the subjects were mildly deprived at the time of the experiment (no food eaten since 9.00 hrs) the artificial sweeteners gave rise to a facilitation of perceived hunger in contrast to the glucose load which markedly suppressed hunger. Statistical analysis revealed a significant effect of time ($F(6,66) = 16.02$, $p < 0.01$) and a significant preload by time interaction ($F(24,264) = 2.30$, $p < 0.01$). The food intake data were equally interesting and are shown in Fig. 7. The effect of preload was marginally significant ($F(4,44) = 2.24$, $p < 0.1$, 2-tailed test). Post-hoc two-sample comparisons (Newman–Keuls) revealed that, compared to water, the glucose load significantly suppressed the amount of food consumed in the test meal ($p < 0.05$). Indeed, the energy reduction brought about by glucose almost precisely matched the energy contained in the preload. In other words, subjects compensated very well for this caloric

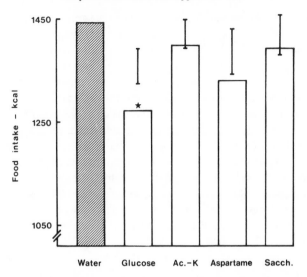

FIG. 7. The effect of consuming glucose, aspartame, saccharin, acesulfame-K and water upon mean food intake (kcal) in a test meal one hour later. Error bars indicate standard error of the mean difference between water and preload. *Significant reduction compared to water ($p<0.05$).

preload. The artificial sweeteners did not suppress food intake, indicating that the residual hunger was functional and maintained consumption. However, it is noticeable that the artificial sweeteners did suppress intake by small amounts ranging from 2% (acesulfame-K) to 8% (aspartame). The low intake for aspartame is a little misleading since, with this treatment, six subjects increased their intake (compared to water load) and six showed reductions. Of these last six, two subjects displayed substantial reductions of 50% and 28% respectively. In these subjects for some reason the aspartame load produced an anorexic response.

One interesting feature of the study is the relationship between the effects of the treatments on hunger and on food consumption. For the glucose load the effects are consistent—a marked suppression of hunger together with a reduction in food consumption. However, the artificial sweeteners—and aspartame in particular—showed elevations in hunger but weak suppressive effects on intake. This dissociation is very unusual in our experience. However, it is not surprising that increases in food intake were not observed. The subjects were hungry at the time of the test meal and ate considerable amounts of food (average of 1450 kcal). Therefore intake was probably maximal for this time of the day and it would have been extremely difficult for any manipulation to improve further on this degree of energy consumption. In addition, it should be kept in mind that subjects were eating from a limited range of foods (those appropriate for the nutritional analysis employed) and especially favoured foods which may have been sought under conditions of enhanced hunger may not have been present. These explanations probably account for the lack of an increase in food intake following artificial sweetener preloads, but why should a mild decrease have occurred? This was probably engendered by a carry-over of the sensory and cognitive processes mediating satiety (see later) which normally help to suppress intake in advance of post-ingestive and post-absorptive effects.

IMPLICATIONS OF UNCOUPLING SWEETNESS AND CALORIES

In all of the experiments described above subjects given oral loads of solutions, high in sweetness and in energy, displayed a consistent profile of responses. Measures of satiation including hedonic ratings, hunger motivation scales and the food item checklist all revealed a concerted pattern of effects. Consistent profiles were also displayed by treatments which were devoid of energy and sweetness. These conditions (water load or no ingestion) did not produce a decline in hedonic ratings (of the sucrose test solutions) and during the course of the testing period (60 minutes) appetitive motivation increased—subjects began to feel more hungry and less full. Consequently, when sweetness and calories co-vary, consistent effects on indices of satiation and upon food consumption are demonstrated. What happens when sweetness and energy are experimentally disengaged through the agency of artificial sweeteners?

In the first series of studies described here the intense sweetener aspartame has been compared with glucose, sucrose and control treatments. In contrast to those treatments in which sweetness and energy were linked, aspartame generally gave rise to a mixed profile of effects—some measures of satiation showing a moderate downward response and others showing no effect or being facilitated. Usually aspartame produced a decline in hedonic ratings but did not reduce, and sometimes enhanced, other motivational measures. Interestingly, a high concentration of aspartame did not strengthen the alliesthesia effect—indeed it appeared weaker. This feature requires further investigation, but suggests that the effects of aspartame may vary in an unpredictable way with the dose applied. This may be particularly important in view of the additional effects on appetite control mechanisms which may be brought into play by the particular chemical composition of aspartame.

Consequently, in experimental investigations in the laboratory, aspartame has been demonstrated to display irregular effects on measures of appetite control. What are the implications of this for artificial sweeteners in general use? First, for people consuming dietary products containing artificial sweeteners it can be predicted that the lowering of energy intake would fail to bring about a normal depression of motivation. This would leave people with a residual hunger, i.e. a tendency to eat if given the opportunity. This was demonstrated to be the case in the last series of experiments where aspartame (and the other artificial sweeteners) failed significantly to depress food consumption in the test meal. Second, the intense sweeteners appear to display ambiguous effects on factors reflecting the operation of satiation (the process which stops eating). This suggests that the appetite control mechanisms will be activated in possibly conflicting ways, with some systems being turned down whilst others remain active. This confusion of psychobiological information cannot help the development of good control over eating. Third, there is evidence that, under some circumstances, aspartame actually stimulated eating. This response appears very variable and probably depends on the dose, time after administration and the characteristics of a particular subject. However, it does mean that certain individuals could respond to aspartame (and other artificial sweeteners) by becoming more rather than less hungry. The circumstances under which this facilitation of hunger leads to increases in food consumption remain to be investigated further.

CAN ARTIFICIAL SWEETENERS PROVIDE SATIATING POWER?

At the present time only a handful of studies have explored the effects of aspartame (and other artificial sweeteners) on appetite and food consumption. Apart from the investigations mentioned above these studies include the three experiments on the substitution of aspartame for sucrose in foods,[1-4] an experiment on aspartame in jelly,[26] a comparison of aspartame and sucrose in milkshake loads,[27] and large doses of aspartame and phenylalanine in capsules bypassing the taste receptors.[28] These studies have produced markedly different effects ranging from an apparent aspartame-induced anorexia[26] to aspartame-induced increases in intake—9% more than placebo, 26% more than sucrose.[27] Interestingly, in a staunch defence of artificial sweeteners Booth[29] has categorically stated that 'all the evidence is that aspartame does not stimulate eating' without even referring to the work of Brala and Hagen.

One of the key questions is whether artificially sweetened products (i.e. sweet but low in energy) can provide the satiating power of high energy sweeteners. That is, do they provide a strong suppression of hunger and an inhibition of later food consumption? The studies reported above suggest that artificial sweeteners do not possess strong satiating power. However, a certain degree of satiety may be present under some circumstances. Thinking on this issue may be clarified by considering the processes set out in Fig. 8. This diagram illustrates various ways in which the ingestion of foods or preloads may inhibit later consumption. It follows that a sweet-tasting solution or food (low in calories) will provide certain sensory and cognitive suppression of intake in the immediate post-ingestive period, but will lack the later post-absorptive actions. Consequently, the belief about

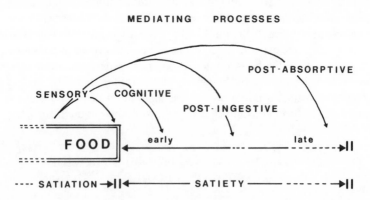

FIG. 8. A conceptualisation of the contributions of sensory, cognitive, post-ingestive and post-absorptive stimuli to satiation and the time course of satiety.

a sweet-tasting product or the triggering of established cue-consequence associations (derived from the consumption of high-calorie sweeteners) may serve to provide short-lived satiety under some circumstances. These mechanisms probably account for the weak inhibition of food consumption by artificial sweeteners in the test meals described above. In experiments on the satiating effect of sweeteners the precise nature of the preload or the sweetened food will be crucial; some products/solutions will impose potent sensory/ cognitive effects while others will be much weaker. However, artificial sweeteners would not be expected to provide late-phase satiety.

The issue of satiating power is clearly relevant to the three studies of Porikos and van Itallie[1-4] in which subjects (a total of 13 obese and 14 lean) consumed food from a menu in which the sucrose content of sweet items had been replaced by aspartame. These elegant experiments fall between clinical trials of a product (aspartame) and studies on energy regulation. Since the designs used were not completely balanced (consumption of sucrose-containing foods always preceded consumption of aspartame-loaded items) the studies cannot readily be used to throw light on the body's capacity to monitor energy intake. The results indicated that, when subjects were switched from the sucrose to the aspartame products, overall energy intake fell. However, despite the technical accomplishments in the use of calorically disguised sweet items, the biological system was not totally deceived and subjects showed a caloric compensation of about 40%. Therefore, on the full aspartame regime the subjects did overeat but not by a large enough margin to achieve full compensation for the lost calories.

However, a number of comments can be made about these very ingenious studies. First, given the elaborate deception, the degree of caloric compensation is quite impressive. In order to regain the lost calories through consumption of the sweet items alone the subjects would have been obliged to consume massive and unacceptable amounts. Since they were obliged by the methodology to sustain a certain energy deficit through the sweet items (by mandatory consumption) which are calorically dense (calories per weight), the degree of overeating required through the other food items to obtain perfect compensation was unrealistic. Second, there is evidence that the normal subjects used were an unrepresentative sample who may have been nutritionally imbalanced before entering the study.

Certainly, the first baseline intake of these subjects was remarkably high and the quality and palatability of the food offered probably caused an artificial elevation of intake over the first few days. In our view, these considerations suggest that a compensation of 40% is rather remarkable. Indeed, taking account of the elevated baselines the compensation may well be nearer 100%.[29]

The satiating power of artificial sweeteners is also questioned by the survey of use of these products carried out by the American Cancer Society. In a preliminary report on more than 78 000 women aged 50–69 'the rate of weight gain (over a one-year period) in AS (artificial sweeteners) users was significantly greater than in nonusers irrespective of initial relative weight' (ref. 30 p. 197). In addition, 'the proportion of AS users who gained ten pounds or more was significantly greater than the proportion of nonusers who gained ten pounds or more at each weight level'. These data should be treated cautiously since all the information was collected retrospectively by questionnaire. Moreover, the users of artificial sweeteners may well have been dieters and it should be asked whether it is the dieting strategy rather than artificial sweetener use (as part of this strategy) which is counterproductive in the attempt to control body weight. Although these data do not prove that artificial sweetener use causes weight gain (although the data are certainly consistent with this view), they certainly demonstrate that artificial sweetener use does not prevent weight gain. Similar findings have been revealed for other dietary products. For example, in a retrospective study of dieters it was found that 'use of slimmers' meal replacements . . . was associated with failure to lose weight during the diet and with failure to maintain lost weight' (ref. 31 p. 197). The authors further assert that 'there is evidence that such products are abused and/or the regulation of claims is inadequate'. Since this study, like that of Stellman and Garfinkel,[30] also relied upon retrospective supply of information the data should be considered with some caution. However, the similarity of the two findings is interesting.

It is noticeable that in the Stellman and Garfinkel analysis the authors present a deliberately balanced view of the outcome, in particular drawing attention to one category of women (the most obese) in which more artificial sweetener users than nonusers lost ten pounds or more. The authors question how these women may differ from the larger numbers who gained weight. The presence of different types of responders gives credibility to the analysis. The major detected effect of artificial sweetener use, to increase weight gain, is consistent with the idea that artificial sweetener use may either facilitate appetite or lead to a build-up of residual hunger.[32, 33] Other dieting strategies may have similar effects.

In the discussion presented above, the major characteristic of artificial sweeteners under consideration has been the capacity to uncouple sweetness from calories. However, in the case of aspartame certain post-ingestive mechanisms could be brought into play by way of triggering of amino acid receptors in the alimentary canal, a release of endogenous satiety hormones or by the adjustment of plasma amino acid profiles and ultimately brain neurotransmitter synthesis. In an attempt to investigate this last issue one study has examined the effects of the administration of very large doses (up to 10·08 g) of phenylalanine and aspartame.[28] Since subjects ingested these amounts in capsules (swallowing as many as 24 capsules in some conditions) the substances by-passed the generation of sweet sensations in the mouth and therefore would avoid triggering cephalic phase reflexes or disrupting learned associations between sweetness and calories. Consequently, this study is not related to the issues investigated in our research presented previously. Nevertheless, it is worth examining. The results apparently failed to support any action of phenylalanine or aspartame on hunger or food consumption. However, no data were shown for the effects of amino acid loads on hunger and no statistical analysis was presented. In the case of food intake (in a test meal) no F values or other statistical data were presented and no post-hoc tests were applied even though one dose of phenylalanine (10·08 g) produced an approximate 16% suppression of intake. It is worth noting that this degree of suppression is greater than that normally achieved by 50 g glucose[34] or by a potent anorexic drug.[22] Lastly, it is worth pointing out that the study was carried out on men who were unrestrained (i.e. not dieting) and hungry at the time of the test meal. As noted previously, this design is insensitive to the detection of increases in food intake and it would be particularly interesting to compare the changes in hunger ratings with food intake (see Figs 6 and 7). Consequently, although this study provides some fascinating data, the report still leaves unanswered a number of critical questions. Evidence from our own studies using much smaller doses of aspartame in capsule form (therefore by-passing the sweet sensation) indicate that this manipulation is not inert.[35] We feel that it is important to consider the possibility that

aspartame may exert effects on more than one mechanism implicated
in appetite and eating control.

POSTSCRIPT

Artificial sweeteners constitute exquisite tools for researchers examining mechanisms controlling appetite and eating; they are also agents of considerable commercial importance. This means that investigations of artificial sweeteners are not just a scientific enterprise but acquire political significance if research outcomes are perceived to have an influence on commercial prospects. It is therefore difficult to carry out research which, whilst throwing light on the action of sweeteners, is not perceived as being advantageous or detrimental to one or another commercial interest. The tendency to view a research outcome in terms of marketing advantage is a great handicap to independent researchers seeking to disclose valid information about important psychobiological manipulations. In a recent report[32] we drew attention to certain paradoxical effects of artificial sweeteners. However, reports in the media were largely focused on one single aspect of this study—namely the likely facilitation of appetite—with a commensurate degree of misrepresentation of the outcome of the research. This action of journalists linked to a particular commercial lobby is undesirable but may be expected. Rather alarmingly, at least one scientific investigator has engaged in a heroic attempt to undermine the essence of the outcome of the above-mentioned report. Although one may expect journalists to get facts wrong or fail to properly understand subtle issues, it is disturbing when scientists display similar weaknesses. In the report alluded to in the footnote* (seen by the present writers in draft form) the distinguished commentator made 8 errors of perception including the misreading of sucrose for glucose.

It is worth repeating that knowledge concerning the effects of artificial sweeteners on appetite is still extremely limited; the field is under-researched and wordy polemic is no substitute for sound experimentation.

Artificial sweeteners in general, and aspartame in particular, are

---

*Citation available but identity withheld here.

fascinating compounds. They are likely to influence psychobiological systems, and effects on appetite and eating should be expected. Research on this issue should be encouraged, not stifled. The nature of the effects generated on appetite remain to be precisely defined; effects may vary with amount ingested, environmental or physiological circumstances and with the type of individual. Our research indicates that these sweeteners may give rise to unexpected effects or to multiple and paradoxical effects. When used as an aid to weight control it should be kept in mind that artificial sweeteners do not *per se* perform a weight-reducing or weight-regulating function. Individuals who consume artificial sweeteners and who assign responsibility to these products may fail to check facilitative effects or the existence of residual hunger. It would seem judicious to point out that the ingestion of artificial sweeteners for weight control should be accompanied by a greater vigilance and greater degree of self-monitoring, not less.

REFERENCES

1. PORIKOS, K. P. (1981). In: *The Body Weight Regulatory System; Normal and Disturbed Mechanisms*, Eds Cioffi, P. W., James, P. W. and van Itallie, T. B., Raven Press, New York, 83–7.
2. PORIKOS, K. P., BOOTH, G. and VAN ITALLIE, T. B. (1977). *Am. J. Clin. Nutr.*, **30**, 1638–44.
3. PORIKOS, K. P., HESSER, M. F. and VAN ITALLIE, T. B. (1982). *Physiol. Behav.*, **29**, 292–300.
4. PORIKOS, K. P. and VAN ITALLIE, T. B. (1984). In: *Aspartame—Physiology and Biochemistry*, Eds Lewis, D., Stegink, L. J. and Filer, J., Marcel Dekker Inc., New York, 273–86.
5. NAIM, M. and KARE, M. R. (1982). In: *Nutritive Sweeteners*, Eds Birch, G. G. and Parker, K. J., Elsevier Applied Science, London, 171–93.
6. BEAUCHAMP, G. K. and COWART, B. J. (1987). In: *Sweetness*, Ed. Dobbing, J., Springer-Verlag, London, 127–40.
7. BOOTH, D. A. (1980). In: *Obesity*, Ed. Stunkard, A. J., Saunders, Philadelphia, 101–43.
8. GARCIA, J., HAWKINS, W. G. and RUSINIAK, K. W. (1974). *Science*, **185**, 824–31.
9. SJOSTROM, L., GARELLICK, G., KROTKIEWSKY, M. and LUYCKX, A. (1980). *Metabolism*, **29**, 901–9.
10. SIMON, C., SCHLIENGER, J. L., SAPIN, R. and IMLER, M. (1986). *Physiol. Behav.*, **36**, 465–9.
11. BERTHOUD, H. R., BEREITER, D. A., TRIMBLE, E. R., SIEGEL, E. G. and JEANRENAUD, B. (1981). *Diabetolog.*, **20**, 393–401.

12. GIBBS, J., FALASCO, J. D. and McHUGH, P. R. (1976). *Am. J. Physiol.*, **230**, 15–18.
13. SMITH, G. P. and GIBBS, J. (1979). *Prog. Psychobiol. Physiol. Psychol.*, **8**, 179–242.
14. KISSILEFF, H. R., PI-SUNYER, F. X., THORNTON, J. and SMITH, G. P. (1981). *Am. J. Clin. Nutr.*, **34**, 154–60.
15. MEI, N. (1985). *Physiol. Rev.*, **65**, 211–37.
16. WURTMAN, R. J. (1983). *New Eng. J. Med.*, **309**, 429–30.
17. COULOMBE, R. A. and SHARMA, R. P. (1986). *Toxicol. Appl. Pharmacol.*, **83**, 79–85.
18. LEIBOWITZ, S. F. and SHOR-POSNER, G. (1986). In: *Psychopharmacology of Eating Disorders: Theoretical and Clinical Advances*, Eds Carruba, M. O. and Blundell, J. E., Raven Press, New York, 29–50.
19. HILL, A. J., LEATHWOOD, P. J. and BLUNDELL, J. E. (1987). *Human Nutr.: Appl. Nutr.*, **41A**, 244–57.
20. HILL, A. J. and BLUNDELL, J. E. (1986). *Nutr. Behav.*, **3**, 133–44.
21. HILL, A. J., MAGSON, L. D. and BLUNDELL, J. E. (1984). *Appetite*, **5**, 361–71.
22. HILL, A. J. and BLUNDELL, J. E. (1986). In: *Advances in the Bio-Sciences*, Vol. 60, Eds Ferrari, E. and Brambilla, F., Pergamon Press, Oxford, 377–89.
23. BLUNDELL, J. E. and HILL, A. J. (1987). In: *Modern Concepts of the Eating Disorders: Research, Diagnosis, Treatment*, Eds Blinder, B. J., Friedman, E., Chaitin, B. F. and Goldstein, R., Spectrum, New York, in press.
24. BLUNDELL, J. E. and BURLEY, V. J. (1987). *Int. J. Obesity*, **11** (Suppl. 1), 9–25.
25. CABANAC, M. (1971). *Science*, **173**, 1103–7.
26. ROLLS, B. J., HETHERINGTON, M., BURLEY, V. J. and DUIJVEN-VOORDE, P. M. (1986). In: *Interaction of the Chemical Senses with Nutrition*, Eds Kare, M. R. and Brand, J. G., Academic Press, New York, 247–68.
27. BRALA, P. M. and HAGEN, R. L. (1983). *Physiol. Behav.*, **30**, 1–9.
28. RYAN-HARSHMAN, M., LEITER, L. A. and ANDERSON, G. H. (1987). *Physiol. Behav.*, **39**, 247–53.
29. BOOTH, D. A. (1987). In: *Developments in Sweeteners – 3*, Ed. Grenby, T. H., Elsevier, North Holland, in press.
30. STELLMAN, S. D. and GARFINKEL, L. (1986). *Prev. Med.*, **15**, 195–202.
31. LEWIS, V. J. and BOOTH, D. A. (1985). In: *Measurement and Determinants of Food Habits and Food Preferences*, Eds Diehl, J. M. and Leitzman, C., EC Workshop Report, Giessen (W. Germany), 187–208.
32. BLUNDELL, J. E. and HILL, A. J. (1986). *Lancet*, **1**, 1092–3.
33. BLUNDELL, J. E. and HILL, A. J. (1987). In: *The Future of Predictive Safety Evaluation*, Eds Worden, A., Parke, D. and Marks, J., MTP Press, Lancaster, 263–82.
34. BLUNDELL, J. E. and HILL, A. J. (1987). *Clin. Neuropharmacol.*, in press.
35. ROGERS, P. J. and BLUNDELL, J. E. (1987). Unpublished report.

12

Nutrient Ingestion and Body Weight Regulation

Y. SCHUTZ

Institute of Physiology, University of Lausanne, Switzerland

ABSTRACT

In individuals who maintain a stable body weight for long periods of their life, total metabolisable energy intake, although quite variable from day to day, must be equal to total energy expenditure. In addition, if body composition is maintained stable, then composition of substrate oxidised by the body over the same period must be equivalent to the metabolisable energy intake; i.e. protein, carbohydrate and fat balance must be equilibrated. Above the minimum requirement level, nitrogen balance is on a weekly basis spontaneously maintained on various protein intakes, and protein represents—in contrast to carbohydrate and fat—a low fraction of total energy intake (12–15%). Thus according to a concept developed by J. P. Flatt, long-term weight maintenance is determined primarily by the extent to which modulation of the metabolism of both carbohydrate (CHO) and fat occurs.

CHO metabolism. Since the body's capacity for storing glycogen is limited to a few hundred grams and, in habitual nutritional conditions, the body's glycogen reserves may be maintained within a relatively stable range, total carbohydrate oxidation over a few days must be equivalent to the total metabolisable CHO ingested.

Conversion of carbohydrate into fat (i.e. 'de novo' lipogenesis) provides a pathway for the disposal of CHO consumed in excess. In man an estimate of new 'de novo' lipogenesis can be obtained by continuous indirect calorimetry (i.e. when the non-protein respiratory quotient (RQ) exceeds 1·0). In order to induce lipogenesis in man, massive amounts of carbohydrate must be given either acutely or chronically. In our laboratory, Acheson et al. have measured the magnitude of thermogenesis and lipogenesis with 500 g malto-dextrin loads. Glucose-induced thermogenesis, which varied according to the antecedent diet of the subjects, was found to be dependent upon the rate of net lipogenesis (range 1 to 9 g/14 h) and a significant correlation (r = 0·82, p < 0·001) was found between these two variables. Furthermore, the rate of lipogenesis of obese individuals was not greater than that observed in matched control subjects.

Only a limited number of chronic carbohydrate (CHO overfeeding) studies have been performed in man. We have measured the changes in 24-h RQ before, during and following CHO overfeeding, using a respiration chamber. After seven days of CHO overfeeding (last day's excess energy intake over requirements: + 2800 kcal/d), it was found that the induction of lipogenesis resulted in substantial fat synthesis from CHO i.e. ~ 150 g/d.

Fat metabolism. It is well known that, in contrast to the CHO stores, the body's fat stores can be largely extended, as evidenced by the degree of obesity attained by some individuals. Recent data obtained in our laboratory have demonstrated that the presence or absence of fat, in a breakfast providing fixed amounts of carbohydrate and protein, had no effect on the composition of the nutrient oxidised during the post-prandial hours. This suggests that the fat oxidation is not dependent upon fat intake.

To elucidate further the role of fat we performed 24-h fat overfeeding studies in young men who stayed in a respiration chamber where their rate of nutrient oxidation was continuously monitored. During the first 24-h period the subjects consumed a mixed maintenance diet containing 30% of calories as fat. An additional amount of 106 ± 6 g of fat/24 h was added to this diet during the following 36 h of their stay in the chamber. The results showed that the supplement of dietary fat failed to promote the use of fat as a metabolic fuel. Overall energy balance was closely correlated with the fat balance (r = 0·96, p < 0·001) but not with the carbohydrate balance (r = 0·12, n.s.). Therefore appreciable imbalance between intake and oxidation of fat appears to be much more likely than for carbohydrate or for protein.

INTRODUCTION

Human beings tend to maintain a stable body weight during adult-hood in spite of large day-to-day fluctuations in nutrient intake. As the adult grows older, there is a general tendency towards an increase in body weight and body fat.[1,2] The regulation of nutrient storage—which allows the body pool of macronutrients to remain essentially constant over a period of time—is assured through the control of nutrient intake and nutrient oxidation. The basic homeostatic mechanism involved in body weight and body composition regulation integrates a number of endogenous and exogenous stimuli. In order to elucidate the respective role of each stimulus involved in this complex homeostatic process, several recent symposia have been devoted to this fascinating subject.[3,4] In addition, confusion has arisen as to whether body weight is 'regulated' (i.e. maintained constant via adjustment of both input and output) or 'controlled' (i.e. constantly adjusted in order to regulate other parameters).

One simple approach for studying the behaviour of a physiological system is to apply an acute or chronic exogenous stimulus and to subsequently measure the overall regulatory response of the organism. For example, the metabolic and physiological response to a change in food intake can be scrutinised in man over various periods of time.

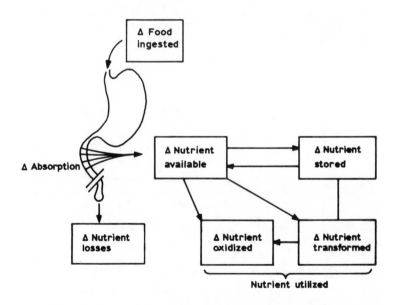

FIG. 1. General outline of the fate of food intake within the body (Δ = change).

The present paper examines the effect of acute or chronic carbohydrate (CHO) overfeeding versus fat overfeeding on three factors (Fig. 1).

1. Changes in digestion and absorption.
2. Changes in the rate of nutrient oxidation and storage.
3. The difference in energy equivalent of body-weight gain.

CHANGES IN DIGESTION AND ABSORPTION

The question has often been raised as to whether or not the regulation of body weight could be accomplished by controlling the rate of nutrient absorption.

Over 30 years ago, the American pioneer Atwater made an extensive number of metabolic balance experiments in three subjects over 3–8 days' duration.[5] The results showed that, with a mixed diet, typical of the early 20th century, 92% protein, 95% fat and 98% carbohydrate were normally digested.

More recently, Southgate and Durnin[6] in England and Göranzon et al.[7] in Sweden performed further metabolic balance studies in individuals who were ingesting either a 'normal' diet or high fibre diets. As shown in Table 1, high fibre diets lead to significantly lower protein, fat and carbohydrate digestibilities. Since the apparent

TABLE 1
Apparent Digestibility Studies in Man: Influence of Dietary Fibres

	Digestibility (%)								
	Protein			Fat			Carbohydrate		
Authors	Low fibre	p	High fibre	Low fibre	p	High fibre	Low fibre	p	High fibre
Southgate and Durnin[6]	89·6	*	86·8	96·4	**	94·8	—		—
	92·1	*	90·8	96·7	**	96·2	—		—
Göranzon et al.[7]	89·7	*	81·4	93·1	***	87·3	96·6	***	93·4

*$p < 0.05$; ** $p < 0.005$; *** $p < 0.001$.

digestibility coefficient of Atwater represents average values, it seems of interest to assess the range of variability involved between subjects: the standard deviation of the percentage digestibility for protein, fat and carbohydrate[7] was in the order of 1–3% with the low fibre diet and 1–7% with the high fibre diet suggesting a limited degree of flexibility for modulating nutrient absorption between healthy individuals. Could overfeeding cause a decreased rate of nutrient availability so that part of the excess nutrient intake could be disposed of by reducing absorption?

Dallosso and James[8] have measured the digestible energy of food in adult men overfed with fat. During fat overfeeding, the average ($\pm$ SD) apparent energy digestibility ($96 \pm 1\%$) was nearly identical to that measured during the normal feeding period ($95 \pm 1\%$).

Similarly when excess CHO is fed in progressively increased amounts to adult men, the rate of digestible energy remains unchanged[9] and during the last three days of overfeeding (when more than 900 g CHO/d was ingested) the percentage apparent digestibility was still of the order of 95–98.

The results are consistent with the view that the normal human gut possesses a large functional reserve for macronutrient absorption. The notion that increased macronutrient losses during overfeeding explain why some individuals gain less weight than others on the same diet is not supported by experimental data.

CHANGES IN NUTRIENT UTILISATION AND STORAGE

In individuals who maintain a stable body weight for long periods of their life, the total metabolisable energy intake, although quite variable from day to day, must be equal to the total energy expenditure. In addition, if body composition is maintained stable, the composition of the substrate which is oxidised by the body over the same period of time must be equivalent to that which is ingested, so that the protein, carbohydrate and fat balances are equilibrated. Deviations from these balances commonly occur from day to day as evidenced by day-to-day fluctuations in body weight. Therefore, the regulation of body weight and body composition implies that a controlled mechanism exists with which it is possible to elicit corrective responses when excessive nutrients are accumulated or are being depleted.

Above the minimum requirement level, nitrogen balance is spontaneously maintained on various protein intakes, and protein represents—in contrast to CHO and fat—a low fraction of total energy intake (12–15%). Thus according to a concept developed by Flatt[10] long-term weight maintenance is determined primarily by the sensitivity with which the metabolism of both carbohydrate and fat can be controlled.

Excess Carbohydrate (CHO) Ingestion

Since the body's capacity for storing glycogen appears to be limited to a few hundred grams, total carbohydrate oxidation over a few days must be equivalent to the total metabolisable CHO ingested. An acute glucose load given either 'per os' or intravenously results in an increased CHO utilisation and increased glycogen storage in the postprandial phase.[11,12].

Conversion of carbohydrate into fat (i.e. 'de novo' lipogenesis) provides a pathway for the disposal of CHO consumed in excess. In man an estimate of net 'de novo' lipogenesis can be obtained by continuous indirect calorimetry (i.e. when the non-protein respiratory quotient (RQ) exceeds 1·0). In order to induce lipogenesis in man, massive amounts of carbohydrate must be given either acutely or chronically. In our laboratory, Acheson et al.[13] have measured the magnitude of thermogenesis and lipogenesis with 500 g dextrin-maltose loads. The rate of glucose-induced thermogenesis—which varied according to the antecedent diet of the subject—was found to be dependent upon the rate of net lipogenesis (range 1 to 9 g/14 h) and a significant correlation ($r = 0·82, p < 0·001$) was found between these two variables. Furthermore, the rate of lipogenesis of obese individuals was not greater than that observed in matched control subjects.[14]

Only a limited number of chronic CHO overfeeding studies have been performed in man (see ref. 15 for review). We have measured the changes in 24-h RQ before, during and following CHO overfeeding, using a respiration chamber. After seven days of CHO overfeeding (last day's excess energy intake over requirements: + 2800 kcal/d), it was found that the induction of lipogenesis resulted in substantial fat synthesis from CHO (~150 g/d). It should be noted that even under these extremely artificial nutritional circumstances, CHO balance was equilibrated;[16] i.e. the stimulation of CHO utilisation could match CHO intake despite massive CHO ingestion (~1000 g/d).

Excess Fat Ingestion

It is well known that, in contrast to the CHO stores, the body's fat stores can be largely extended, as is evident from the degree of obesity attained by some individuals. Recent data obtained in our laboratory[17] have demonstrated that the presence or absence of fat in a breakfast providing fixed amounts of carbohydrate and protein had no effect on the composition of the nutrient oxidised during the postprandial hours. This suggests that total fat oxidation measured in the postprandial phase is not dependent upon fat intake (Table 2).

To elucidate further the role of fat we performed more prolonged fat overfeeding studies in young men[18] who stayed in a respiration chamber for three nights and days, during which time their rate of nutrient oxidation was continuously measured by indirect calorimetry.

During the first 24-h period the subjects consumed a mixed maintenance diet containing 30% of calories as fat. An additional amount of 106 ± 6 g of fat/24 h was added to this diet during the following 36 h of their stay in the chamber. The results showed that the supplement of dietary fat failed to promote the use of fat as a metabolic fuel (Table 2). Overall energy balance was closely correlated with the fat balance ($r = 0.96$, $p < 0.001$) but not with the carbohydrate balance ($r = 0.12$, n.s.).

TABLE 2

Nutrient Oxidation and Balance in Response to Excess Fat Intake Given as a Single Breakfast[17] or as 3 Meals/day[18]

	Nutrient					
	Intake		Oxidation		Balance	
	CHO	Fat	CHO	Fat	CHO	Fat
1. Single breakfast (9-h response)			g/9 h			
Control	73	6	79 ± 8	37 ± 7	-5 ± 8	-31 ± 6
Fat supplement	73	46	79 ± 9	39 ± 4	-5 ± 9	6 ± 4***
2. 3 meals/day (24-h response)			g/24 h			
Control	335 ± 8	106 ± 2	307 ± 19	111 ± 8	28 ± 15	-5 ± 9
Fat supplement	336 ± 8	212 ± 5	321 ± 16	112 ± 8	15 ± 12	$+100 \pm 9$***

*** $p < 0.001$.

There is a paucity of data on chronic fat overfeeding in man. Recently, Dallosso and James[8] have studied eight young men who maintained their weight on a baseline diet for one week and were then overfed with fat for another week, so that the percentage fat in the diet increased from 30% to 50% of the energy. The study showed that 88% of the excess metabolisable energy intake was stored in the body. Interestingly, fat overfeeding did not change the rate of CHO storage (+ 2 kcal/d) whereas it substantially enhanced fat storage (+ 1386 kcal/d), so that all the energy surplus was retained in the form of fat. This study confirms the notion that short-term fat over-feeding does not stimulate the rate of fat oxidation in man so that the excess fat is stored in adipose tissue with a high energy efficiency. The influence of dietary fat on fat oxidation thus appears to be far less than the effects which dietary carbohydrate exert to make carbo-hydrate oxidation commensurate with their intake. Appreciable imbalances between intake and oxidation appear therefore to be much more likely for fat than for carbohydrate.

The lack of increase in fat oxidation in response to extra fat intake observed in short-term studies must be only a transient phenomenon for the following reasons:

1. If long-term fat oxidation in the presence of excess fat would remain constant, the rate of fat storage would continuously increase (and hence body weight would never plateau). This is

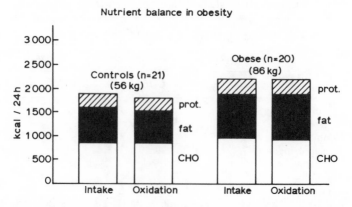

FIG. 2. Carbohydrate (CHO), fat and protein balances in obese women in the static phase of obesity when compared with thin controls (see basic data, Table 3).

not observed experimentally: body composition should eventually stabilise at a level at which the increased rate of fat oxidation allows a new level of fat balance to be maintained.

2. Experimental data show that the absolute rate of fat oxidation of obese individuals in the static phase of obesity is greater than that of thin individuals (Fig. 2) despite the fact that the proportion of fuel mix oxidised is the same as evidenced by the same RQ. As shown in Table 3 this is partly explained by the significantly greater rate of energy expenditure commonly observed in obese individuals.[19,20] It should be recalled that the excess body weight of obese individuals is not made up only of fat tissue but also of fat-free tissue, as an average 75% fat and 25% fat-free mass.[21] The increase in the latter compartment may explain the elevated energy expenditure observed in obesity.

CHANGES IN THE ENERGY EQUIVALENT OF BODY WEIGHT GAIN

Calculation of the energy equivalent of weight gain (i.e. the rate of energy retained per unit of weight gain) is of interest since it provides an index of the composition of weight gain.[22] The metabolisable energy ingested in excess of the total energy expenditure is stored in the form of macronutrients. Carbohydrate storage in the liver and muscles is accompanied by water retention ('wet' glycogen) so that the energy density of the glycogen–water pool is much lower (~ 1 kcal/g or $4 \cdot 2$ kJ/g) than the glycogen itself ($4 \cdot 2$ kcal/g or $17 \cdot 6$ kJ/g). Garrow[23] has shown that the relationship between the day-to-day weight change and the day-to-day energy imbalance in a given individual was highly significant ($p < 0 \cdot 001$) and the slope of the regression line was found to be $1 \cdot 1$ kcal/g indicating that there was a change in weight of 90 g for every 100 kcal of energy imbalance. This corresponds to a glycogen–water mixture of 1 g glycogen binding with approximately 3 g of water:

$$\left(\frac{4 \cdot 2 \text{ kcal}}{4 \text{ g}} = 1 \cdot 1 \text{ kcal/g} \right).$$

In contrast to CHO, average fat ($9 \cdot 3$ kcal/g or $38 \cdot 9$ kJ/g) is stored in adipose tissue with little associated water ($\sim 15\%$ by weight) so

TABLE 3

Energy Expenditure and Respiratory Quotient (RQ) in Obese and Nonobese Women[24]

	Age (y)	Body weight (kg)	Body fat (% body wt)	E intake (kcal/day)	24-h RQ	24-h EE (kcal/day)
Control (n=21)	26±5	56·3±5·8	25·1±3·5	1 849±192	0·84±0·03	1 761±132
Obese (n=20)	26±5	86·1±14·1	38·5±3·5	2 203±234	0·85±0·03	2 138±280
p	NS	<0·001	<0·001	<0·001	NS	<0·001

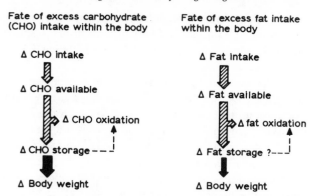

FIG. 3. Different metabolic responses of a surplus of carbohydrate (Δ CHO) versus an excess of fat (Δ fat) on CHO and fat oxidation respectively and body weight.

that the energy density of adipose tissue remains elevated (7·9 kcal/g or 33·1 kJ/g). In order to illustrate this point the energy equivalent of body-weight change observed was calculated from the data given in the previously mentioned fat overfeeding study,[8] i.e. when fat stores are expected to be expanded: the average increase in energy stores averaged 1383 kcal/d for a weight gain of 174 g/d yielding an energy equivalent of 7·95 kcal/g corresponding exactly to that of adipose tissue.

The present approach based on the energy equivalent of weight gain does confirm the results obtained with the classical fat balance method (see above). The above consideration implies that for a given energy retention the short-term weight change will be eight times greater when glycogen is stored than when adipose tissue is stored (Fig. 3).

CONCLUSIONS

Man eats a variable quantity of nutrient from day to day and therefore in order to maintain nutrient homeostasis the body must in the long term adequately cope with this dynamic pattern of changes in nutrient intake:

1. Since the glycogen stores are quantitatively limited to a few hundred grams, excess CHO intake will result in both an initial

increase in glycogen storage and, concomitantly, a rapid compensatory stimulation in CHO utilisation. This suggests the presence of an efficient mechanism regulating CHO stores within a certain range.

2. Since the fat stores can be quantitatively expended to a large degree, excess fat intake does not appear to stimulate fat oxidation immediately; it only increases fat storage. Therefore, the short-term mechanism regulating fat storage appears to be less sensitive and less precisely controlled for fat than for CHO. However, since total fat oxidation in obese individuals is greater than that of their lean counterparts, a new equilibrium must be reached at a higher level of fat balance.

Future research should focus on further exploring the mechanism involved in the regulation of nutrient balance and whether the greater fat oxidation observed in obesity is due to an increase in adipose tissue 'per se' as postulated by Flatt[10] or rather due to the effect of the increased fat-free mass which generally accompanies the obese state.

ACKNOWLEDGEMENT

The author thanks Professors E. Jéquier, K. J. Acheson and J. P. Flatt for their interest and encouragement.

REFERENCES

1. BRAY, G. A. (1983). The energetics of obesity, *Med. and Science in Sports and Exercise*, **15**, 32–40.
2. SIMOPOULOS, A. P. and VAN ITALLIE, T. B. (1984). Body weight, health and longevity, *Annals of Int. Med.*, **100**, 285–95.
3. CIOFFI, I. A., JAMES, W. P. T and VAN ITALLIE, T. B. (Eds) (1981). *The Body Weight Regulatory System: Normal and Disturbed Mechanisms*, Raven Press, New York.
4. BENDER, A. E. and BROOKES, L. J. (Eds) (1987). *Body Weight Control: The Physiology, Clinical Treatment and Prevention of Obesity*, Churchill Livingstone, Edinburgh, London, Melbourne and New York.
5. ATWATER, W. O. and BRYANT, A. P. (1955). Rep. Storrs Agric. Exp. Sta. 1899, p. 73 as quoted by Widdowson, E. Assessment of the energy value of human foods, *Proc. Nutr. Soc.*, **14**, 142–54.
6. SOUTHGATE, D. A. T. and DURNIN, J. V. G. A. (1970). Calorie

conversion factors. An experimental reassessment of the factors used in the calculation of the energy value of human diets, *Brit. J. Nutr.*, **24**, 517–35.

7. GÖRANZON, H., FORSUM, E. and THILEN, M. (1983). Calculation and determination of metabolizable energy in mixed diets to humans, *Am. J. Clin. Nutr.*, **38**, 954–63.

8. DALLOSSO, H. M. and JAMES, W. P. T. (1984). Whole-body calorimetry studies in adult men. 1. The effect of fat over-feeding on 24 h energy expenditure, *Brit. J. Nutr.*, **52**, 49–64.

9. ACHESON, K. J., SCHUTZ, Y., BESSARD, T., ANANTHARAMAN, K., FLATT, J. P. and JÉQUIER, E. (1988). Glycogen storage capacity and *de novo* lipogenesis during massive carbohydrate overfeeding in man, *Am. J. Clin. Nutr.* (accepted for publication).

10. FLATT, J. P. (1987). Dietary fat, carbohydrate balance, and weight maintenance: effects of exercise, *Am. J. Clin. Nutr.*, **45**, 296–306.

11. FELBER, J. P. and JÉQUIER, E. (1982). Glucose storage deficiency as a cause of insulin resistance in obese-hyperinsulinaemic diabetes, *Int. J. Obes.*, **6** (Suppl. 1), 131–5.

12. THIÉBAUD, D., SCHUTZ, Y., ACHESON, K. J., JACOT, E., DEFRONZO, R. A., FELBER, J. P. and JÉQUIER, E. (1983). Energy cost of glucose storage in man during glucose/insulin infusion, *Am. J. Physiol.*, **244**, E216–E221.

13. ACHESON, K. J., SCHUTZ, Y., BESSARD, T., RAVUSSIN, E., JÉQUIER, E. and FLATT, J. P. (1984). Nutritional influences on lipogenesis and thermogenesis after a carbohydrate meal, *Am. J. Physiol.*, **246**, E62–E70.

14. ACHESON, K. J., SCHUTZ, Y., BESSARD, T., FLATT, J. P. and JÉQUIER, E. (1987). Carbohydrate metabolism and *de novo* lipogenesis in human obesity, *Am. J. Clin. Nutr.*, **45**, 78–85.

15. SCHUTZ, Y., ACHESON, K. J. and JÉQUIER, E. (1985). Twenty-four-hour energy expenditure and thermogenesis: response to progressive carbohydrate overfeeding in man, *Int. J. Obes.*, **9** (Suppl. 2), 111–14.

16. JÉQUIER, E. and SCHUTZ, Y. (1983). Long-term measurements of energy expenditure in humans using a respiration chamber, *Am. J. Clin. Nutr.*, **38**, 989–98.

17. FLATT, J. P., RAVUSSIN, E., ACHESON, K. J. and JÉQUIER, E. (1985). Effects of dietary fat on postprandial substrate oxidation and on carbohydrate and fat balances. *J. Clin. Invest.*, **76**, 1019–24.

18. SCHUTZ, Y., JÉQUIER, E. and FLATT, J. P. (1986). Failure of a 1000 kcal supplement of dietary fat to promote fat oxidation in man, *Experientia*, **42**, 709 (abstract).

19. RAVUSSIN, E., BURNAND, R., SCHUTZ, Y. and JÉQUIER, E. (1982). Twenty-four-hour energy expenditure and resting metabolic rate in obese, moderately obese, and control subjects. *Am. J. Clin. Nutr.*, **35**, 566–73. Balances. *J. Clin. Invest.* **76** (1985). 1019–24.

20. SCHUTZ, Y., BESSARD, T. and JÉQUIER, E. (1984). Diet-induced thermogenesis measured over a whole day in obese and nonobese women, *Am. J. Clin. Nutr.*, **40**, 542–52.

21. WEBSTER, J. D., HESP, R. and GARROW, J. S. (1984). The composition of excess weight in obese women estimated by body density, total body water and total body potassium, *Hum. Nutr. & Clin. Nutr.*, **38C**, 299–306.
22. SCHUTZ, Y. (1985). Terminology, factors and constants in studies of energy metabolism of humans. In: *Human Energy Metabolism: Physical Activity and Energy Expenditure Measurements in Epidemiological Research Based upon Direct and Indirect Calorimetry*, Ed. van Es, A. J. H., *Euro-Nut Report 5*: Den Haag, 153–68.
23. GARROW, J. S. (1974). *Energy Balance and Obesity in Man*, 1st Edn, North-Holland Publ. Comp. Amsterdam, 43.
24. SCHUTZ, Y. and JÉQUIER, E. (1986). Energy expenditure, *Lancet*, **i**, 101–2.

13

Genetic Differences in Metabolic Rate

C. GEISSLER

*Department of Food and Nutritional Sciences,
King's College, University of London, UK*

ABSTRACT

The paper reviews the literature concerning genetic influences on metabolic rate and presents data from our research group on measured differences between subjects of different ethnic origin and on subjects who are either naturally lean or with a predisposition to obesity.

European subjects were shown to have higher metabolic rates during standardised activities than either African or Asian subjects. Energy expenditure of the Europeans was 10–17% higher than for subjects of other ethnic origin, of the same size and performing the same activities. The daily energy expenditure of women with a predisposition to obesity was measured to be on average 15% lower than that of women of the same size and with the same pattern of activity, but who have no weight problem.

The implications of these findings are discussed in reference to food intake and the possible role of low-calorie foods.

INTRODUCTION

There is still a great deal of controversy about how energy balance and body weight are controlled. The relative importance of factors affecting energy intake and energy expenditure is the subject of much research and debate particularly in relation to the development of obesity. Probably the accepted wisdom of the majority of the general public and even of the medical profession is that people are fat because they are lazy and gluttonous. However, increasing evidence of metabolic defects, which reduce metabolic rate in the obese, refute this simplistic view.

The controversy remains because of two principal reasons: (1) obesity is not a single entity but is likely to have several causes; and (2) the techniques we have for measuring both energy intake and expenditure in the long term are so poor that knowledge of energy balance in normal life is impossible to the requisite level of accuracy. The closest we can get is to make these measurements in a respiration chamber but few subjects are willing to stay in one room for even several days.

Evidence that the amount of food consumed is closely controlled, via centres in the hypothalamus of the brain, comes mainly from animal studies but even in animals this control can be overridden with palatable cafeteria diets. In humans the pressures to override any hypothalamic mechanisms of intake control are plenty. We rarely eat because we are hungry: we eat when it is time for lunch or dinner. Few of us eat food as boring as rat chow: an abundant variety of foods tempts our appetites so that we can easily devour the strawberries and cream when we are already full. In fact many of us are lazy gluttons but some can cope with variable food intake and remain lean; some cannot and become obese. There is little evidence that the obese eat more than the lean. Most studies show that they eat similar quantities or less. It seems that, for obesity to occur, two conditions are necessary: (1) an ample varied food supply; and (2) a pre-disposition to weight gain which can be genetically based.

GENETIC FACTOR IN OBESITY

A genetic component in obesity has been clearly shown in animal studies, and indicated in human studies of families, twins, adopted children, and ethnic groups.

Genetic selection has long been used in animal husbandry to improve the growth and fattening qualities of pigs and cattle, and more recently to reduce the fat content of meat following consumer and nutritional demands for less fat in the diet. The type of feeding also affects the deposition of fat. Estimates of the relative importance of genetics and environment in farm animal breeding indicate that half of the total variance in fatness is due to genetic differences.[1]

Animal models of obesity include strains of mice and rats that are genetically obese and several forms exist. Inheritance may be by a single dominant or recessive gene, or polygenic. These are reviewed by Bray and York.[2] Miller[3] and Bouramand-Naini[4] estimated the relative roles of nature and nurture in the deposition of fat in rodents and showed that, for a variety of strains, including obese and wild rats, the fraction of variation in body fat due to genetics is 83% and that due to diet only 7%. When only the more genetically restricted laboratory rats are examined, the proportions are respectively 13% and 50%.

The evidence that obesity is largely genetically transmitted is overwhelming in animals.[5] In general, obese strains consume more food than the non-obese but the abnormality is not simply hyperphagia. Many of these strains use food energy more efficiently so that when pair-fed with lean litter mates they still deposit excessive quantities of fat. They expend less energy per unit body weight than the non-obese and their heat production in response to thermogenic stimuli is impaired.[6]

HUMAN STUDIES

Families

Obesity runs in families. If both parents are normal weight then less than 10% of their children are obese, compared with 50% if one parent is obese and 80% if both parents are.[7-9] The relationship is even stronger if the grandparents are also obese.[10]

Thousands of observations show a clear correlation of fatness between parent and child of approximately 0·25, a level to be expected from polygenic inheritance.[11] The fatness of children increases when pairs of parents are classified by different combinations of fatness level from lean × lean through lean × medium, medium × medium, medium × obese to obese × obese.[12,13]

Early maturation seems to be associated with obesity, possibly as another expression of the genetics of fatness. Women who mature early are fatter by the time they are 30 than late maturers and remain so even at 70. Obese boys, girls, men and women tend to be the offspring of early maturing mothers and the lean of late maturing mothers.[14-16]

Such studies indicate that genetic inheritance is important. However, families live in the same environment; therefore the correlations could also be attributed to similar family patterns of eating and activity. Spouses tend to resemble each other in their degree of fatness and it is a moot point whether this is due to selective mating or merely to living together: family members living together go up and down in fatness level together;[17] parent–child correlations increase during years of growth and decrease after adulthood and leaving home[18] and obese adults tend to have obese pets.[19]

However, these caveats do not negate the possibility of a genetic factor but only show that environment is also important. Genetic and socioeconomic factors in fatness and obesity have recently been reviewed by Garn.[20]

Twins and Adopted Children

The separate influence of genes and environment can be better distinguished in studies of twins brought up in the same and in a different environment, and from adopted children in comparison with their genetic and adoptive parents. Such studies have been reviewed by Bray[21] and some examples presented here.

Newman et al.[22] found that the mean differences in weight between pairs of siblings at the same age was 10·4 lb, between non-identical twins 10·0 lb but between identical twins only 4·1 lb. He also found more variability in the differences between siblings and non-identical twins than between identical: the percentages of pairs differing by more than 12 lb were 32%, 34% and 2% respectively.

Shields[23] found the mean weight difference of adult identical twins, whether brought up together or brought up in different environments, to be 10·5 lb while non-identical twins who had lived together had a mean weight difference of 17·3 lb.

Brook and colleagues[24] measured skinfolds of over 200 pairs of 3–15-year-old twins of the same sex, a third of whom were identical. The triceps and subscapular skinfold were extremely well correlated within identical twins ($r = 0·72, 0·83$) and less well within non-identical twins ($r = 0·49, 0·34$). On the assumption that, if fatness were entirely genetically determined, the coefficient of correlation for monozygous twins would be 1 and for dizygous twins would be 0·5, the authors calculated the heritability, i.e. the proportion of total variance due to genetics, of skinfold thickness. They conclude that most (84–98%) of the variation in older children is genetically determined and the contribution of non-genetic familial effects small. In younger children heritability is the main contributor but is smaller (52–76%) and the environment plays a larger part, probably due to the greater influence of parents over their food intake.

Ethnicity or Race

Most of the human genetic studies of obesity have looked at related individuals. There is less in the literature about the relative predisposition of various races or ethnic groups to obesity. Most seems to come from the literature on diabetes and the susceptibility of such groups as Pima and other American Indians, Polynesians and Micronesians in developing diabetes on adoption of a Western diet.[25-30] This is accompanied by a high prevalence of obesity. Neel[31] hypothesised that these problems result from the introduction of a steady food supply in societies where people have developed a 'thrifty genotype' with an ability to store energy efficiently.

Genetic Differences in Metabolic Rate

The evidence presented up until now strongly suggests a genetic influence on energy balance in the form of weight or fat storage but does not show whether it is due to excess intake or reduced expenditure.

In humans, evidence of hyperphagia in the obese is small and more interest and research is being devoted to differences in adaptation to the great intra- and inter-individual variability of food intake. Little direct evidence of the role of inheritance in energy expenditure exists. There is, however, a larger amount of indirect evidence by comparison of the energy expenditure of the obese and the lean on the assumption, from the studies described above, that an important proportion of the obesity trait is inherited.

One model for study of the genetic influence on energy expenditure is identical twins. In six pairs of male identical twins Poehlman and colleagues[32] measured resting metabolic rate (RMR) and the thermic effect of a 1000 kcal meal, before and after 22 days of overfeeding on an extra 1000 kcal per day. The results are not presented in a way that allows comparison of absolute metabolic rates within the twin pairs but they do show a significant resemblance within pairs in the increased thermic effect of the meal on overfeeding. The response of RMR to overfeeding showed less resemblance within pairs; however, there was twice as much variance between twin pairs as within. These results suggest genetic control on the adaptive response to overfeeding and therefore ultimately to body fatness.

A less stringent identification of genetic inheritance is in racial or ethnic groups. Measurements of the energy cost of standardised activities of men and women in various countries show considerable variation but, in general, European and American values are higher than those in developing countries. This variation could be due to differences in techniques, body size, age, environmental temperature, diet or genetics. The genetic factor cannot be isolated unless the different racial groups are measured under the same conditions of environment and experimental protocol. This has been done in very few studies.

Mason and colleagues[33] compared the basal metabolic rate (BMR) of upper-class Indian and European women aged 20–78 years in Bombay and, by regression analysis, showed the BMR of European women to be significantly higher than that of Indian. This racial difference could not be explained by differences in age, height, weight, or muscle mass, and was therefore likely to have a genetic basis.

Dieng and colleagues[34] compared the energy cost of lying and standing between French and West African subjects of comparable age and weight, and found the standing value to be significantly higher in French subjects than in the African.

We measured the cost of activities that could be strictly standardised, in European, African and Asian subjects[35] who were all University postgraduate students and staff in London and therefore equally affluent and all acclimatised. A group of subjects of each race was randomly selected and the cost of lying, sitting and standing measured. This showed the Europeans to have higher expenditure for each of these activities when the results were expressed in absolute values and per unit body size. However, they were also taller and heavier than the Africans and Asians and so, to obviate any possible differences due to body size, a further selection was made within these subjects of those who fell within a narrower range of height (165–175 cm), weight (63–75 kg) and Body Mass Index (BMI) (20–25) such that the body size of the two groups was strictly comparable. The resulting European, Asian and African groups were therefore very closely matched for age (26·1, 26·4, 28·8), height (169·6, 169·5, 171·8 cm), weight (67·9, 68·5, 68·4 kg), BMI (23·6, 23·8, 23·2), fat % (18·5, 17·7, 16·7) and Lean Body Mass (LBM) (55·3, 56·3, 56·9). Even between these strictly matched groups the energy cost of each activity was 10–20% higher in Europeans than in

TABLE 1
Energy Cost of Standardised Activities
(kcal/min/kg LBM)[35]

Matched subjects	Lie	Sit	Stand
European ($n=8$)	1·43	1·60	1·76
Asian ($n=7$)	1·2	1·43	1·54
African ($n=9$)	1·19	1·35	1·58

Anovar differences between races significant $p<0.001$.

Asians and Africans whether expressed per individual, per kg body weight or per kg LBM (Table 1). We take this to indicate genetic differences in metabolic rate, although the role of diet and stimulants cannot be ruled out.

Ideally, prospective studies could be carried out to identify metabolic factors in individuals who later become obese or who remain lean so as to determine genetic predisposition to obesity. However, such long-term studies are difficult to do.

The closest substitute to such a study was carried out by Griffiths and Payne.[36] On the assumption that the children of obese parents are genetically much more likely to become obese they measured energy intake and expenditure in normal 4–5-year-old children. Those with an obese parent expended 20% less energy over the whole day and also at rest than those with normal-weight parents. This indicates that low metabolic rate predates obesity and is genetically determined.

Once obesity has been identified, comparison of energy expenditure between the obese and lean is fraught with difficulties because of differences in body size and composition. If the absolute RMR of an already obese person is compared to that of a lean, it is generally similar or higher for the simple reason that there is more of him/her. If it is standardised in the traditional way by expressing per unit LBM this pretends that fat tissue is inert, or by expressing per unit body mass this assumes fat to be as equally active metabolically as lean tissue such as muscle, which is known not to be the case.

To study the question of whether those with a predisposition to obesity have different metabolic rates from those who are naturally lean, we therefore chose to compare the next-best model to the pre-obese, the post-obese. We matched individuals in two groups of

TABLE 2
Daily Energy Expenditure at Three Levels of Activity[37]

	Energy expenditure (kcal)		
	Sedentary	Normal	Normal + aerobics
Post-obese (n = 16) (PO)			
Mean	1 273	1 601	1 823
SE	54	69	83
Lean controls (n = 16) (L)			
Mean	1 538	1 882	2 132
SE	69	56	65
(PO/L)	0·83	0·85	0·86

16 (post-obese, lean) very carefully for age (mean 32, 32 yr), weight (60·8, 61·8 kg) and height (165, 166 cm). One group had been obese but now maintained weight at a normal level by dietary control, the other lean group maintained weight without any conscious food restriction. We measured their daily energy expenditure in a room respirometer on three different occasions, each at different levels of activity; sedentary, normal, and including 'aerobic' exercise. The metabolic rate of the post-obese was some 15% lower than the naturally lean at all levels of activity (Table 2).[37]

This indicates a metabolic factor in energy expenditure and balance which is likely to be largely genetic. This conclusion was strengthened by comparing the metabolic rates of all subjects with a family history of obesity with those with no such history. The significance of the difference was even greater ($p < 0.0001$) than was the difference between those with and without a personal history of obesity ($p < 0.0002$).

Further indirect evidence for energy expenditure mechanisms in genetic obesity comes from studies on the thermogenic response to various stimuli. Many studies show that the response of the obese or post-obese is lower than that of the lean to the following thermogenic stimuli:

1. food;[38–48]
2. potentiation of food effect by exercise;[49, 50]
3. cold;[51–53]

4. caffeine[54,55] and
5. ephedrine.[56,57]

These latter studies cannot prove a genetic influence on energy expenditure, including thermogenesis, but suggest a mechanism in the control of energy expenditure for genetic predisposition to obesity for which the evidence is so strong.

Social Factors Modifying the Expression of Genetic Inheritance
Social factors modify genetic differences. This is apparent from several observations. Poorer children of both sexes are leaner than their better-off peers. This also applies to men but, in women over the age of 15, the relationship is reversed, poorer women are fatter than richer.[58,59] This may be because poorer women are under less media pressure to slim and do not spend money on slimming clubs. At 50 years of age the average low-income woman in the US is 8 kg heavier than the average high-income woman, though shorter.[60,61] The relative role of genetics and environment receives varying emphasis from study to study[62-64] but it is clear that, whatever the genetics, the environment is still important.

COROLLARY

The genetics/environment debate is important in determining the underlying causes of obesity and therefore in influencing treatment and attitudes. The obese still suffer from the stigma of the general unsympathetic misconception that their problem is all their own fault in that they lack the willpower to control their eating or to do more exercise. However, in practice at the present time, treatment is the same whether the obese are regarded with sympathy or not. The pharmaceutical industry has taken up the quest from academic research[65] to develop drugs to normalise energy metabolism in the obese without the untoward side effects of those presently available. However, until there are acceptable drugs on the market the only sensible recourse is to reduce energy intake and increase activity. Various aids exist to help reduce intake such as bulking agents and appetite depressants but they tend to spoil the enjoyment of food which is one of the great pleasures of life. The wide variety of low-calorie products now makes calorie restriction less of a hardship and social blight. Instead of cutting out meals or foods or drastically restricting quantities, these foods can be substituted for their higher-calorie equivalents and can be used in normal meal patterns and without spoiling the gastronomic and social occasion of meals.

REFERENCES

1. McCarthy, J. C. (1979). Normal variation in body fat and its inheritance. In: *Animal Models of Obesity*, Ed. Festing, M. F. W. Macmillan Press Ltd, London, 1–14.
2. Bray, G. A. and York, D. A. (1971). Genetically transmitted obesity in rodents, *Physiol. Rev.*, **51**, 598–646.
3. Miller, D. S. (1979). Non genetic models of obesity. In: *Animal Models of Obesity*, Ed. Festing, M. F. W., Macmillan Press Ltd, London, 131–40.
4. Bouramand-Naini, M. (1977). *Nutrition and Genetics*, PhD Thesis, University of London.
5. Festing, M. F. W. (Ed.) (1979). *Animal Models of Obesity*, Macmillan Press Ltd, London.
6. York, D. A. (1979). The characteristics of genetically obese mutants. In: *Animal Models of Obesity*, Ed. Festing, M. F. W., Macmillan Press Ltd, London, 39–64.
7. Mayer, J. (1957). Correlation between metabolism and feeding behaviour and multiple etiology of obesity, *Bull. NY Acad. Med.*, **33**, 744.
8. Garn, S. M. and Clark, D. C. (1975). Nutrition, growth, development and maturation findings from Tenstate Nutrition Survey 1968–70, *Pediatrics*, **56**, 306–19.
9. Garn, S. M. and Clark, D. C. (1976). Trends in fatness and the origins of obesity, *Pediatrics*, **57**, 443–56.
10. Garn, S. M., Bailey, S. M., Solomon, M. A. and Hopkins, P. J. (1981). Effect of remaining family members on fatness prediction, *Am. J. Clin. Nutr.*, **34**, 148–53.
11. Garn, S. M., Bailey, S. M. and Higgins, I. T. T. (1980). In: *Childhood Prevention of Atherosclerosis and Hypertension*, Eds Laner, R. M. and Shekelle, R. B., Raven Press, New York, 187–204.
12. Angel, J. L. (1949). Constitution in female obesity, *Am. J. Phys. Anthrop.*, **7**, 433–68.
13. Garn, S. M., Bailey, S. M. and Cole, P. E. (1980). In: *Nutrition, Physiology and Obesity*, Ed. Schemmel, R., CRC Press, Palm Beach, Florida, 51–78.
14. Garn, S. M., Rosenberg, K. R. and Higgins, I. T. T. (1979). Menarcheal timing and the long term persistence of fatness levels, *Ecol. Fd Nutr.*, **8**, 1–2.
15. Sherman, B., Wallace, R., Bean, J. and Schlabaugh, L. (1981). Relationship of body weight to menarcheal and menopausal age: implications for breast cancer risk, *J. Clin. Endo. Metab.*, **52**, 488–93.

16. GARN, S. M., LA VELLE, M., ROSENBERG, K. R. and HAWTHORNE, V. (1986). Maturational timing as a factor in female fatness and obesity, *Am. J. Clin. Nutr.*, **43**, 879–83.
17. GARN, S. M., BAILEY, S. M. and COLE, P. E. (1979). Synchronous fatness changes in husbands and wives, *Am. J. Clin. Nutr.*, **32**, 2375–7.
18. GARN, S. M., LA VELLE, M. and PILKINGTON, J. J. (1984). Obesity and living together, *Marr. Fam. Rev.*, **7**, 33–47.
19. MASON, E. (1970). Obesity in pet dogs, *Vet. Rec.*, **86**, 612–16.
20. GARN, S. M. (1986). Family-life and socioeconomic factors in fatness and obesity, *Nutr. Rev.*, **44** (12), 381–6.
21. BRAY, G. A. (1981). The inheritance of corpulence. In: *The Body Weight Regulatory System: Normal and Disturbed Mechanisms*, Eds Cioffi, L. A., James, W. P. T. and van Itallie, T. B., Raven Press, New York, 185–95.
22. NEWMAN, H. H., FREEMAN, F. N. and HOLTZINGER, J. J. (1937). *Twins: a Study of Heredity and Environment*, Chicago University Press.
23. SHIELDS, J. (1962). *Monozygotic Twins Brought Up Apart and Brought Up Together. An Investigation into the Genetic and Environmental Causes of Variation in Personality*, Oxford University Press, London.
24. BROOK, C. G. D., HUNTLEY, R. M. C. and SLACK, J. (1975). Influence of heredity and environment in determination of skinfold thickness in children, *Brit. Med. J.*, **2**, 719–21.
25. JACKSON, M. Y. (1986). Nutrition in American Indian Health: past, present, and future. A review, *J. Am. Diet. Ass.*, **86** (11), 1561–5.
26. KNOWLER, W. C., PETTITT, D. J., SAVAGE, P. J. and BENNETT, P. H. (1981). Diabetes incidence in Pima Indians: contributions of obesity and parental diabetes, *Am. J. Epidem.*, **113** (2), 144–56.
27. ZIMMET, P., FAAIUSO, S., AINUU, J., WHITEHOUSE, S., MILNE, B. and DeBOER, W. (1981). The prevalence of diabetes in the rural and urban Polynesian population of Western Samoa, *Diabetes*, **30**, 45–51.
28. ZIMMET, P., ARBLASTER, M. and THOMA, K. (1978). The effect of westernisation on native populations. Studies on a Micronesian community with a high diabetes prevalence, *Aust. NZ J. Med.*, **8**, 141–6.
29. EVANS, J. G. and PRIOR, I. A. M. (1969). Indices of obesity derived from height and weight in two Polynesian populations, *Br. J. Prev. Soc. Med.*, **23**, 56–9.
30. TONKIN, S. (1970). Height weight and haemoglobin study of adolescent Maoris and Europeans, *NZ Med. J.*, **72**, 323–7.
31. NEEL, J. V. (1962). Diabetes mellitus: a thrifty genotype rendered detrimental by 'progress'?, *Am. J. Hum. Genet.*, **14**, 353.
32. POEHLMAN, E. T., TREMBLAY, A., FONTAINE, E., DEPRES, J. P., NADEAU, A., DUSSAULT, J. and BOUCHARD, C. (1986). Genotype dependency of the thermic effect of a meal and associated hormonal changes following short term overfeeding, *Metabolism*, **33** (1), 30–6.
33. MASON, E. D., JACOB, M. and BALAKRISHNAN, V. (1964). Racial group difference in the basal metabolism and body composition of Indian and European women in Bombay, *Hum. Biol.*, **36**, 374–96.
34. DIENG, K., LEMONNIER, D., BLEIBERG, F. and BRUN, T. A. (1980).

Differences in the rate of energy expenditure of resting activities between European and African men, *Nutr. Rep. Internat.*, **21**, 183–7.

35. GEISSLER, C. and ALDOURI, M. S. H. (1985). Racial differences in the energy cost of standardised activities, *Ann. Nutr. Metab.*, **29**, 40–7.

36. GRIFFITHS, M. and PAYNE, P. R. (1976). Energy expenditure in small children of obese and non-obese parents, *Nature*, **260**, 698–700.

37. GEISSLER, C., MILLER, D. S. and SHAH, M. (1987). The daily energy expenditure of the post-obese and the lean, *Am. J. Clin Nutr.*, **45**, 914–20.

38. JEQUIER, E. (1983). Does a thermogenic defect play a role in the pathogenesis of human obesity?, *Clin. Physiol.*, **3**, 1–7.

39. BESSARD, T., SCHUTZ, Y. and JEQUIER, E. (1983). Energy expenditure and postprandial thermogenesis in obese women before and after weight loss, *Am. J. Clin. Nutr.*, **38**, 680–93.

40. HAWTHORNE, B. E., BREWER, W. D. and OHLSON, M. A. (1956). Metabolic patterns of a group of overweight, underweight, and average weight women, *J. Nutr.*, **60**, 391–411.

41. KAPLAN, M. L. and LEVEILLE, G. A. (1976). Calorigenic response in obese and non-obese women, *Am. J. Clin. Nutr.*, **29**, 1108–13.

42. PITTET, P. H., ACHESON, K., CHAPPUIS, P. H., TECHTERMANN, F. and JEQUIER, E. (1976). Thermic effect of glucose in obese subjects studied by direct and indirect calorimetry, *Br. J. Nutr.*, **35**, 281–92.

43. STORDY, B. J., MARKS, V., KALUEY, R. S. and CRISP, A. H. (1977). Weight gain, thermic effect of glucose and resting metabolic rate during recovery from anorexia nervosa, *Am. J. Clin. Nutr.*, **30**, 138–46.

44. SHETTY, P. S., JUNG, R. T., JAMES, W. P. T., BARRAND, M. A. and CALLINGHAM, B. A. (1981). Post prandial thermogenesis in obesity, *Clin. Sci.*, **60**, 519–25.

45. ZED, C. A. and JAMES, W. P. T. (1982). Thermic response to fat feeding in lean and obese subjects, *Proc. Nutr. Soc.*, **41**, 32A.

46. SCHUTZ, Y., BESSARD, T. and JEQUIER, E. (1984). Dietary induced thermogenesis measured over a whole day in obese and nonobese women, *Am. J. Clin. Nutr.*, **40**, 542–52.

47. SCHUTZ, Y., GOLAY, A., FELLIER, J. P. and JEQUIER, E. (1984). Decreased glucose induced thermogenesis after weight loss in obese subjects: a predisposing factor for relapse of obesity, *Am. J. Clin. Nutr.*, **39**, 380–7.

48. SWAMINATHAN, R., KING, R. F. G. J., HOLNIFIELD, J., SIWEK, R. A., BAKER, M. and WALES, J. K. (1985). Thermic effect of feeding carbohydrate, fat and protein and mixed meal in lean and obese subjects, *Am. J. Clin. Nutr.*, **42**, 177–81.

49. SEGAL, K. R. and GUTIN, B. (1983). Thermic effect of food and exercise in lean and obese women, *Metabolism*, **32** (6), 581–9.

50. SEGAL, K. R., PRESTA, E. and GUTIN, B. (1984). Thermic effect of food during graded exercise in normal weight and obese men, *Am. J. Clin. Nutr.*, **40**, 995–1000.

51. ANDERSON, J., SHORT, A. and YAFFE, M. (1974). The relationship between physiological and psychological measurements in obesity. In:

Recent Advances in Obesity Research, Ed. Howard, A., John Liddey, London, 201–4.

52. ANDREWS, F. and JACKSON, F. (1978). Increasing fatness inversely related to increase in metabolic rate but directly related to decrease in deep body temperature in young men and women during cold exposure, *Irish J. Med. Sci.*, **147**, 329–30.

53. BLAZA, S. and GARROW, J. S. (1983). Thermogenic response to temperature, exercise and food stimuli in lean and obese women, studied by 24-hour direct calorimetry, *Brit. J. Nutr.*, **49**, 171–80.

54. JUNG, R. T., SHETTY, P. S., JAMES, W. P. T., BARRAND, M. A. and CALLINGHAM, B. A. (1981). Caffeine. Its effect on catecholamines and metabolism in lean and obese humans, *Clin. Sci.*, **60**, 527–35.

55. DULLOO, A. G., GEISSLER, C. A., MILLER, D. S., HORTON, T. and COLLINS, A. Effect of low doses of caffeine on fasting metabolic rate, diet induced thermogenesis, and on daily energy expenditure in lean and post-obese human volunteers, in press.

56. MORGAN, J. B., YORK, D. A., WASILEWSKA, A. and PORTMAN, J. (1983). A study of the thermic response to a meal and to a sympathomimetic drug (ephedrine) in relation to energy balance in man, *Br. J. Nutr.*, **47**, 21–32.

57. DULLOO, A. G. and MILLER, D. S. (1986). The thermogenic properties of ephedrine/methylxanthine mixtures: human studies, *Int. J. Obesity*, **10**, 467–81.

58. UNITED STATES DEPARTMENT OF HEALTH, EDUCATION AND WELFARE (1972). *Tenstate Nutrition Survey 1968–1970*, US DHEW no (HSM) 72-8132 Govt. Print Office, Washington.

59. RIMM, I. J. and RIMM, A. A. (1974). Association between socioeconomic status and obesity in 59,556 women, *Prev. Med.*, **3**, 543–72.

60. GOLDBLATT, P. B., MORE, M. E. and STUNKARD, A. J. (1965). Social factors in obesity, *J. Am. Med. Ass.*, **192** (12), 97–102.

61. GARN, S. M. and RYAN, A. S. (1981). Replicating the income related reversal of fatness, *Ecol. Fd Nutr.*, **10**, 237–9.

62. BOUCHARD, C., SAVARD, R., DEPRES, J. P., TREMBLAY, A. and LEBLANC, C. (1985). Body composition in adopted and biological siblings, *Hum. Biol.*, **57**, 61–75.

63. STUNKARD, A. J., FOCH, J. T. and HRUBEK, Z. (1986). Twin study of human obesity, *J. Am. Med. Ass.*, **256**, 51–4.

64. HARTZ, A., GIEFER, A. and RIMM, A. A. (1977). Relative importance of the effect of family environment and heredity on obesity, *Ann. Hum. Genet.*, **41**, 185–93.

65. MILLER, D. S. and DULLOO, A. G. (1987). The experimental use of drugs for treating obesity. In: *Body Weight Control*, Eds Bender, A. E. and Brookes, L. E., Pitman, London, 169–77.

14

Consequences of Obesity

N. FINER

Guy's and St Thomas's Hospitals, University of London, UK

ABSTRACT

Epidemiological evidence, from both cross-sectional and cohort studies, shows that the development of obesity, the storage of excessive amounts of fat, is associated with a variety of undesirable physiological and medical consequences. It is probable that the risks of a modest degree of overweight have been exaggerated and there has been an upward shift recently in the standards for ideal weight.

It is often difficult to disentangle the causes and effects of obesity. Environmental factors (for example dietary fat intake) may independently contribute to weight gain and ill health; they may also, as in the case of cigarette smoking, confound the relationship of obesity to disease.

Metabolism, and cardiovascular, respiratory, and endocrine physiology are altered in the obese. These abnormalities are usually secondary to the obesity and reverse with weight loss. For example, the increased energy expenditure of the obese (due to the increased muscle development that accompanies excess adipose tissue) falls towards normal with weight loss.

Increasing adiposity is associated with increased insulin secretion, and diminished insulin sensitivity. Recent work has pointed to the importance of fat distribution in these abnormalities. In women, fat in an upper body distribution is associated with impaired hepatic insulin extraction and an increase in androgenic activity. Both these factors may be independent pathophysiological factors for the development of hypertension, diabetes mellitus and hypertriglyceridaemia.

The insulin resistance present in obesity may also affect central serotoninergic neurotransmission, and alter feeding behaviour and mood. Abnormalities of growth hormone, thyroid and prolactin secretion, on the other hand, may relate more to altered dietary intake rather than adiposity itself.

Our understanding of the causes of obesity and its various consequences has been hindered by an inability to define different subgroups; recognition of body fat distribution and the diet composition as independent factors may change this.

INTRODUCTION

An association between obesity and ill-health has been clearly demonstrated by cross-sectional and cohort surveys.[1-8] Although these studies confirm the epidemiologically important links between obesity and diseases affecting the cardiovascular, metabolic, respiratory and musculo-skeletal systems, clinicians need to know what factors at an individual level make obesity dangerous. Since obesity has heterogeneous aetiologies it is not surprising that clinical features, complications and responses to treatment vary widely between individuals who are grouped solely by being overweight or obese. In order to understand better these differences, we need to know how to distinguish between 'the obesities'. A further problem in interpreting the link between obesity and ill-health lies in the difficulty of determining which factors may cause ill-health independently of their role in causing obesity.[9] For example, dietary fat appears to be a risk factor for ischaemic heart disease independently of its ability to promote weight gain.[10-12] This issue is not just of academic interest. Treatment of obesity has a high failure rate and it could be argued that dietary changes that do not result in weight loss, and which might be more readily achieved by the obese, could be as beneficial as weight loss itself.[13] An underlying problem of interpreting epidemiological studies remains a difficulty in defining obesity as an absolute rather than relative entity.

DEFINITIONS OF OBESITY

Body fat can be estimated from skinfold thickness but more accurately by measuring lean body mass (by isotopic methods,[14] densitometry,[15] CT scanning[16–18] or perhaps electrical bio-impedance[19]) and subtracting this from body weight. None of these time-consuming or invasive methods is applicable to epidemiological surveys or general clinical practice. For these purposes obesity is often equated to overweight. Overweight may be defined relative to some norm or population average (as in the Build and Blood Pressure studies[7, 8]) or by an index derived from body weight as a function of height such as the Quetelet or Body Mass Index (BMI).[20]

Obesity and overweight are only loosely equivalent: the National Health and Nutrition Survey[21] found that the proportion of men and women defined as overweight was significantly higher than the proportion who were defined as obese by skinfold thickness measurements. BMI correlates closely with skinfold thicknesses, but accounts for only about half of the variance in adiposity.[22] The practical working definition of obesity was for many years a weight of more than 120% of the 'acceptable' range of body weight for height based on the 1960 Metropolitan Life Insurance Tables,[23] equivalent to a BMI of greater than 27. Current values defined from the more recent

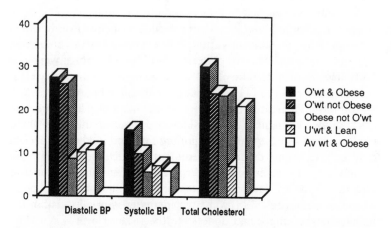

Fig. 1. Age-adjusted percentage of men aged 20–75 years with elevated blood pressure (diastolic >95 mm Hg, systolic >160 mm Hg) and serum total cholesterol levels (>260 mg/dl) defined as either obese (sum of triceps and subscapular skinfold thicknesses above 85th percentile) or overweight (Body Mass Index above the 85th percentile) or both. Underweight and lean defined as below the 15th percentile for Body Mass Index and skinfold thicknesses. Data from NHANES I, as quoted by Van Itallie.[24]

NHANES II data (BMI of more than 27·8 for men and 27·3 for women) are slightly higher.[24] This survey makes the distinction between overweight (based on relative weight) and obese (based on skinfold thickness), allowing a complex classification based on whether subjects are obese, overweight or both. Although complicated, this classification does show a differing incidence of complications in the different groups (Fig. 1).

An attractively simple classification based on BMI has been suggested by Garrow for clinical rather than epidemiological purposes.[25] Grade I obesity (BMI 25–29·9) affects 34% of men and 24% of women aged between 16 and 65 years in the UK. Grade II or moderate obesity (BMI 30–40) affects about 7% of the population, while severe or Grade III obesity (BMI >40) occurs in only about 0·1% of individuals.[26]

CONSEQUENCES OF OBESITY ON LONGEVITY

Four large insurance studies, The Framingham 30-year follow-up study, The American Cancer Society study and many other smaller studies have shown that the obese tend to die young.

The 1979 Build Study, based on 4·2 million insured lives between 1954 and 1972, showed a logarithmic rise in mortality risk as relative weight increased.[8] Men who were 115–125% of average weight at entry had a mortality ratio of 134%; at 135–145% of average weight this ratio had risen to 141%, and at 155–165% the figure was 227%.

Comparative figures from the 1959 Build and Blood Pressure Study showed a higher risk for all levels of overweight.[7] Part of the explanation for the apparent melioration of the ill-effects of obesity may be the improvement of treatment for diseases arising from obesity (e.g. hypertension). The rise in smoking during the 1950s, and the tendency for smokers to be lighter than non-smokers,[27] would also tend to bias towards an increased mortality risk in the lighter-weight ranges and understate the risks of overweight (Fig. 2).[28]

In the American Cancer Society Study of 750 000 men and women[3] the overall mortality among men and women 30–40% heavier than average was nearly 50% higher than in those of average weight. This study allowed an analysis of the independent effect of smoking.

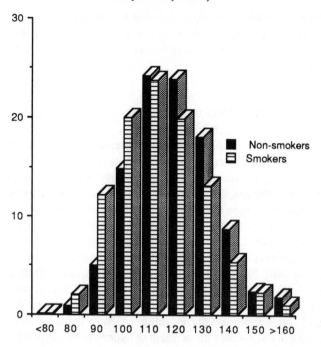

FIG. 2. Distribution of men aged 30–59 years in the Framingham Heart Study by smoking status and percentage Metropolitan Relative Weight at baseline. Data from Feinlieb.[29]

Throughout the range of BMI, smoking was associated with a near doubling of mortality risk. An alternative way of looking at this is that smoking conferred a similar risk upon an average weight man or woman as being 35–50% overweight.

All of these studies demonstrate that duration of overweight is of great importance in modifying the global risk figures. The mortality risk to men (aged 15–39 at entry to the study) of being 25–35% above average weight rose from 110%, in the first five years of follow-up in the 1979 Build Study, to 170% after between 15 and 22 years of follow-up.[8] Thirty-year follow-up data on over 2000 men in the Framingham study confirms that the risks of obesity increase with duration.[29] Smoking also interacts with the effect of time on mortality from overweight: an excess mortality for those more than 40% overweight was apparent after six years in smokers, but only after 18 years in non-smokers.[29]

OBESITY AND CORONARY HEART DISEASE

Hypertension and coronary heart disease are usually cited as, numerically and clinically, the most important sequelae of obesity.

In the large American Cancer Society study, coronary heart disease was the major factor accounting for the higher mortality of the overweight; men and women 30–40% heavier than average were 55% more likely to die from coronary artery disease than those of average weight; for those above 140% the risk rose to 200%.[3] The risk of coronary artery disease is greatest in younger overweight men but may only become apparent after many years.[30] Only after 16 years' follow-up did overweight men under the age of 40 years at entry show an excess of coronary heart disease in the Manitoba study.[6] Early data from the Framingham study failed to demonstrate obesity as a risk factor independent of hypertension, hyperlipidaemia or diabetes mellitus.[31] However, after 20 years of follow-up the Framingham data show a clear contribution of obesity to cardiovascular disease, independent of its association with blood pressure, LDL (low-density lipoprotein)-cholesterol and blood glucose.[32]

Not all epidemiological studies have shown a link between obesity and coronary heart disease. Keys' Seven Countries study failed to find a significant positive relationship between obesity and coronary heart disease after 10 years[12] or 15 years.[33] Although the Pooling Project review of data on white men aged 40 to 64 (from eight North American surveys with five to ten years' prospective follow-up) found an overall linear relationship of relative weight to coronary heart disease, there were marked differences between cohorts.[34]

A consensus view, as expressed by the Royal College of Physicians[35] and the National Institutes of Health[1] is that mild and moderate degrees of overweight do increase the mortality risk from coronary heart disease, although long-term follow-up is necessary to demonstrate this relationship. A complementary interpretation of the data by Barrett-Connor suggests that, while there is little doubt that the overweight or obese are likely to have unfavourable heart disease risk factors, the incidence of ischaemic heart disease in the overweight is much less than would be predicted on the basis of these risks.[9]

One reason for the confusion in the literature may be the very heterogeneity of obesity. One aspect, fat distribution, is being recognised as being of especial importance as a pathogenic factor. Vague[36] first suggested that in women, android, central or upper-body segment obesity was more commonly associated with metabolic complications such as diabetes mellitus than gynaecoid, peripheral or lower-body segment obesity.

Recent Swedish surveys show that the ratio of waist to hip circumference (which correlates highly with computed tomography measures of the ratio of intra-abdominal to subcutaneous fat[37]) predicts ischaemic heart disease better than the degree of obesity itself.[38,39] Furthermore, lean men with a high waist–hip ratio were at greater risk of developing coronary heart disease than more obese men with a high ratio.[40,41] This latter finding adds particular strength to the suggestion that metabolic consequences of abdominal fat deposition, rather than obesity itself, may mediate some of the deleterious effects of obesity.

OBESITY AND HYPERTENSION

Overweight Americans aged 20–45 years are nearly six times as likely to be hypertensive as non-overweight Americans of the same age.[24] The Framingham data showed a 6 mm rise in systolic blood pressure and a 4 mm rise in diastolic blood pressure for a 10% gain in body fat.[23] Weight gain over a six-year period was strongly associated with the development of hypertensive levels of blood pressure in another study,[42] which also showed that weight loss lowered blood pressure towards normal. This is a consistent finding.[43,44]

Fat distribution,[45] and fat cell size,[46] are also important determinants for the development of hypertension. The finding, to be discussed later, that hyperinsulinaemia is associated with abdominal rather than peripheral obesity, indirectly supports a role for insulin in the pathogenesis of hypertension. Short-term studies show that hyperinsulinaemia increases sodium re-absorption and may contribute to the development of hypertension.[47] An alternative hypothesis that hypertension may result from an inappropriately raised cardiac output in the presence of a relatively restricted arterial capacity (due to the low vascularity of adipose tissue) has also been proposed.[48]

METABOLIC AND ENDOCRINE CONSEQUENCES OF OBESITY

Basal metabolic rate and energy expenditure on thermogenesis and exercise are increased in obesity.[49,50] It is the increase in lean body mass, rather than adipose tissue, that accounts for increased energy expenditure.[51, 52] It therefore follows that, to maintain their over-weight, the obese must continue to consume an increased caloric intake. Weight loss results in a decrease in both lean body mass and fat; a fall in energy expenditure, in addition to any adaptive changes (such as decreased tri-iodothyronine levels), is thus inevitable. Unless lean body mass or daily energy expenditure is increased (by for example increased exercise) a permanently lower caloric intake must be maintained by the slimmed obese if they are to remain at their lower body weight.[53–55]

Other metabolic consequences depend more on the increase in adipose tissue, and in particular it seems, adipose tissue distribution. Abdominal fat (most easily measured by a high waist–hip circumference ratio) will accurately predict those women likely to develop metabolic abnormalities such as raised plasma triglyceride, glucose and insulin levels.[56,57] Elegant metabolic studies by Kissebah's group in Wisconsin demonstrate that both the degree of adiposity and the site of fat deposition independently influence splanchnic insulin metabolism.[58,59] Increased pancreatic insulin secretion, both basally and in response to glucose stimulation, relates (in pre-menopausal women) to the total excess of fat. The other factor that determines peripheral insulinaemia, is the rate of removal and degradation by the liver, of insulin that has been secreted into the portal circulation. As much as 70% of insulin is extracted and degraded in its first pass through the liver in normal weight subjects.[60] Hepatic insulin extraction falls, however, with increasing abdominal fat, contributing to the marked peripheral hyperinsulinaemia in women with high waist–hip circumference ratios.[58]

Several possibilities could account for the association of upper-body obesity with these metabolic abnormalities. Abdominal fat deposition could result from the metabolic abnormalities or vice versa. Alternatively a third, independent, factor could lead to both the metabolic abnormalities and the abdominal fat deposition. Kissebah, favouring the latter possibility, has suggested that the increased androgenic to oestrogenic activity that is found in upper-body obese pre-menopausal women,[61] and is also present in normal-weight men, could be this third factor.

Obesity is associated with increased production and turnover of cortisol[62] and androgens.[63] Evidence points to an increased ACTH drive to the adrenals as the cause, more probably related to the increased energy intake than the obesity itself.[64]

The increased levels of testosterone and androstenedione found in obese women result in increased plasma levels of oestradiol and oestrone because of peripheral conversion of androgens to oestrogens in fat.[65] Kissebah found a strong correlation of abdominal, but not thigh, fat with increasing androgenic activity as evidenced by a decreased sex hormone binding globulin and increased free testosterone levels.[59] The increased androgen concentrations in plasma could enhance hepatic very low density lipoprotein (VLDL)-triglyceride secretion and increase peripheral plasma triglycerides, which would account for some of the increased cardiovascular risk of being centrally obese. Androgens could also play a primary role in the deposition of abdominal fat during over-feeding.[59]

Not all data support abdominal obesity as an additive and independent metabolic risk. The Swedish studies which examined body fat distribution in relation to coronary heart disease found that increased cardiovascular risk related to the waist–hip ratio but not the degree of obesity.[40] This finding poses a therapeutic problem, since substantial weight loss over six months does not result in a fall in waist–hip ratio despite substantial reductions in hip and waist circumferences (Fig. 3). Further prospective studies are clearly needed to establish whether the factors involved in fat deposition are environmentally or genetically determined.

NEUROENDOCRINE CONSEQUENCES OF OBESITY

Neuroendocrine alterations in the obese are well documented. Disorders of growth hormone release in response to insulin-induced hypoglycaemia,[66] arginine infusion and exercise have been described,

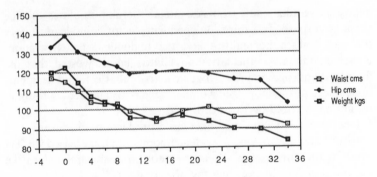

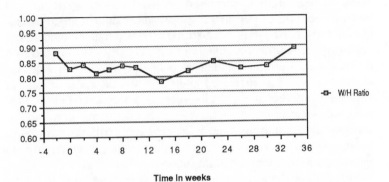

Time in weeks

FIG. 3. Change in waist and hip circumference, and weight over 34 weeks dieting. Thirty women (average weight 118·7 kg) were treated for eight weeks with a 380 kcal formula diet, and then received a diet of between 800 and 1200 kcal daily (according to measured energy expenditure) for 26 weeks. Waist–hip ratio was calculated from waist and hip circumferences in cm. Data (unpublished) Finer and Finer.

but it seems that they are dependent on over-feeding rather than obesity itself. Weight loss restores growth hormone (GH) secretion to normal in most subjects,[67] although not all studies have confirmed this.[68] The finding that GH responses to GH-releasing factor are also impaired suggests a pituitary rather than a hypothalamic cause;[69,70] these alterations also reverse with weight loss suggesting that the dysfunction is a consequence rather than a cause of obesity.

Prolactin secretion is abnormal in some overweight women,[68,71] due to a hypothalamic disorder that is not reversible with weight loss.[72] Isocaloric feeding with a diet high in carbohydrate may induce similar changes in prolactin secretion in obese subjects with previously normal prolactin release, but not in normal weight volunteers.[73]

A substantial body of evidence now exists to suggest that the macronutrient composition of food may affect central neurotransmission, and in particular serotoninergic pathways, with consequent effects on mood and subsequent eating behaviour.[74]

Insulin release following a carbohydrate meal increases the plasma concentration of tryptophan relative to the other large neutral amino acids (plasma tryptophan ratio) that compete for uptake into the brain.[75] Increasing the plasma tryptophan ratio enhances brain serotonin synthesis,[76] while a decrease, such as occurs after a protein meal, will have an opposite effect.[77] Obese subjects who are insulin-resistant have lower plasma tryptophan ratios (and hence predicted brain serotonin synthesis) than lean controls and smaller responses to carbohydrate ingestion.[78]

Pharmacological evidence for the role of serotoninergic pathways in the control of appetite is shown by the anorectic and weight-reducing activity of serotonin agonists.[79,80]

Some obese women,[81] and also patients suffering with seasonal affective disorder syndrome[82] show a specific appetite for carbohydrates. It is postulated that 'carbohydrate craving' could arise from a 'need' or 'desire' for increased brain serotoninergic activity perhaps because of its effect on mood.[83,84] One study shows that the obese need to consume twice as much glucose as lean subjects to achieve a significant rise in plasma tryptophan ratio.[85] One might predict therefore that 'carbohydrate cravers' would be characterised by marked insulin resistance (and therefore also have an abdominal distribution of their fat), but no data have been reported on this.

CONCLUSION

Several recent reviews have explored in greater detail than here the clinical and pathophysiological consequences of obesity[86] and in particular the respiratory,[87] cardiovascular,[9] endocrine and metabolic.[64,88] This short review has attempted to show how the recently recognised importance of fat distribution may lead to a refined classification of the obesities and improve our understanding of the reasons for the medical consequences of being overweight.

REFERENCES

1. ANON. (1985). *Ann. Int. Med.*, **103**, 1073–7.
2. SORENSON, T. I. A. and SONNE-HOLM, S. (1977). *J. Chron. Dis.*, **30**, 359–67.
3. LEW, E. A. and GARFINKEL, L. (1979). *J. Chron. Dis.*, **32**, 563–76.
4. DYER, D. R., STAMLER, J., BERKSON, D. M. and LINDBERG, H. A. (1975). *J. Chron. Dis.*, **28**, 109–23.
5. HUBERT, H. B., FEINLIEB, M., MCNAMARA, P. M. and CASTELLI, W. P. (1983). *Circulation*, **67**, 968–77.
6. RABKIN, S. W., MATHEWSON, F. A. L. and HSU, P. H. (1977). *Amer. J. Cardiology*, **39**, 452–8.
7. BUILD AND BLOOD PRESSURE STUDY (1959). Vol. 1, Chicago: Society of Actuaries.
8. BUILD STUDY (1979). Chicago: Society of Actuaries and Association of Life Insurance Medical Directors of America.
9. BARRETT-CONNOR, E. L. (1985). *Ann. Int. Med.*, **103**, 1010–19.
10. KANNEL, W. B., CASTELLI, W. P., GORDON, T. and MCNAMARA, P. M. (1971). *Ann. Int. Med.*, **24**, 1–12.
11. KALLER, L. H. (1976). *Amer. J. Epidemiology*, **104**, 425–96.
12. KEYS, A. (1980). *Seven Countries: A multivariate analysis of death and coronary heart disease*, Harvard University Press, Cambridge, Mass., USA.
13. PUSKA, P., IACONO, J. M., NISSINEN, A., KORHONEN, H. J., VARTIAINEN, E., PIETINEN, P., DOUGHERTY, R. and LEINO, U. (1983). *Lancet*, **1**, 1–5.
14. WARD, G. M., KRZYWICKI, H. J., RAHMAN, D. P., QUASS, R. L., NELSON, R. A. and CONSALAZIO, C. F. (1975). *Am. J. Clin. Nutr.*, **28**, 162–9.
15. BROZEK, J., GRANDE, F., ANDERSON, J. T. and KEYS, A. (1963). *Ann. NY Acad. Sci.*, **110**, 113–40.
16. GRAUER, W. O., MOSS, A. A., CANN, C. E. and GOLDBERG, H. I. (1984). *Am. J. Clin. Nutr.*, **39**, 631–7.
17. TOKUNAGA, K., MATSUZAWA, Y., ISHAKAWA, K. and TARUI, S. (1983). *Int. J. Obesity*, **7**, 437–45.
18. DIXON, A. K. (1983). *Clin. Radiol.*, **34**, 189–91.
19. BEYNEN, A. C. and GUNDLACH, B. L. (1985). *Medicographia*, **7**, 39–43.
20. FLOREY, C. DU V. (1970). *J. Chron. Dis.*, **23**, 93–104.
21. ABRAHAM, S., CARROLL, M. D., NAJJAR, M. F. and FULWOOD, R. (1983). *Vital and Health Statistics, Series 11*, 230.
22. STAVIG, G. R., LEONARD, A. L., IGRA, A. and FELTEN, P. (1984). *J. Chron. Dis.*, **37**, 255–62.
23. RESEARCH ON OBESITY (1976). Report of the DHSS/MRC Group, HMSO, London.
24. VAN ITALLIE, T. B. (1985). *Ann. Int. Med.*, **103**, 983–8.
25. GARROW, J. S. (1981). *Treat Obesity Seriously: A Clinical Manual*, Churchill Livingstone, London.

26. JAMES, W. P. T. (1984). *Clin. in Endocrinol. Metab.*, **13**, 635–59.
27. KHOSLA, T. and LOWE, C. R. (1971). *Br. Med. J.*, **4**, 10–12.
28. GARRISON, R. J., FEINLIEB, M., CASTELLI, W. P. and MCNAMARA, P. M. (1983). *J. Am. Diet. Assoc.*, **249**, 2199–203.
29. FEINLIEB, M. (1985). *Ann. Int. Med.*, **103**, 1019–24.
30. SIMOPOULOS, A. P. and VAN ITALLIE, T. B. (1984). *Ann. Int. Med.*, **100**, 285–95.
31. TRUETT, J., CORNFIELD, J. and KANNEL, W. (1967). *J. Chron. Dis.*, **20**, 511–20.
32. HUBERT, H. B., FEINLIEB, M., MCNAMARA, P. M. and CASTELLI, W. P. (1983). *Circulation*, **67**, 968–77.
33. KEYS, A., MENOTTI, A. and ARAVANIS, C. (1984). *Prev. Med.*, **13**, 141–54.
34. THE POOLING AND GROUP RESEARCH PROJECT (1978). *J. Chron. Dis.*, **31**, 201–306.
35. Obesity: A Report of the Royal College of Physicians (1983). *J. Roy. Coll. Phys.*, **17**, 5–65.
36. VAGUE, J. (1953). *La differentiation sexuelle humaine: ses incidences en Pathologie*, Masson, Paris.
37. ASHWELL, M., COLE, T. J. and DIXON, A. K. (1985). *Br. Med. J.*, **290**, 1692–4.
38. LAPIDUS, L., BENGTSSON, C., LARSSON, B., PENNERT, K., RYBO, E. and SJORSTROM, L. (1984). *Br. Med. J.*, **289**, 1257–61.
39. LARSSON, B., BJORNTORP, P. and TIBBLIN, G. (1981). *Int. J. Obesity*, **5**, 97–116.
40. LARSSON, B. (1985). In: *Metabolic Complications of Obesity*, Eds Vague, J., Bjorntorp, P., Guy-Grand, B. and Rebuffe-Scrive, M., Elsevier Science Publishers BV, Amsterdam, 21–9.
41. LARSSON, B., SVARDSUDD, K., WELIN, L., WILHELMSEN, L., BJORNTORP, P. and TIBBLIN, G. (1984). *Br. Med. J.*, **288**, 1401–4.
42. TYROLER, H. A., HEYDEN, S. and HARNES, C. G. (1975). In: *Epidemiology and Control of Hypertension*, Ed. Paul, O., Stratton International, New York, 177–202.
43. STAMLER, J. (1979). In: *Medical Complications of Obesity*, Eds Mancini, M., Lewis, B. and Contaldo, F., Academic Press, London, 191–216.
44. REISEN, E., ABEL, R., MODAN, M., SILVERBERG, E. S., ELIAHOU, H. E. and MODAN, B. (1978). *N. Engl. J. Med.*, **298**, 1–6.
45. KALKHOFF, R. K., HARTZ, A. H., RUPLEY, D., KISSEBAH, A. H. and KELBER, S. (1983). *Journal of Laboratory and Clinical Medicine*, **102**, 621–7.
46. BERGLUND, G., LJUNGMAN, S., HARTFORD, M., WILHELMSEN, L. and BJORNTORP, P. (1982). *Hypertension*, **4**, 692–6.
47. DEFRONZO, R. A., COOKE, C. R. and ANDRES, R. (1975). *J. Clin. Invest.*, **55**, 845–55.
48. MESSERLI, F. H. (1982). *Lancet*, **1**, 1165–8.
49. JAMES, W. P. T., DAUNCEY, M. J. and DAVIES, H. L. (1978). *Lancet*, **2**, 472.
50. PRENTICE, A. M., BLACK, A. E., COWARD, W. A., DAVIES, H. L.,

GOLDBERG, G. R., MURGATROYD, P. R., ASHFORD, J. and SAWYER, M. (1986). *Br. Med. J.*, **292**, 983–7.

51. HALLIDAY, D., HESP, R., STALLEY, S. F., WARWICK, P., ALTMAN, D. G. and GARROW, J. S. (1979). *Int. J. Obesity*, **3**, 1–6.

52. RAVUSSIN, E., BURNAND, B., SCHUTZ, Y. and JEQUIER, E. (1982). *Amer. J. Clin. Nutr.*, **35**, 566–73.

53. WURTMAN, R. J., WALDHAUSER, F. and LIEBERMAN, H. R. (1983). In: *The Pineal Gland and its Endocrine Role*, Eds Axelrod, J., Fraschini, F. and Velo, G. P., Plenum Publishing Corporation, 551–73.

54. FINER, N., SWAN, P. C. and NAYLOR, M. N. (1983). *Clin. Sci.*, **65**, 87–97.

55. WELLE, S. L., AMATRUDA, J. M., FORBES, G. B. and LOCKWOOD, D. H. (1984). *J. Clin. Endocrinol. Metab.*, **59**, 41–4.

56. KROTKIEWSKI, M., BJORNTORP, P., SJOSTROM, L. and SMITH, U. (1983). *J. Clin. Invest.*, **72**, 1150–62.

57. EVANS, D. J., HOFFMAN, R. G., KALHOFF, R. K. and KISSEBAH, A. H. (1984). *Metabolism*, **33**, 68–75.

58. PEIRIS, A. N., MUELLER, R. A., SMITH, G. A., STRUVE, M. F. and KISSEBAH, A. H. (1986). *J. Clin. Invest.*, **78**, 1648–57.

59. KISSEBAH, A. H., EVANS, D. J., PEIRIS, A. and WILSON, C. R. (1985). In: *Metabolic Complications of Human Obesities*, Eds Vague, J., Bjorntorp, P., Guy-Grand, B. and Rebuffe-Scrive, M., Elsevier Science Publishers BV, Amsterdam, 115–30.

60. BRATUSCH-MARRAIN, P. R., HALDAUSL, W. K., GASIC, S. and HOFER, A. (1984). *Metabolism*, **33**, 151–7.

61. EVANS, D. J., HOFFMAN, R. G., KALHOFF, R. K. and KISSEBAH, A. H. (1983). *J. Clin. Endocrinol. Metab.*, **57**, 304–10.

62. MIGEON, C. J., GREEN, O. C. and ECKERT, J. P. (1963). *Metabolism*, **12**, 717–30.

63. FEHER, T. and HALMY, L. (1975). *Can. J. Biochem.*, **53**, 215–22.

64. JUNG, R. (1984). *Clin. in Endocrinol. Metab.*, **13**, 597–612.

65. SCHINDLER, A. E., EBERT, A. and FRIEDRICH, E. (1972). *J. Clin. Endocrinol. Metab.*, **35**, 627–30.

66. BLAZA, S. (1983). *J. Roy. Soc. Med.*, **76**, 213–16.

67. CROCKFORD, P. M. and SALMON, P. A. (1970). *Can. Med. Assoc. J.*, **103**, 147–50.

68. JUNG, R. T., JAMES, W. P. T., CAMPBELL, R. G. and CALLINGHAM, B. A. (1982). *Lancet*, **1**, 1043–6.

69. KOPELMAN, P. G., NOONAN, K., GOULTON, R. and FORREST, A. J. (1985). *Clin. Endocrinol.*, **23**, 87–94.

70. WILLIAMS, T., BERELOWITZ, M., JOFFE, S. N., THORNER, M. O., RIVIER, J., VALE, W. and FROHMAN, L. A. (1984). *N. Engl. J. Med.*, **311**, 1403–7.

71. KOPELMAN, P. G., PILKINGTON, T. R. E., WHITE, N. and JEFFCOATE, S. L. (1979). *Lancet*, **1**, 747–9.

72. KOPELMAN, P. G., PILKINGTON, T. R. E., JEFFCOATE, S. L. and WHITE, N. (1980). *Br. Med. J.*, **281**, 358–9.

73. KOPELMAN, P. G., FINER, N., WHITE, N., McGARRICK, G., HANG-

ZHENG, W. and JEFFCOATE, S. L. (1983). *J. Obesity and Weight Reg.*, **2**, 162–80.
74. WURTMAN, R. J. (1983). *Lancet*, **1**, 1145–7.
75. MARTIN-DU PAN, R., MAURON, C., GLAESER, B. and WURTMAN, R. J. (1982). *Metabolism*, **31**, 937–43.
76. FERNSTROM, J. D. and WURTMAN, R. J. (1972). *Science*, **178**, 414–16.
77. LIEBERMAN, H. R., CABALLERO, B. and FINER, N. (1986). *J. Neural Trans.*, **65**, 211–17.
78. CABALLERO, B., FINER, N. and WURTMAN, R. J. (1987). In: *Amino Acids in Health and Disease: New Perspectives. UCLA Symposia on Molecular and Cellular Biology, New series*, Eds Kaufman, S., Fernstrom, J., Roth, R. and Woo, S., Allan R Liss, Inc., New York, 369–82.
79. FINER, N., CRADDOCK, D., LAVIELLE, R. and KEEN, H. (1985). *Curr. Ther. Res.*, **38**, 847–54.
80. WURTMAN, J. J., WURTMAN, R. J., MARK, S., TSAY, R., GILBERT, W. and GROWDON, J. (1985). *Int. J. Eating Disorders*, **4**, 89–99.
81. WURTMAN, J. J., WURTMAN, R. J., GROWDON, J. H., HENRY, P., LIPSCOMBE, A. and ZEISEL, S. H. (1981). *Int. J. Eating Disorders*, **1**, 2–11.
82. ROSENTHAL, N., SACK, D. and GILLIN, J. (1984). *Arch. Gen. Psychiatr.*, **41**, 72–80.
83. SPRING, B., MALLER, O., WURTMAN, J. J., DIGMAN, L. and COZOLINO, L. (1983). *J. Psychiatr. Res.*, **17**, 155–67.
84. LIEBERMAN, H. R., CORKIN, S., SPRING, B. J., WURTMAN, R. J. and GROWDON, J. H. (1985). *Am. J. Clin. Nutr.*, **42**, 366–70.
85. FINER, N., CABALLERO, B. and WURTMAN, R. J. (1986). *Int. J. Obesity*, **10**, 347.
86. BRAY, G. A. (1985). *Ann. Int. Med.*, **103**, 1052–62.
87. KOPELMAN, P. G. (1984). *Clin. in Endocrinol. Metab.*, **13**, 613–34.
88. BJORNTORP, P. (1984). *Eur. J. Clin. Invest.*, **14**, 239–41.

15

The Importance of Energy-Reduced Diets in the Management of Diabetes

J. A. METCALFE

British Diabetic Association, London, UK

ABSTRACT

Advocates of energy-reduced diets as the means of achieving weight loss amongst overweight or obese individuals tend to emphasise the benefits of weight loss in terms of long-term health and mental well-being. In the management of diabetes, an immediate effect on blood glucose is seen once the individual commences a reduced energy intake. This confirms the importance of this therapeutic application of an energy-modified food plan to both diabetics and their professional advisers. One would hope that such an improvement would be a powerful motivator of the diabetic to maintain the diet in order to achieve the continued short-term benefits of blood glucose control and ultimately, with significant improvements in body weight, beneficial changes in blood lipids as well. However, among the thousands of obese diabetics, many fail to achieve continued weight loss and remain well above their ideal body weight. It is clear that diabetics as much as any other overweight or obese group need continuous encouragement if they are to maintain an energy-reduced diet over a long enough period of time to achieve substantial weight loss. Unlike the cosmetic slimmer, for the diabetic group, the clinical benefits of a successful diet warrant a continued commitment from professionally qualified staff to provide both education and encouragement for the diabetic to adopt the correct dietary strategies.

A diet requiring long-term commitment is only likely to be maintained if it features a practical and palatable food plan. Therefore it is vital that in the management of any diabetic the diet is individualised and that it features readily available foods. The growing awareness by the food industry of consumer demand for products offering energy savings will benefit the diabetic. The modifications that would be particularly beneficial for the diabetic requiring an energy-reduced diet will be discussed.

DIABETES—INTRODUCTION

It is estimated that approximately 1·5% of the United Kingdom's population has diabetes mellitus. This is a condition which is characterised by the body's inability to regulate food metabolism. Diabetes is often perceived solely as a failure to control carbohydrate metabolism due to an ineffective insulin supply. This is an over-simplification since insulin is also involved in the body's regulation of fat and protein metabolism. Hence, the modern-day dietary treatment of diabetes concerns itself with total food energy intake and not solely carbohydrate.

Diabetes can present at any age, although it is rare under the age of two and it is extremely common in old age. It is estimated that at any one time, over half the diabetic population is of pensionable age.

Diabetes used to be classified according to the age of presentation, i.e. juvenile onset or maturity (senile) onset; the former referring to those diabetics that required insulin injections, the latter to those that could be controlled by diet alone or diet and oral hypoglycaemic agents. However, the absurdity of the occasional 60+-year-old with a diagnosis of juvenile diabetes or the 40-year-old with senile onset diabetes led to a review of the nomenclature. Diabetes is now most commonly referred to as insulin-dependent diabetes (IDD) and non-insulin-dependent diabetes (NIDD). Some patients who are classically NIDDs may require insulin treatment because of failure of diet control or other intervening medical conditions, but in Britain the majority of insulin-taking diabetics are truly insulin-deficient. The relative proportions of IDD to NIDD in the population is believed to be approximately 1:4.

THE DIET

Information from individual clinical studies and epidemiological reviews of morbidity and mortality from diabetes throughout the world led, in 1982, to a change in the basic precepts of dietary management of diabetes.

The principal consideration when advising the newly presenting diabetic is to establish and maintain an optimum energy intake for that individual. Providing this condition has been satisfied, the relative proportion of carbohydrate, fat and protein should be flexible, but ideally should mirror that advice given to the general population and particularly to those groups at risk of cardiovascular disease. This is because diabetes in the western world is still characterised by a two-fold increase in the incidence of cardiovascular disease. For the majority of non-insulin-dependent diabetics, it is cardiovascular disorders which are the primary cause of death or disabling disease.

In 50–70% of all cases energy control will actually involve energy restriction in order to achieve weight loss. If weight loss can be attained and maintained, improvements in the parameters of diabetic control such as blood glucose and lipids, are excellent. Clinical studies have demonstrated an immediate effect upon blood glucose of reducing energy intake. If maintained in the longer term, further improvements in glucose and lipid metabolism are seen. The majority of those involved in diabetic management and education feel the case for energy-reduced diets in the management of diabetes is proven. It is the practical implementation of advice that can achieve energy reduction that must concern the diabetic, their professional advisers, the food industry and the legislative bodies.

IMPLEMENTATION

Obesity has not been shown to have a direct causal effect on the development of diabetes, but it is a precipitating factor in the diabetically susceptible individual. The majority of obese diabetics are obese at diagnosis, but a small number (particularly adolescent females) do become overweight as a consequence of stabilisation on an inappropriate food intake.

As previously described, the majority of diabetics are in the older age group, and each will have eating habits which have been established over decades. Also in this older group, obesity, while perhaps recognised as undesirable physically or socially, is not perceived as unacceptable as it would be by individuals in the younger age group, where social pressure and health concerns are more pronounced. Maintenance of a reduced energy intake for a period long enough to result in a measurable reduction in body weight, necessitates the co-operation of the patients and their family members.

The individual will be more motivated to achieve and maintain the weight loss once they themselves desire it, rather than because weight loss has been dictated by their medical or dietetic advisers. Only when the individual recognises that the serious health consequences of diabetes are amplified by obesity because the potential complications outweigh the disadvantages of making changes in their food selection, do they become personally motivated.

RATE OF WEIGHT LOSS

Very low energy intakes may result in impressive short-term weight loss, but the British Diabetic Association's policy and that of the majority of diabetologists and dietitians is to encourage slow and steady long-term weight loss and maintenance as achieved by a realistic energy reduction programme. This rarely justifies recourse to diet plans below 800 kilocalories (3·4 MJoules) per day.

The diabetic must learn to make use of ordinary foods as part of an appropriate food intake. Learning how to make appropriate food selections will in the long term ensure that any weight loss is actually maintained. It is realistic to expect that an individual who is about two stone (13 kg) overweight at presentation will take between four and six months to achieve their target weight. This assumes that their previous intake can be realistically and consistently reduced by approximately 500 kilocalories (2·1 MJoules) per day, over this period. For some individuals, reductions greater or smaller than this will be achievable and expected weight loss will need to be adjusted

TABLE 1
Requirements for Successful Implementation

They require:
(1) adequate education on the type of food they should select,
(2) easy access to appropriate foods,
(3) that these foods be palatable,
(4) that no financial disadvantage results.

accordingly. Successful long-term changes in eating habits can be achieved if the criteria in Table 1 are met.

EDUCATION

The education and motivation for weight loss amongst diabetics is primarily a task for those involved in diabetes management. There are however aspects where the food industry and legislative bodies can be of assistance. Particularly important is the area of informative and practical nutritional food labelling. Knowledge of energy content per item/serving, is information that the individual could and should utilise when making food selections. The food industry has a responsibility to ensure that statements about nutritional content are not open to misinterpretation. Currently the British Diabetic Association is increasingly concerned by the use of statements such as 'low/reduced-sugar', 'sugar-free', 'no animal fat' etc. on products which are not offering significant energy savings. It is clear that many consumers interpret such statements wrongly. They assume the product is excluding all forms of energy-containing sugars (which often is not the case) or is low in fat, when there is merely a substitution of fat. They fail to recognise that such products need to be very carefully considered before including them in their restricted food plan.

REDUCED-ENERGY FOODS

The obese diabetic can certainly be taught to seek out less energy-dense foods and to adopt cooking methods which will achieve a significant saving in energy intake. However, an important component in successfully achieving a reduction in energy intake depends on a number of factors. The individual must know what foods to select but of equal importance is the availability of suitable foods. There is a need for foods that imitate popular products in terms of taste and texture, but which offer significant savings in energy, to be widely available. To date, the majority of products that are offering energy savings achieve these by modifying their fat and/or simple sugar content.

The increasing availability of low-fat spreads, reduced-fat meat and dairy products, reduced-fat crisps, low-calorie drinks, diet yoghurts, etc. are all important innovations that have helped the obese or overweight diabetic to select popular foods within a reduced-energy intake. This is particularly important when the obese diabetic is a member of a family. It is obviously easier if the whole family will accept these modified foods which simplifies shopping and catering for family meals. The diabetic requires education and information in order to help them make the correct quantitative as well as qualitative choice of such foods, but it is encouraging to see dietary compliance improve when the main principles are on selection of foods to 'have' rather than the previous emphasis on foods to 'have not'.

The potential market for products that offer substantial savings in fat and therefore total energy is significant. There is a growing awareness amongst the general population of the value of a reduction in animal fat intake. This means a market not just from the diabetic or the dieter, but from the whole population. The need for more and better reduced-fat products, possibly with the aid of safe reduced-energy fat or oil replacements, is a challenge that the food industry should respond to.

Until such replacements are available, food technologists have a responsibility to review existing recipe formulations to ascertain what fat savings can be achieved. A start has been made in terms of popular products such as sausages, crisps, yoghurts, etc. Other popular items which are particularly sought after by the diabetic and their family members, are baked products, confectionery, ice-creams and biscuits.

For some products, this may require changes in industries' Codes of Practice and/or legislation, since minimum fat content is specified for a number of products. It is obviously not conducive to the food industry or the consumer if the products that they wish to market/buy can no longer be classified as normal, solely because their nutritional content has been manipulated in a positive and beneficial direction.

The growing use of new and palatable intense sweeteners to replace simple sugars as sweetening agents in many products has been welcomed by diabetics. However, it is important for the sweetening industry to remember their obligation to review intake of these new sweeteners amongst consumer groups, as recommended at the time the new sweeteners were approved for use. Whilst there is no convincing evidence that intakes are excessive or likely to have a deleterious effect upon health, information on likely intakes, particularly amongst specific groups such as diabetics, should be available.

The diabetic consumer in particular would benefit from the availability of a palatable reduced-energy bulk sweetener which could be used in baked goods, desserts and confectionery, both within the home and the food industry. Unfortunately, the current bulk sweeteners have failed to show convincing evidence of reduced-energy availability. This is obviously an area of further development and research for the food and chemical industries. In the interim, a successful combination of intense and bulk sweeteners combined with a reduced-energy bulking agent, appears to offer the best potential for reduced energy content in baked goods, desserts, etc.

ENERGY REDUCTIONS

The British Diabetic Association was forced to lobby hard and long during the last review of the Food Legislation relating to products making specific nutritional claims. As a result, products making a diabetic claim must achieve at least a 50% reduction in energy content when compared to a comparable product. Failure to do so commits the producer to a warning statement on the packaging itself. This warning statement reads 'This product is not suitable for the overweight diabetic'. This stark statement has proved invaluable in educating the diabetic and the non-diabetic purchaser against the indiscriminate use of products which may offer savings in rapidly absorbed carbohydrate but little, if any, energy saving.

Current legislation requires only a 25% saving in energy for products making a 'reduced-energy' claim. Unfortunately, as with the slogans mentioned previously, such a statement is often interpreted wrongly by the diabetic and probably other consumer groups as well. Many perceive reduced-energy as being a description of low energy, indeed this is sometimes a mistake made by the food industry itself. There is clearly a need for clearer labelling of such products. Ideally more manufacturers should adopt the convention of including a comparison, with a normal product, expressed per serving; this will clarify the amount of energy being saved.

CONCLUSION

Of approximately one million diabetics, at least 500 000–700 000 actually require a modification in their energy intake. The growing availability of reduced-energy products has benefited the diabetic and continued developments are to be encouraged. In the development of such products, the food industry needs to be conscious of the needs of diabetics and their families. Any foods that are developed must be palatable, widely available and most importantly, clearly labelled.

No diet can be successful unless it is followed; the food industry, by responding to the needs of diabetics, has a vital role in improving dietary compliance and ultimately the health of many thousands of diabetics in the United Kingdom.

16

Caloric Value of Fibre and Guar Gum

G. Livesey and I. R. Davies

AFRC Institute of Food Research, Norwich, UK

ABSTRACT

Fibre is often considered to help subjects lose body fat or maintain lowered fat stores, but precise studies which adequately address the underlying mechanisms are few. Modifications of food intake, metabolisable energy available from the diet and of the efficiency of metabolism are mechanisms difficult (or expensive) to quantify in humans, whereas all three can be demonstrated in animals. The contribution from each depends on the type of fibre.

The background to the food energy assessment systems and some relevant observations on the metabolic events in the human colon will be described briefly. One current philosophy is to extend the Atwater or similar food energy factors to include fibre as a fourth proximate with a factor between 0 and 4 kcal/g. For some applications the validity of this is questionable. The energy factors are used in two ways. First they predict the metabolisable energy value of diets and energy intake. Second, and far more importantly, they predict whether intakes of energy meet requirements and whether changes in intake will result in appropriate changes in energy balance. The second application is invalid in the case of substances affecting metabolic efficiency. Under these circumstances a net energy system appears to be valid. When applied to guar gum or solka floc cellulose in rats this system assigns negative net energy values for fattening.

It is concluded that the energy balance trial is still the most realistic approach to the determination of the energy values of unavailable carbohydrates and that various indirect approaches, though convenient, can give false values. Further, it may be inappropriate to compare the 'slimming' effects of some unavailable carbohydrates if this property is predicted from their metabolisable energy values.

INTRODUCTION

Interest in the caloric value of dietary fibre is rising steadily. Various dietary guidelines advocate increased consumption of fibre to 30 g per day per average adult.[52] High-fibre diets are specifically beneficial to diabetics[6] because such diets result in improved control over blood glucose. Guar gum is especially beneficial in this respect.[36] The high-fibre diets, e.g. the F-plan diet,[26] are considered by some to help individuals with slimming. Until very recently, however, the evidence that fibre was an aid to slimming was considered insubstantial[59,60] and an appropriate caloric value for fibre could not be identified by an *ad-hoc* expert committee.[3] The value of fibre as a means to the control of body weight or energy balance has been reasserted[4,43,65] but the mechanism(s) by which high-fibre diets, or diets supplemented with fibre isolates, bring about control over energy balance in man remain inadequately investigated.

The nutritional and physiological properties of dietary fibre or other unavailable carbohydrates are varied and complex.[7, 9,22,31,58,59] Properties relevant to the regulation of energy balance include effects on hunger.[10,19,24,25,43,56,74] The expression of this property would, of course, result in the consumption of fewer calories from all components of the diet. Another property appears to be an effect on the efficiency of energy metabolism such that energy absorbed from the gastrointestinal tract is more readily released as heat than deposited as fat.[21] The stool bulking effect of dietary fibre is well known[11,37] and this is related to the indigestibility of fibre relative to the available carbohydrates such as sugar and some starches.[33,67,73] The extent of the degradation of fibre in man and animals is, however, dependent on many factors[14,15] some of which are discussed below.

ACCURACY AND PRECISION FOR THE DETERMINATION AND ESTIMATION OF METABOLISABLE ENERGY VALUES

Several different methods have been suggested for the estimation (calculation, prediction) of the metabolisable energy value of human diets. Each is based on the chemical analysis of foods and the application of prediction equations (Table 1). The worth of each

TABLE 1
Methods for Calculating Metabolisable Energy Using the Composition of
Human Diets

(a)	Rubner[61]	ME = 4·1P + 9·3F + 4·1C
(b)	Atwater and Bryant[5]	ME = 4·0P + 8·9F + 4·0C
(c)	McCance and Widdowson[47]	ME = 4·1P + 9·3F + 3·75Cm
(d)	Southgate and Durnin[67]	ME = 4·0P + 9·0F + 3·75Cm
(e)	Levy *et al.*[44]	ME = 0·976GE − 7·959N − 59·8
(f)	Miller and Payne[51]	ME = 0·95GE − 7·5N
(g)	Southgate[66]	ME = 0·977GE − 6·6N − 4UC
(h)	Miller and Judd[50]	ME = (0·95 − Fb)GE − 7·5N

The factorial approaches (a to d) combine the prediction of gross energy and digestibility (GE × D) in a single energy factor. The empirical approaches (e to f) determine gross energy and predict the digestibility. ME, metabolisable energy (kcal); P, weight of protein (g); F, weight of fat (g); C, weight of mixed carbohydrate (g); Cm, weight of available carbohydrate expressed as monosaccharide (g); GE, gross energy (kcal); N, nitrogen (g); UC, unavailable carbohydrate (g); Fb, fibre (g/100 g dry wt of food).

equation is judged by its accuracy in estimating the metabolisable energy value of human diets. The absolute reference standard for comparison is the metabolisable energy value of the diets as determined by metabolic balance experiment.

One limitation to the accuracy of this standard is the precision with which metabolisable or digestible energy can be determined. Coefficients of variation for the determination of digestibility of energy are shown in Fig. 1 for humans and rats separately. The precision of data obtained with humans equals that obtained in experiments with rats. There is too little evidence to know whether the precision can be improved by extending the duration of the balance trial in humans beyond one week whereas in rats this is evident. With balance trials of 28 days' duration using rats, the coefficient of variation is as low as 0·12% for semisynthetic fibre-free diets and a little higher, at about 0·5%, for diets containing fibre supplements (10 g of either cellulose or guar gum per 100 g diet). Careful experiments in humans with a trial of one weeks' duration can be expected to produce coefficients of variation of about 1%. As with rats, higher values, when not due to technical problems, are due to greater variations between individuals in their ability to utilise the dietary energy.

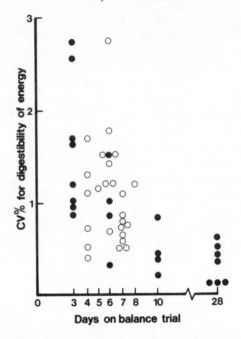

FIG. 1. The coefficient of variation for the measurement of digestible energy values of complete diets in humans and rats. The closed circles (●) are for rat experiments recently conducted at the Institute of Food Research, Norwich. The lower group of values at 28 days were with fibre-free diets whereas the higher group of data are for diets containing dietary supplements of either solka floc cellulose or guar gum 10 g/100 g diet. The open circles (○) are for human experiments with data taken from published sources. Data at each day's duration of the balance trial are from separate sources: 4 days, van Es *et al.*;[69,70] 5 days, Prynne and Southgate;[57] 6 days, Göranzon *et al.*;[29] 7 days, Southgate and Durnin;[67] 8 days, Bernstein *et al.*[8]

The importance of conducting precise energy balance experiments clearly becomes apparent when attempting to assess the contribution of dietary fibre or other unavailable carbohydrate to the availability of energy from the diet. Thirty grams dietary fibre per day in a 2000 kcal diet is equivalent to 6% of the gross energy intake. The coefficient of variation associated with the estimated apparent digestibility of energy for the fibre is then about 16% of its mean gross energy value (i.e. 100 ÷ 6).

With diets of low fibre content their metabolisable energy can generally be predicted from careful proximate analysis to an accuracy of within 5%.[8,12,29,67] Prediction of the gross energy of a diet from proximate analysis is only a little more accurate.[67] These authors concluded that efforts to improve the accuracy should emphasise gross energy determinations. For diets of moderate to high fibre content the accuracy of prediction of metabolisable energy is presently uncertain. The various equations for its prediction (Table 1) give different values.[29,50] It must be emphasised that the accuracy of prediction of metabolisable energy from proximate analysis is better than that from data in food tables because the latter cannot account for variations in the relative proportions of the proximate constituents and water. Further, the accuracy of prediction from compositional analysis is limited by variation in the gross energy values of protein and fat and by the accuracy of the analytical methods. The latter has made it difficult to identify the energy value of fibre in studies aimed primarily at assessing the adequacy of different approaches to predicting energy values.

APPROACHES TO THE ESTIMATION OF HUMAN FOOD ENERGY VALUES

The various approaches suggested for the prediction of metabolisable energy value of diets based on chemical analysis are summarised in Table 1. Generally, earlier suggestions employ a factorial approach in which the energy factors for each proximate constituent combine the prediction of gross energy with digestibility. More recent suggestions employ empirical equations which offer several advantages. First, gross energy is the major variable in the prediction equations just as it is in the equation for determining metabolisable energy in the energy balance trial (i.e. metabolisable energy = (gross energy × digestibility of energy) − urinary energy). Second, gross energy is determined rather than predicted. This is particularly important since there are relatively wide variations in the gross energy values of proteins, fats and carbohydrates from different sources.[45] Third, gross energy can be determined experimentally with more accuracy than can carbohydrate (analysed directly or indirectly by difference), fat (where the extent of solvent extraction may be problematic) and protein (where the factor for converting the analytical value for nitrogen to protein varies and may be unreliable). Fourth, there is less ambiguity over the choice of analytical methods and, with regard to carbohydrate, no uncertainty about expression of the analytical value (e.g. carbohydrate by difference, including the weight of hydrated and anhydrous sugars and polymers or carbohydrate as monosaccharide). Fifth, the procedure makes no assumptions about the source of energy that enters the faeces as is required by the factorial approach. Sixth, the gross energy values of protein, fat and carbohydrate in faeces are not assumed to equal those for the corresponding proximates in the diet. Seventh, fewer assumptions are made about interactions between dietary components and which of these affects the digestibility of one or more components. There is at least one disadvantage of the empirical approach over the factorial approach. It is that the digestibility of protein, fat, carbohydrate or available carbohydrate differ. Therefore, the digestibility factor for gross energy will depend on the composition of the diet. For the UK, USA and Sweden, diets

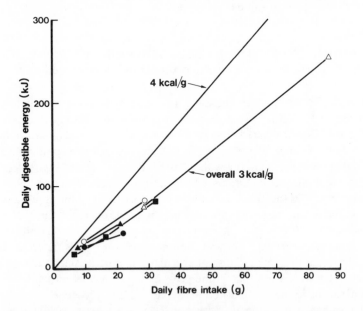

FIG. 2. True digestible energy available from dietary fibre at various levels of fibre intake. True digestible energy available from fibre was calculated from the data of Göranzon et al.[29] (△, mixed age and sex) and Southgate and Durnin[67] (●, young men; ■, young women; ○, elderly men; ▲, elderly women). Separate symbols are given for each experimental group. True digestible energy was calculated as the product of the weight of fibre intake, its digestibility and gross energy value. The digestibility of fibre in the work by Göranzon et al.[29] was estimated assuming no losses of sugars and starch to the faeces.[67]

completely free of dietary fibre show directly[12] or indirectly by extrapolation (see Figs 2 and 3), a digestibility for fat of 95–97% and a digestibility for protein of 92–94%. The digestibility of available carbohydrate is 100% by definition. For habitual diets it is likely that this source of error in the empirical equations will be no greater than about 3%. Potentially, this source of error can be accounted for by calculation of more specific digestibility factors based on the protein, fat and carbohydrate composition of the diet. Nevertheless, even without such a correction, this disadvantage seems to be outweighed by the advantages of the empirical approach over the factorial approach. What needs to be resolved, however, is the most appropriate way of accounting for the contribution made by dietary fibre and unavailable carbohydrate to the energy value of the diet.

The empirical equation suggested by Southgate[66] (ME = 0·977GE − 6·6N − 4UC) implies that fibre modifies the intercept of plots of metabolisable (or digestible) energy intake on gross energy intake whereas the equation suggested by Miller and Judd[50] (ME = (0·95-Fb)GE − 7·5N) implies it is the slope that is affected. Levy *et al.*[44] compared the metabolisable energy of 23 diets determined by the

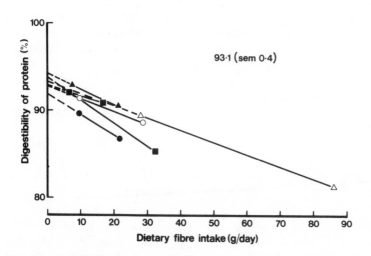

FIG. 3. Apparent digestibility of protein at various levels of fibre intake. Data are from Göranzon *et al.*[29] (△, mixed age and sex) and Southgate and Durnin[67] (●, young men; ■, young women; ○, elderly men; ▲, elderly women). Separate symbols are given for each experimental group.

energy balance technique and found that such plots gave a negative intercept consistent with fibre affecting the intercept, not the slope. The data of Southgate and Durnin[67] analysed by Southgate[66] show an effect on the intercept. There are three other possible difficulties with the equation proposed by Miller and Judd.[50] First, the term 7·5N implies an average 100% apparent digestibility for dietary nitrogen (protein). A value closer to 6·6N corresponds to an apparent digestibility for dietary nitrogen (protein) of 0·88, a value expected for diets with recommended dietary fibre intakes of 30 g/day per adult. Second, the digestibility term 0·95 is lower than predicted for a fibre-free diet (see below), and is more in keeping with a diet containing 20–50 g dietary fibre whereas the 0·977 and 0·976 digestibility terms in the Levy et al.,[44] and Southgate[66] equations are predicted for a fibre-free diet. The data of Göranzon et al.,[29] suggest a value of about 0·98 also. Third, the Southgate[66] equation predicts ME values for different foods which can be added together to give the ME value of the whole diet whereas some error is introduced when adding together the ME values for separate food items as predicted by the Miller and Judd[50] equation. This is notable for combinations of high-energy low-fibre foods and low-energy high-fibre foods. Miller and Judd,[50] however, noted that their equation predicted the energy value of their diets more accurately than did the Southgate equation. By contrast, the Southgate equation predicts the metabolisable energy values of the Southgate and Durnin[67] diets more accurately than the Miller and Judd[50] equation (Livesey, G., unpublished). At present it seems that the digestibility and metabolisability of all human diets cannot be predicted reliably to an accuracy of greater than 8% of the true value even when the gross energy value of the diet is known.

EFFECTS OF FIBRE ON THE APPARENT DIGESTIBILITY OF PROTEIN AND FAT

Unavailable carbohydrate increases the faecal loss of protein and fat in some circumstances[12,17,29,39,40,50,54,67] but not all.[49,57,63] If one can generalise, natural or conventional diets of increasing fibre content appear to be associated with the increased losses of non-fibre energy in faeces. Isolates of mixed fibre components or of higher chemical purity fed to man may also enrich the faeces with non-fibre energy.

For example, losses of nitrogen, and therefore of energy as protein, to the faeces, increase with the consumption of oat bran,[12] wheat bran,[16,27,32] pectin,[17] and hemicellulose.[42] Ispagula husks (Isogel), on the other hand, when fed as a supplement (rather than closely combined with other food components) decreased the apparent digestibility of protein in only one of four subjects studied. In all the subjects a small decrease in the apparent digestibility of fat was observed but this was substantial in one only.[57]

The apparent digestibility of protein in rodents is decreased by incorporating fibre into the diet in the form of wheat bran, sugar-beet fibre, guar gum, pectin,[54,62] carob bean gum, sodium alginate, agar-agar, carrageenan,[30] hemicellulose and lignin.[41,62] It is notable, however, that 10% crystalline cellulose decreased the apparent protein digestibility in rats[34] but in humans no significant effects have been observed.[49,63] However, crystalline cellulose may 'wash-out' microorganisms from the hind gut.[71] When this occurs the overall rate of microbial growth may decline resulting in lower losses to the faeces of microbial nitrogen.

At this time the source of the additional nitrogen in the faeces is uncertain. Suggestions include a decrease in the true digestibility of protein, increased losses of protein from the tissues of the intestinal tract and increased microbial protein synthesis with the end products of mammalian protein catabolism, ammonia and urea, being the source of nitrogen. There is less speculation on the source of the additional fat in faeces when fibre is consumed. A decreased true digestibility of fat probably contributes to this. The effects of artificial unavailable carbohydrates on protein and fat excretion are largely untested. Including Polydextrose® in the diet (10 g/100 g diet) only slightly decreased the apparent digestibility of nitrogen in rats,[13] from 86 (sem 1%) to 84 (sem 1%) or equivalent to only 5% of the energy content of the Polydextrose® eaten. In man, 50 g lactitol mono-hydrate daily decreased the digestibility of nitrogen[69] from 86·9 (sem 1·2%) to 83·6 (sem 3·9%) or equivalent to 5% of the lactitol energy consumed. Whether these effects are representative is uncertain; the digestibilities of nitrogen in the basal diets of the rats fed Poly-dextrose® and in the basal diet of the humans fed lactitol mono-hydrate were already lower than expected for most human diets. Further, lactulose increased faecal nitrogen losses in man to an extent similar to that expected for dietary fibre in conventional diets.[72] There is a considerable need for more quantitative information on the effects of alternative carbohydrates on nitrogen and energy losses to the faeces.

FURTHER ANALYSIS OF PUBLISHED ENERGY BALANCE DATA ASSOCIATED WITH LOW, MEDIUM AND HIGH FIBRE INTAKES

At this time the apparent metabolisable energy value of dietary fibre from conventional foods and diets has been suggested to be well above 0 kcal/g,[29] on average about zero,[67] and sometimes well below zero.[50] The last report provides too little information to allow a proper quantitative assessment of the apparent metabolisable energy value of fibre. However, its conclusion that the Atwater system overestimates the metabolisable energy value of their diets by as much as 20% with a daily intake of about 2000 kcal and 45 g fibre is consistent with the apparent metabolisable energy of fibre being as negative as −4 to −5 kcal/g.

In the data of Southgate and Durnin[67] and Göranzon et al.[29] information was provided on some of the individual chemical components of dietary fibre. It is difficult to distinguish between their separate effects on the availability of energy from the diet. For the present analysis, therefore, dietary fibre has been calculated to include all the individual components reported (cellulose, non-cellulosic polysaccharides, lignin, etc.) and the data considered as if the fibre was a single entity.

The contribution to dietary energy of digestible energy made available directly from fibre was estimated as the product of its gross energy value (taken as 4 kcal/g), its digestibility (fibre intake minus faecal fibre losses/dietary fibre intake) and dietary fibre intake (g). Increasing the daily fibre intake from 6 g to 86·5 g appears to result in an increased contribution of energy from fibre (Fig. 2). The 'true' digestible energy value of fibre calculated in this way is about 2–3 kcal/g. The precise value, however, is dependent on a number of factors to be discussed below. At the highest level of fibre intake shown, the energy supplied from fibre, 260 kcal (86·5 g × 3 kcal/g) represents 11% of the total digestible energy intake which was 2268 kcal.

Despite the considerable 'true' contribution to the digestible energy made by dietary fibre, the digestibility of energy for the whole

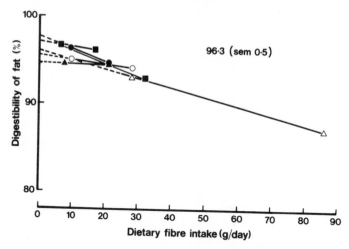

FIG. 4. Apparent digestibility of fat at various levels of fibre intake. Data are from Göranzon *et al.*[29] and Southgate and Durnin[67] with the symbols as described in Fig. 3.

diet is considerably decreased with increasing fibre intake. This is partly attributed to the effect fibre has on the losses of protein and fat. Figures 3 and 4 show that, with increasing daily fibre intake from 6 to 86·5 g, the digestibilities of these energy sources progressively decrease.

The apparent digestible energy values for the dietary fibre were calculated here separately for each experiment reported.[29,67] An experiment reported by Farrel *et al.*,[27] provided data for the calculation of additional comparative information. Two procedures were used to estimate the apparent digestible energy values of the dietary fibre. First, plots of digestible energy intake/gross energy intake versus gross energy intake from fibre/gross energy intake, gave slopes equal to the digestible energy from fibre/gross energy from fibre.[67] The latter was multiplied by the gross energy value of fibre (for convenience taken to be 4 kcal/g) to give the apparent digestible energy value. Second, the apparent digestible energy value was calculated as the sum of the true digestible energy value of the fibre (that is digestibility multiplied by 4 kcal/g) plus or minus the effect fibre had on the excretion of faecal protein and fat, each expressed in units of kcal/g fibre intake. Since dietary fibre was consumed at two levels in each experiment, the latter procedure provided twice the number of estimates.

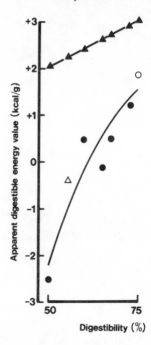

FIG. 5. The relationship between true and apparent digestible energy values and the digestibility of dietary fibre. Apparent digestible energy values were calculated from Göranzon et al.[29] (○), Southgate and Durnin[67] (●) and Farrel et al.[27] (△). The corresponding true digestible energy values (▲) were calculated as digestibility × gross energy of the fibre using data from the same sources. Slopes of the plots for digestibility of energy for whole diets versus the fraction of gross energy intake due to fibre gave the apparent digestibility of energy in fibre. The latter multiplied by the gross energy value gave the apparent digestible energy values. The curve, fitted by eye, is constrained also by data in Fig. 6.

The apparent digestible energy values calculated by the above two methods are shown in Figs 5 and 6 as a function of the digestibility of the dietary fibre. Three observations can be made. First, the two procedures give similar estimates for the apparent digestibility of energy for dietary fibre. Second the apparent digestible energy value of fibre is well below the true digestible energy value. Third, the apparent digestible energy value of fibre is related to the digestibility of the fibre. The last can be interpreted to mean that some additional losses of protein and fat to the faeces occur with increasing loss of fibre to the faeces rather than with increasing fibre intake *per se*.

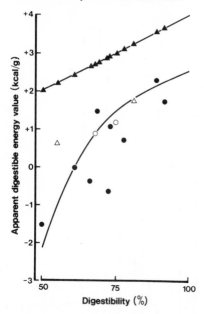

FIG. 6. The relationship between true and apparent digestible energy values and the digestibility of dietary fibre. Apparent digestible energy values were calculated from the data of Göranzon *et al.*[29] (○), Southgate and Durnin[67] (●) and Farrel *et al.*[27] (△) as the sum of the true digestible energy value of the fibre (△) plus the additional protein and fat losses to the faeces that can be attributed to fibre intake. The curve, fitted by eye, is constrained by data in Fig. 5.

Figures 5 and 6 show that the data of Southgate and Durnin,[67] Göranzon *et al.*[29] and Farrel *et al.*[27] are entirely consistent. However, the apparent digestible energy value of fibre and its digestibility varies considerably between experimental groups.

FACTORS AFFECTING THE DIGESTIBILITY OF DIETARY FIBRE

Cummings[14,15] describes a number of factors affecting the digestibility of unavailable carbohydrates. Two factors of considerable importance are the chemical composition of the fibre and the transit time for passage through the alimentary tract, in particular the hind gut. In general non-cellulosic polysaccharides are readily digested

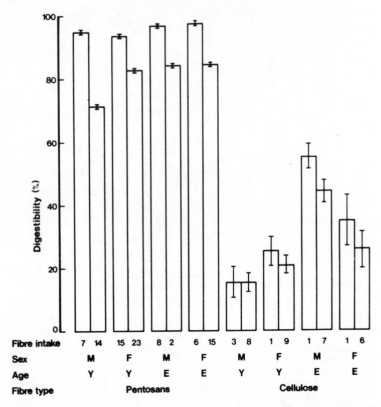

FIG. 7. Digestibility of pentosans and cellulose. The data are from Southgate and Durnin.[67] The daily level of intake (g) of each class of fibre component is indicated together with gender (M, male; F, female) and age group (Y, young; E, elderly).

(fermented) whereas cellulose is less well fermented as illustrated in Fig. 7 which is constructed directly from data published by Southgate and Durnin.[67]

In Fig. 6 the digestibility of the fibre components is lower at the higher levels of intake, but this has been attributed to qualitative differences in the fibre fractions. It is notable that the digestibility of the cellulose varied consistently between experimental groups. The low digestibility of cellulose (~15%) in the young men and the high digestibility (~50%) in the elderly men (Fig. 7) can perhaps mostly be attributed to differences in the transit times. In the young men the transit times were very short or about 24h (Southgate, D. A. T., personal communication). The digestibility of cellulose can also be very high. Cummings[15] notes that in subjects with transit times of >50h duration the digestibility of cellulose is about 90%.

MICROBIAL FERMENTATION—UNCERTAINTY AND IMPLICATIONS FOR THE ASSESSMENT OF ENERGY VALUES

The fermentation of unavailable carbohydrate produces heat and combustible gases. This energy is not available to the host when carbohydrate is fermented in the hind gut. One consideration therefore is that this quantity of energy should be deducted from the digestible or metabolisable energy value of the diet. In ruminants about 22% of the caloric energy is lost as methane or hydrogen and about 3% as heat.[35] Hence it had been thought that as much as 25% of the carbohydrate gross energy should be deducted if it were completely fermented. In man, however, about 35 g of carbohydrate are fermented each day,[18,64] but only about 150 ml of methane and 600 ml of hydrogen are produced.[28,46] This quantity of combustible gas represents only 2% of the gross energy of the carbohydrate. Together with the heat of fermentation this makes only 5% of the carbohydrate energy which is known to be unavailable to the host. Alternative stoichiometries for the fermentation of carbohydrate in man have therefore been proposed.[23] What is uncertain is what happens to the excess reducing power generated during fermentation. Either the hydrogen is used to reduce substances which are absorbed and used by the host or these substances are lost to the faeces. In either event the metabolisable energy balance trial would account for the absorption or not of this energy. A further implication is that during fermentation of carbohydrate, energy is transferred from carbon, which is released as CO_2, to hydrogen which is either absorbed or lost to the faeces subsequent to reduction of other molecules. Hence tracing the carbon of carbohydrate does not necessarily trace the utilisation of energy when fermentation is involved and measurement of molecular hydrogen gas production may not account for all the energy transferred from carbon to hydrogen or other reduced substances.

THE APPARENT DIGESTIBLE ENERGY VALUE OF GUAR GUM

Guar gum is a relatively pure galactomannan which is viscous in solution. Although being almost completely utilised when included in the diets of rats[21,54,55] and man[55] dietary guar gum results in a substantial increase in the bulk of faeces due to more solids. Like the dietary fibre of conventional diets, guar gum elevates the losses to the faeces of both protein[54] and fat.[38] The extent of the faecal bulking properties of guar gum in both rat and man is similar and consistent with an apparent digestible energy value of about 10 or 12 kJ/g. The apparent digestible energy has been determined in the rat to be 10 kJ/g by the measurement of gross energy content of food and faeces in energy balance experiments.[21] In these experiments guar was mixed with other components of the diet. Whether the apparent digestible energy value of guar depends on this, or whether when taken in solution a different value would result is uncertain.

THE EFFECTS OF DIETARY FIBRE AND GUAR GUM ON BODY FAT RETENTION

Fibre may affect body fat retention in three ways. First it does so by affecting hunger, second by diluting dietary calories and third by modifying the efficiency of metabolism (see Introduction). Increasing intakes of fibre[4,65] and guar gum[43,68] have been considered causal to their effects of lowering body weight and body fat in man. Guar gum, however, has not always been associated with a lowering of body weight.[48] Observations such as these have not been made in properly conducted energy balance trials and it is highly unlikely that body weight changes can accurately reflect changes in the storage of energy as fat even in long-term feeding studies particularly when the intake of guar is low and there is no control over food intake. Further, guar gum modifies the distribution of tissue masses in the rat[20] and a similar effect in man would exclude inferences about energy balance made from body weight measurements.

Careful and precise energy balance studies in the rat showed supplements of guar gum (10 g/100 g diet) to be associated with a depression of body fat deposition.[21] This was shown to be inde-

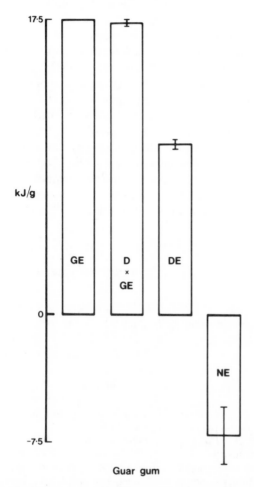

FIG. 8. Values of gross energy, true digestible energy, apparent digestible energy and net energy for fat production for guar gum fed to rats. The data are for a 28-day balance experiment with guar gum fed as a supplement (10 g/100 g basal diet) to male Wistar rats[21] housed at 21°C. The net energy for fat production is the difference in body fat deposition between the guar gum-fed animals and animals pair-fed the same quantity of basal diet related to the weight of the supplement eaten over the duration of the balance trial. The bars show the standard errors of the means.

pendent of effects on either food intake or malabsorption of energy. Expression of the difference in body fat deposition, attributed to the presence in the diet of guar gum, relative to the weight of the supplement eaten, gives the 'net energy value for fat production' which for guar gum was negative (Fig. 8). Comparison between the true digestible energy value, the apparent digestible energy value and the net energy value for fat production gave significantly different values for guar gum in these experiments (Fig. 8). It remains to be established whether similar effects on body fat deposition would result in man. However, for individuals who tend to eat more dietary energy than they spend (i.e. the overweight) it must not be assumed that the relative caloric values of dietary fibre, polysaccharides such as guar gum (and possibly other unavailable carbohydrate) are best represented by the digestible or metabolisable energy system. A net energy system, as used for domestic animals,[1,2,53] could well be more appropriate.

ACKNOWLEDGEMENTS

Thanks are due to Dr D. A. T. Southgate for his interest and comments on the manuscript. I.R.D. is supported by an AFRC studentship.

REFERENCES

1. ARC (1980). *The nutritional requirements of ruminant livestock*, Commonwealth Agricultural Bureaux, Slough.
2. ARC (1981). *The nutrient requirements of pigs*, Commonwealth Agricultural Bureaux, Slough.
3. ALLISON, R. G. and SENTI, F. R. (1983). *A perspective on the application of the Atwater system of food energy assessment*, Life Science Research Office, FASEB, Bethesda, USA.
4. ANDERSON, B., TERNING, K. and BJONTORP, P. (1987). Dietary treatment of obesity located in different regions: the effect of fibre on relapse, *Int. J. Obesity*, **11** (Suppl. 1), 79–85.
5. ATWATER, W. O. and BRYANT, A. P. (1900). *The availability and fuel value of food materials*, 12th Annual Report (1899) of the Storrs, C.T. Agricultural Experimental Station.
6. BDA (1982). Dietary recommendations for diabetics for the 1980s. A policy statement by the British Diabetic Association, *Hum. Nutr.: Appl. Nutr.*, **36A**, 378–94.
7. BALCH, C. C., OSBORN, D. F., COATES, M. E. and JENKINS, K. N.

(1984). Symposium: Nutritional implications of microbial action in the non-ruminant alimentary tract, *Proc. Nut. Soc.*, **43** (1), 1–86.

8. BERNSTEIN, L. M., GROSSMAN, M. I., KRYZWICKI, H., HARDING, R., BERGER, F. M., MCGARY, V. E., FRANCIS, E. and LEVY, L. M. (1955). *Comparison of various methods for determination of metabolizable energy value of a mixed diet in humans*, Report No. 168. Medical Nutrition Laboratory. US Army, Fitzsimons Army Hospital, Denver, USA.

9. BIRCH, G. G. and PARKER, K. J. (1983). *Dietary Fibre*, Applied Science Publishers, London and New York.

10. BLUNDELL, J. E. and BURLEY, V. (1987). Satiation, satiety and the action of fibre on food intake, *Int. J. Obesity*, **11** (Suppl. 1), 9–25.

11. BURKITT, D. P., WALKER, A. R. P. and PAINTER, N. S. (1972). Effect of dietary fibre on stools and transit times and its role in the causation of disease, *Lancet*, **2**, 1408–12.

12. CALLOWAY, D. H. and KRETSCH, M. J. (1978). Protein and energy utilization in men given a rural Guatemalan diet and egg formulas with and without added oat bran, *Am. J. Clin. Nutr.*, **31**, 1118–26.

13. COOLEY, S. and LIVESEY, G. (1987). The metabolizable energy value of Polydextrose® in a mixed diet fed to rats, *Brit. J. Nutr.*, **57**, 235–43.

14. CUMMINGS, J. H. (1978). Diet and transit through the gut, *J. Plant Foods*, **3**, 83–95.

15. CUMMINGS, J. H. (1982). Polysaccharide fermentation in the human colon. In: *Colon and Nutrition*, Ed. Kasper, H. and Goeball, H., 91–102 (Falk Symposium 32). MTP Press Ltd, Lancaster, UK.

16. CUMMINGS, J. H., HILL, M. J., JENKINS, D. J. A., PEARSON, J. R. and WIGGINS, H. S. (1976). Changes in faecal composition and caloric function due to cereal fiber, *Am. J. Clin. Nutr.*, **29**, 1468–73.

17. CUMMINGS, J. H., SOUTHGATE, D. A. T., BRANCH, W. J., WIGGINS, H. S., HOUSTON, H., JENKINS, D. J. A., JIVRAJ, T. and HILL, M. J. (1979). The digestion of pectin in the human gut and its effect on calcium absorption and large bowel function, *Br. J. Nutr.*, **41**, 477–85.

18. CUMMINGS, J. H., ALLISON, C. and MCFARLANE, G. T. (1986). Significance of fermentation in the large intestine of man, *Abs. J. Appl. Bacteriol.*, **61** (6), 17.

19. DAVIES, J. D. and COLLINS, M. A. (1978). Distention of the small intestine, satiety and the control of food intake, *Am. J. Clin. Nutr.*, **31**, S255–8.

20. DAVIES, I. R. and LIVESEY, G. (1985). Guar gum modifies distribution of tissue mass in young male Wistar rats, *Abs. XIII International Congress of Nutrition*, 97.

21. DAVIES, I. R., JOHNSON, I. T. and LIVESEY, G. (1987). Food energy values of dietary fibre components and decreased deposition of body fat, *Int. J. Obesity*, **11** (Suppl. 1), 101–5.

22. DAVIES, S. E. and LEWIS, B. A. (1975). Physiological effects of mannans, galactomannans and glucomannans. In: *Physiological Effects of Food Carbohydrates*, Eds Allen, J. and Hodge, J., American Chemical Society, Washington, DC, 296–311.

23. ELIA, M. and LIVESEY, G. (1988). Appendix: Some physiological and

242   G. Livesey and I. R. Davies

biochemical sources of error in the interpretation of data acquired by
indirect calorimetry, *Am. J. Clin. Nutr.*, in press.

24. ELLIS, P. R., APLING, E. C., LEEDS, A. R., PETERSON, D. B. and
JEPSON, E. M. (1985). Guar bread and satiety: effects of an acceptable
new product in overweight diabetic patients and normal subjects, *J. Plant
Foods*, **6**, 253–62.

25. EVANS, E. and MILLER, D. S. (1975). Bulking agents in the treatment of
obesity, *Nutr. Metabol.*, **18**, 199.

26. EYTON, A. (1982). *F-Plan Diet*, Penguin Books, Harmondsworth.

27. FARREL, D. J., GIRLE, L. and ARTHUR, J. (1978). Effects of dietary fibre
on the apparent digestibility of major food components and on blood
lipids in men, *Aust. J. Expt. Biol. Med.*, **56**, 469–79.

28. FLEMMING, S. E. and CALLOWAY, D. H. (1983). Determination of
intestinal gas excretion. In: *Dietary Fibre*, Eds Birch, G. G. and Parker,
K. J., Applied Science Publishers, London and New York, 221–54.

29. GÖRANZON, H., FORSUM, E. and THILÉN, M. (1983). Calculation and
determination of metabolizable energy in mixed diets to humans, *Am. J.
Clin. Nutr.*, **38**, 954–63.

30. HARMUTH-HOENE, A. E. and SCHWERDTFEGER, E. (1979). Effect of
indigestible polysaccharides on protein digestibility and nitrogen retention in growing rats, *Nutr. Metab.*, **23**, 399–407.

31. HEATON, K. W. (1983). Dietary fibre in perspective, *Human Nutr.:
Clinical Nutr.*, **37C**, 151–70.

32. HEUPKA, W. (1943). *Deut. 2 Verdauungs-Stottwechselkranlch*, **7**, 49.

33. HOPPERT, C. A. and CLARK, A. J. (1945). Digestibility and effects on
laxation of crude fiber and cellulose in certain common foods, *J. Am.
Dietet. Assoc.*, **21**, 157–94S.

34. HOVE, E. L. and KING, S. (1979). Effect of pectin and cellulose on
growth feed efficiency and protein utilization and their contribution to
energy requirements and cecal volatile fatty acids in rats, *J. Nutr.*, **109**,
1274–8.

35. HUNGATE, R. E. (1966). *The Rumen and its Microbes*, Academic Press,
New York.

36. JENKINS, D. J. A. (1980). Dietary fiber and carbohydrate metabolism.
In: *Medical Aspects of Dietary Fiber*, Eds Spiller, G. A. and Kay, R. M.,
Plenum Publishing Corporation, New York, 175–92.

37. JENKINS, D. J. A., HILL, M. S. and CUMMINGS, J. H. (1975). Effect of
wheat fiber on blood lipids, fecal steroid excretion and serum iron, *Am.
J. Clin. Nutr.*, **28**, 1408–11.

38. JENKINS, D. J. A., LEEDS, A. R., GASSULL, M. A., HOUSTON, H.,
GOTT, D. V. and HILL, M. J. (1976). The cholesterol-lowering properties of guar and pectin, *Clin. Sci. Mol. Med.*, **51**, 8–9.

39. JUDD, P. A. (1982). The effects of high intakes of barley on gastrointestinal function and apparent digestibility of dry matter, nitrogen and
fat in human volunteers, *J. Plant Foods*, **4**, 79–88.

40. KELSAY, J. L., BEHALL, K. M. and PRATHER, E. S. (1978). Effect of
fiber from fruit and vegetables on metabolic responses of human subjects. I. Bowel transit time, number of defecations, fecal weight, urinary

excretions of energy and nitrogen and apparent digestibilities of energy, nitrogen and fat, *Am. J. Clin. Nutr.*, **31**, 1149–53.

41. KIEM, K. and KIES, C. (1979). Effects of dietary fibre on nutritional status of weanling mice, *Cereal Chem.*, **56**, 73–8.

42. KIES, C. and FOX, H. M. (1977). Dietary hemicellulose interactions influencing serum lipid patterns and protein nutritional status of adult men, *J. Food Sci.*, **42**, 440–3.

43. KROTKIEWSKI, M. (1984). Effect of guar gum on body weight, hunger rating and metabolism in obese subjects, *Br. J. Nutr.*, **52**, 97–105.

44. LEVY, L. M., BERNSTEIN, L. M. and GROSSMAN, M. I. (1958). *The calorie content of urine of human beings and the estimation of metabolizable energy of foodstuffs*, Report No. 226. United States Army Medical Research and Nutrition Laboratory, Fitzsimons Army Hospital, Denver, USA.

45. LIVESEY, G. and ELIA, M. (1985). Food energy values of artificial feeds for man, *Clin. Nutr.*, **4**, 99–111.

46. MARTHINSEN, D. and FLEMING, S. E. (1982). Excretion of breath and flatus gases by humans, *J. Nutr.*, **112**, 1133–43.

47. McCANCE, R. A. and WIDDOWSON, E. H. (1946). *Special Report Series, No. 235, 2nd Edn*, Medical Research Council, London.

48. McIVOR, H. E., CUMMINGS, C. C. and MENDORFF, A. I. (1985). Long-term ingestion of guar gum is not toxic in patients with non-insulin dependent diabetes mellitus, *Am. J. Clin. Nutr.*, **41**, 891–94.

49. MICKELSON, O., MAKDANI, D. D., COTTON, R. H., TITCOMB, S. T., COLNEY, J. C. and GATTY, R. (1979). Effects of a high fiber bread diet on weight loss in college-age males, *Am. J. Clin. Nutr.*, **32**, 1703–9.

50. MILLER, D. S. and JUDD, P. A. (1984). The metabolizable energy value of foods, *J. Sci. Food Agric.*, **35**, 111–16.

51. MILLER, D. S. and PAYNE, P. R. (1959). A ballistic bomb calorimeter, *Br. J. Nutr.*, **13**, S01–S08.

52. NACNE (1983). *Proposals for Nutritional Guidelines for Health Education*, Health Education Council, London.

53. NRC (1981). National Research Council, *Nutritional energetics of domestic animals and glossary of terms*, National Academic Press, Washington, DC.

54. NYMAN, M. and ASP, N.-G. (1982). Fermentation of dietary fibre components in the rat intestinal tract, *Br. J. Nutr.*, **47**, 357–66.

55. NYMAN, M., ASP, N.-G., CUMMINGS, J. and WIGGINS, H. S. (1986). Fermentation of dietary fibre in the intestinal tract: comparison between man and rat, *Br. J. Nutr.*, **55**, 487–96.

56. PORIKOS, K. and HAGAMEN, S. (1986). Is fibre satiating? Effects of a high fibre preload on subsequent food intake of normal-weight and obese young men, *Appetite*, **7**, 153–62.

57. PRYNNE, C. J. and SOUTHGATE, D. A. T. (1979). The effects of a supplement of dietary fibre on faecal excretions by human subjects, *Br. J. Nutr.*, **41**, 494–503.

58. ROTH, H. P. and MEHLMAN, M. Y. (1978). Symposium: The role of dietary fiber in health, *Am. J. Clin. Nutr.*, **31** (10), Supplement.

244   G. Livesey and I. R. Davies

59. ROYAL COLLEGE OF PHYSICIANS OF LONDON (1980). *Medical Aspects of Dietary Fibre*, Pitman Medical, London.
60. ROYAL COLLEGE OF PHYSICIANS OF LONDON (1983). *Obesity. Report of a Working Party*, Royal College of Physicians, London.
61. RUBNER, M. (1901). Der Energiewert der Kost des Menschen, *Ztschr. f. Biologie*, **42**, 261–305.
62. SHAH, N., ATALLAH, M. T., MAHONEY, R. R. and PELLETT, P. L. (1982). Effects of dietary fibre components on faecal nitrogen excretion and protein utilization in growing rats, *J. Nutr.*, **112**, 658–66.
63. SLAVIN, J. L. and MARLETT, J. A. (1980). Effects of refined cellulose on apparent energy, fat and nitrogen digestibilities, *J. Nutr.*, **110**, 2020–6.
64. SMITH, C. J. and BRYANT, M. P. (1979). Introduction to metabolic activities of intestinal bacteria, *Am. J. Clin. Nutr.*, **32**, 149–57.
65. SMITH, U. (1987). Dietary fibre, obesity and diabetes mellitus, *Int. J. Obesity*, **11** (Suppl. 1), 33–43.
66. SOUTHGATE, D. A. T. (1975). Fiber and other unavailable carbo-hydrates and energy effects in the diet. In: *Proceedings of the Western Hemisphere Nutrition Congress IV*, Eds White, P. L. and Selvey, N., Publishing Science Group Inc., Acton MA, 51–5.
67. SOUTHGATE, D. A. T. and DURNIN, J. V. G. A. (1970). Caloric con-version factors. An experimental reassessment of the factors used in the calculation of the energy value of human diets, *Br. J. Nutr.*, **24**, 517–35.
68. TUOMILEHTO, J., VOUTILAINEN, E., HUTTUNEN, J., VINNI, S. and HOMAN, K. (1980). Effect of guar gum on body weight and serum lipids in hypercholesterolaemic females, *Acta Med. Scand.*, **208**, 45–8.
69. VAN ES, A. J. H., DEGROOT, L. and VOGT, J. E. (1986). Energy balances of eight volunteers fed on diets supplemented with either lactitol or saccharose, *Br. J. Nutr.*, **56**, 545–54.
70. VAN ES, A. J. H., VOGT, J. E., NIESSEN, C. H., VETH, J., RODENBURG, V., TEEUWSE, V. and DHUYVETTER, J. (1984). Human energy meta-bolism below, near and above energy equilibrium, *Br. J. Nutr.*, **52**, 429–42.
71. VAN SOEST, P. J. (1984). Some physical characteristics of dietary fibres and their influence on microbial ecology of the human colon, *Proc. Nut. Soc.*, **43**, 25–33.
72. WEBER, F. L. (1979). The effect of lactose on urea metabolism and nitrogen excretion in cirrhotic patients, *Gastroenterology*, **77**, 518–23.
73. WILLIAMS, R. D. and OLMSTEAD, W. H. (1936). The effect of cellulose, hemicellulose, and lignin on the weight of the stool: a contribution to the study of laxation in man, *J. Nutr.*, **11**, 433–99.
74. YUDKIN, J. (1959). The causes and cure of obesity, *Lancet*, **2**, 1135.

17

Methodology in the Measurement of Caloric Availability

D. C. HOBBS

Pfizer, Central Research, Groton, Connecticut, USA

ABSTRACT

Alternative carbohydrates replace the bulk, but not necessarily the sweetness, of sucrose in various food products. To be purposeful they must provide fewer calories than the food ingredients which they replace. Methods to measure the caloric value of these products, when incorporated into a total diet, must take into account the low fortification in the diet, all of the routes by which calories can be made available, and the losses associated with fermentation in the intestinal tract. The methods must also be applicable to humans. The balance method can be applied to humans but does not normally take into account the losses associated with fermentation (e.g. methane). In addition, since the calculations rely on the difference between two large, and inevitably variable values, the method lacks adequate precision for ingredients which are a small fraction of the total diet. The growth curve method cannot be applied to humans, although in animals it may properly reflect all of the energy delivered. It requires very closely controlled experimental conditions and, like the balance method, lacks adequate precision. Calorimetry is difficult to apply to humans and does not distinguish between energy delivered to the host animal and that delivered to its intestinal bacteria, an important factor for products which are fermented. The direct method involves the measurement of labelled CO_2 in breath following administration of isotopically labelled substrate. It can be applied to humans, has good precision, and can distinguish between mammalian and bacterial utilisation. Examination of excreta to quantitate losses of energy can provide supportive data. The direct radiolabel method has been *applied in rats and man to several alternative carbohydrates of diverse types. The results are consistent across species and the sum of caloric availability plus losses in excreta provides good material balance.*

INTRODUCTION

The low-calorie sucrose replacements being considered in this volume are of two general types, high-intensity sweeteners and bulking agents. The high-intensity sweeteners are used to provide sweetness in products, where they replace sucrose and other natural sweeteners. Their potency is many-fold that of the materials which they replace, and the calories they might provide, even if they were completely metabolically available, are negligible. They will not be considered further, except to note that they are sometimes incorporated into foods containing bulking agents of reduced intrinsic sweetness.

The other type of product, the bulking agent, is designed to replace the bulk of natural sweeteners, in order to retain texture, bakeability, bulk, etc. Several products have been developed which have the necessary physical properties for this use; some can also replace a portion of the fat in certain foods. Sweetness is also present in some of these products, obviating the need for concomitant incorporation of high-intensity sweeteners.

To the extent that these bulking agents are used by diabetics, an additional desirable attribute is a reduction in the hyperglycaemia which occurs after ingestion of material containing glucose or readily converted to glucose. A reduced yield of glucose from such products, however, does not necessarily imply a reduction in calories, since many of these bulking agents can give rise to other readily metabolised compounds.

In that the major attribute of these materials is the reduction in calories afforded by their use, methods to accurately measure their caloric yield are necessary. An appropriate method must be sufficiently accurate to quantitate the caloric value of a substance comprising no more than 10% of the total diet. In addition to accuracy, the method must be responsive to all of the routes, direct and indirect, by which calories are made available, yet must not measure as calories those routes by which energy is lost. The method must also have the ability to measure caloric availability from a wide range of

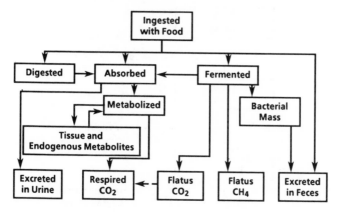

FIG. 1. Flow of energy from bulking agents.

bulking agents in humans consuming the material under conditions appropriately reflective of actual use in foods.

Energy acquisition and loss can take place by a variety of routes (Fig. 1). A substance such as glucose is absorbed directly, metabolised, and about 60% appears as CO_2 in the breath within a few hours. The remainder is incorporated into endogenous metabolites and tissue, but is eventually also metabolised to CO_2 as part of the normal turnover of body constituents. A substance such as mannitol can be absorbed, but excreted so rapidly in the urine[1] that the directly absorbed material yields little energy. Substances such as starch are digested, their component parts absorbed and metabolised to endogenous nutrients, and the resulting CO_2 exhaled in the breath. The yield of CO_2 from starch is similar to that from glucose.

Some substances, such as cellulose and a major fraction of polydextrose, are not digested or absorbed and appear in faeces where they can be quantitated by chemical assay or by other means. To the extent that these materials appear in faeces they are calorically unavailable. Some substances, such as a portion of the polydextrose[2,3] or most of lactitol[4] are fermented by the bacterial flora of the lower intestinal tract. Some of the material fermented appears as additional bacterial mass, some as methane and hydrogen, and some as volatile fatty acids which are absorbed and metabolised to CO_2 and tissue.[5] In the process of converting nutrients to fatty acids and methane, CO_2 is also formed by the bacteria. Most of this appears in

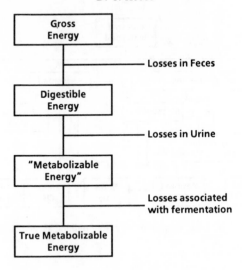

FIG. 2. Losses of energy associated with disposition of bulking agents.

the flatus, but some can cross the intestinal wall into the blood stream and appear in respired air.[6]

The energy losses are summarised in Fig. 2. Gross energy is the total energy available in the substance, as determined for example by bomb calorimetry. After accounting for losses in faeces, the remainder is termed digestible energy. After provision for losses in urine, the remainder is the metabolisable energy in the substance. Most nutrients are absorbed, directly or after digestion, and the metabolisable energy is an accurate reflection of all of the energy made available to the human or animal. However, a number of the bulking agents, under consideration here, undergo fermentation. Caloric availability methods which subtract the losses in faeces and urine from gross energy to obtain metabolisable energy do not account for the additional losses associated with fermentation.

The pathways by which carbohydrates undergo fermentation have been extensively studied, primarily in association with animal nutrition.[7] The major end products of this process are CO_2, methane, and the short-chain fatty acids (Fig. 3). The fatty acids are absorbed and made calorically available to the animal, but the methane is lost. Careful studies in ruminants have shown that about 15% of the energy in the fermented food can be lost as methane. There do not

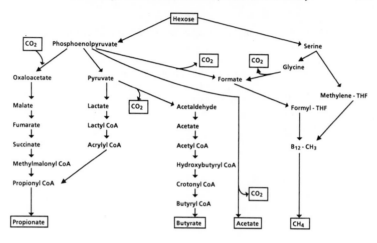

FIG. 3. Fermentation of carbohydrates.

appear to be any studies in humans which have quantitated the extent to which fermented substances yield methane. Qualitative studies, however, have clearly demonstrated the formation of methane and its discharge in flatus following meals containing fermented ingredients.[8,9] It is reasonable to assume that the yield of methane per unit of fermented substrate is the same in man as it is in animals. Since it has been clearly demonstrated that several of the alternative carbohydrates under review here are fermented, in whole or in part, methods which quantitate the energy yields to the human or animal must take into account the losses associated with fermentation.

AVAILABLE METHODS

Several methods have been used to determine caloric availability (Table 1). They can be categorised as partial methods, indirect methods, and direct methods.

Susceptibility to Digestive Enzymes

The *in vitro* susceptibility of bulking agents to the enzymes associated with digestion can be readily determined. The results, however, are misleading and do not reflect overall caloric availability to the whole animal. For example, a substance might be highly

TABLE 1
Methods Used in the Measurement of Caloric Availability

Partial methods
— Susceptibility to digestive enzymes
— Absorption from the small intestine
— Recovery in excreta

Indirect methods
— Balance method
— Calorimetry

Direct methods
— Growth curves
— Isotopic disposition

TABLE 2
Susceptibility of Bulking Agents to Digestive Enzymes

Substrate	mg glucose/100 mg substrate in 4 h
Starch	33·7
Maltose	51·6
Maltitol	5·4
Polydextrose	7·7
Isomalt	36·4

resistant to digestive enzymes, yet readily fermented to available nutrients by the bacterial flora of the lower intestinal tract. Conversely, a substance might be degraded by the digestive enzymes, but the product not absorbed or, if absorbed, not metabolically available due to rapid excretion. In one such study[10] the extent of digestion was determined by measuring the rate of glucose formation from polydextrose, maltitol, and isomalt; corn starch and maltose were included as positive controls. Each incubation contained 10 mg substrate, 5 units of α-amylase, and 1 unit each of maltase and isomaltase in 0·05 M (pH 6·9) phosphate buffer plus 0·01 M KCl. Samples were shaken for 4 hours at 37°C. Control incubations, with no enzyme, released insignificant amounts of glucose, measured by the glucose oxidase method. The results (Table 2) show the expected good yield of glucose from starch and maltose. Maltitol was almost completely resistant to enzyme degradation, as was polydextrose. The presence of about 5% free glucose in polydextrose accounted for most of the glucose seen there. In contrast, isomalt was highly susceptible to enzymic degradation under these conditions. In fact, since total hydrolysis of isomalt will yield 0·5 mole of glucose per mole of substrate, the extent of enzymic hydrolysis is double the 36% indicated here.

The resistance of polydextrose to enzymic hydrolysis does not necessarily indicate its lack of caloric availability, since other studies have shown that polydextrose is partially fermented by the intestinal flora to volatile fatty acids.[3] Thus it is more available than these data would indicate. In contrast, isomalt is readily hydrolysed by this mixture of digestive enzymes. Since glucose formation was the measure of isomalt digestion, these results suggest that isomalt is calorically available via its component parts, glucose, sorbitol, and mannitol.

Absorption from the Small Intestine

As with susceptibility to digestive enzymes, persistence within an isolated segment of the small intestine is not an accurate indicator of caloric availability. Although glucose is well absorbed under such conditions, it has been shown that lactitol is not removed from a solution perfused through the human jejunum.[11] This finding, however, should not be taken to indicate that lactitol has a low caloric availability; fermentation of lactitol in the lower intestinal tract is known to be extensive, releasing absorbable short-chain fatty acids.[4]

Quantitation in Excreta

Where appropriate methodology exists, quantitation of the unaltered bulking agent in excreta is a valuable indicator of loss of energy by this route. As will be shown, it does not account for all losses, but is frequently useful in setting an upper limit to the caloric availability of a substance. In a study with polydextrose,[12] two groups of eight male rats were individually placed in metabolism cages with free access to water and powdered rat-feed fortified with 10% cornstarch or 10% polydextrose. After acclimatisation, faeces were collected, dried, and weighed daily. Polydextrose in the faeces was also assayed by a specific chemical method involving exclusion chromatography, hydrolysis, and measurement of the released glucose. The results (Table 3) indicate similar food consumption and weight gain. Over the ten-day period, 61% of the ingested polydextrose appeared in faeces as excess weight. By chemical assay, 50% of the ingested polydextrose was present in faeces. The discrepancy between these two values suggests that 11% of the polydextrose was incorporated into bacterial mass. This incorporation into bacteria is another route by which calories can be lost to the host

TABLE 3
Recovery of Polydextrose in Rat Faeces

	10% corn starch	*10% polydextrose*
Food consumption, g/day	20·2	19·8
Wt gain, g/10 days	96	96
Faecal weight, g/day	3·3	4·4
Excess weight, g/day	—	1·1
Fraction of ingested polydextrose in faeces		
—by weight	—	0·61
—by assay	—	0·50

animal. There was no bacterial adaptation to polydextrose in this study, the recoveries in the final days being virtually the same as those in the initial days of the experiment. These results indicate a firm upper limit of 39% on the amount of polydextrose available for energy in these rats.

Studies which employ radiolabelled bulking agents have also yielded data regarding losses in excreta, as will be discussed later.

Balance Method

In the balance method, energy in the ingested food is determined or calculated from tables of food values, and energy in excreta is determined by bomb calorimetry.[13] The difference between these two values is termed the metabolisable energy (ME) of the ingested food. To estimate the caloric value of a bulking agent, two dietary periods are employed. In one, a fraction of the diet, generally no more than 10%, is replaced by the bulking agent under study; in the other, a reference substance such as starch or sucrose is used at the same level of fortification in the diet. The study can be parallel, using matched groups of animals or humans or sequential, using the same subjects. The diets and collections are continued for several days to smooth out day-to-day fluctuations in such factors as faecal elimination rates. A comparison of metabolisable energy from the two regimens can then be used to calculate the energy in the bulking agent, given a known energy value in the reference substance.

The calculation necessarily involves the comparison of two large numbers, the ME values of the two diets, to compute a much smaller value, the energy provided from the bulking agent. It is thus highly dependent upon the accuracy with which the two ME values are determined. A review of recently published balance studies has indicated that, under carefully controlled conditions by experienced investigators, a relative standard error of no better than about 2%

TABLE 4
Variability in Human Balance Studies

Investigators	Study type	n	% SE
Norgan and Durnin[14]	Control diet	6	5·8
Calloway and Chenoweth[15]	Lactose malabsorbers	4	8·6
Calloway and Kretsch[16]	Various diets	6	3·3, 3·1, 2·4, 1·4, 3·8
Göranzon et al.[17]	Various diets	6	14, 11, 9, 7, 8

can be achieved (Table 4). In many instances, the standard error was appreciably greater than this. The impact of the precision in the measurement of ME in the diet on the accuracy of determination of the caloric value of the bulking agent can be expressed as follows:

$$V_b = (1 - 1/p)^2 V_r + (1/p)^2 V_t$$

where V_b, V_r, and V_t are the variances in the metabolisable energies of the bulking agent, reference diet, and test diet, respectively, and p is the fraction of the diet which is replaced by the bulking agent.[18] The plot of error in the measurement in the bulking agent as a function of error in the ME of the total diet is shown for three levels of fortification (Fig. 4). For the bulking agents under consideration here, fortification above 10% is not possible, due to the incidence of diarrhoea and the fact that higher fortification levels are not reflective of actual use conditions.

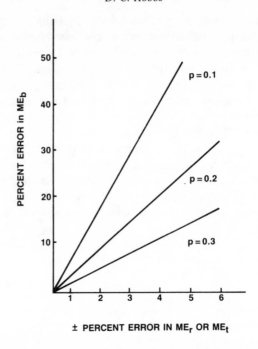

± PERCENT ERROR IN ME$_r$ OR ME$_t$

FIG. 4. Variability in the calculated ME of a bulking agent as a function of variability in the measured ME of the reference and test diets, for different levels of fortification.

Assuming an optimistic standard error of only 2% in the measurement of ME in the diet and a fortification of 10%, the 95% confidence bounds on the computed caloric value of a bulking agent are clearly far too broad to permit a meaningful determination (Table 5).

In addition to these statistical difficulties, the balance method is also inappropriate to measure the caloric value of substances which are fermented. As noted previously, fermentation is inevitably associated with the formation of methane and hydrogen. This appears as a part of the 'excreta' which is not normally quantitated in a balance study. The values obtained in a balance study are thus erroneously high to the extent that the bacterial flora of the intestinal tract convert the bulking agent to materials other than volatile fatty acids. Although the total amount 'wasted' in this manner has not been quantitated in man, studies in ruminants have shown it to be a substantial fraction of the fermented materials in the diet.

TABLE 5
Variability in the Calculated Caloric Value as a Function of the Standard
Error in the Measured ME of the Diet[a]

Standard error in ME of diet	95% confidence bounds on calculated caloric value of bulking agent
2% of mean	2·0±2·12
3% of mean	2·0±3·16
4% of mean	2·0±4·24

[a] Assume 10% fortification and a mean caloric value of 2·0 kcal/g.

Calorimetry

In whole body calorimetry, the animal or human is placed in a chamber with a closely controlled environment and given a carefully measured diet. The heat output of the subject is then measured over a period of several days, with careful control over diet, temperature, activity, etc. This therefore makes it difficult to carry out in humans. Since it is not possible to distinguish between the heat output of the animal and that of the bacteria contained within its intestinal tract, utilisation of the bulking agent by the bacterial flora is indistinguishable from the energy contributed to the host animal.

In indirect calorimetry, the oxygen consumption and CO_2 evolution of the animal or human is measured over a controlled period after meals with and without the bulking agent. Careful control over environmental parameters is again essential.[19]

In both types of calorimetry studies, a period on a control diet is compared with that on a diet containing the bulking agent. The statistics are the same as in balance studies, so the precision in the calculated caloric availability of the bulking agent is again dependent upon the precision with which the total heat output or oxygen consumption is measured. Table 6 indicates the standard errors associated with calorimetry studies reported from experienced laboratories in the recent literature. As in the balance method,[26] it is difficult to achieve a standard error below 2%. As shown previously, errors of this magnitude lead to unacceptably broad confidence bounds on the calculated caloric availability of the bulking agent.

TABLE 6
Variability in Human Calorimetry Studies

Investigators	n	% SE
Dauncey[20]	8	2·7
Dauncey[21]	9	1·8
	9	1·7
Hurni et al.[22]	11	1·2
	11	1·4
Ravussin et al.[23]	30	2·1
Webb[24]	15	3·1
Van Es et al.[25]	7	2·9
	8	2·4

Growth Curves

In the growth curve method,[26] carefully matched groups of young animals are fed a basal diet which is complete except for calories. To the basal diets of the control animals are added a measured amount of a reference substance such as starch or sucrose. The test animals receive the same amount of the bulking agent. The growth of the animals is then carefully determined over a period of several days or weeks. The weight gain in the animals receiving the bulking agent is compared with the gain in the animals receiving the same amount of a reference substance of known caloric value. One can then calculate, by proportionation, the caloric value of the bulking agent. In a variation of this procedure, several levels of reference material are used and the level which gives a weight gain matching that of the animals receiving the bulking agent is used to calculate the caloric value of the latter.

The weight gain method is direct in that it measures all calories delivered to the animal and is not responsive to calories lost by any route, including fermentation losses. However, the energy associated with weight maintenance is not necessarily the same as that for growth,[27] and the values determined may vary with the age and physiological state of the animal. Animals have many mechanisms for maintaining weight gain despite a deficit in calories; these include piloerection, reduced activity, and lowered body surface temperature. Environmental conditions must be carefully controlled; in one study, a room temperature difference of 4° led to a 34% change in weight gain.[26] Finally, the growth curve method cannot be applied to adult animals and it would be totally unethical to apply it to young humans.

Disposition Method

In the disposition method the uniformly radiolabelled bulking agent is administered in food at a dose representative of that projected for human use. Excretion of labelled material in faeces, urine, and exhaled CO_2 is measured. Quantification of label in the faeces and urine gives accurate values for losses by those routes. Expired CO_2 represents the sum of nutrients delivered directly to the animal as well as indirectly after the fermentative action of the intestinal bacteria. It is thus responsive to all of the routes by which energy is provided to the host. A portion of the nutrients delivered to the host is not converted to CO_2 over the duration of the experiment but is incorporated into tissue and endogenous metabolites. Studies with glucose and fatty acids have shown that 60% of the label is consistently cleared in the breath over the period of several hours.[28,29] The excretion of label then falls to a very low level as tissue constituents are turned over. A comparison of the CO_2 yield following the bulking agent with that after a fully metabolised reference substance such as glucose provides a direct and reliable measure of the systemic intake of energy-yielding material. To the extent that the bulking agent is available as a result of fermentation, some of the bacterially generated CO_2 will pass into the circulation and be exhaled via the lungs, biasing the results on the high side; this contribution is believed to be slight, however. In animal experiments, where the CO_2 is collected from a chamber enclosing the animal, the samples will include all of the CO_2 generated from the bacteria, much of which is expelled in the flatus. This will bias the results high to a greater extent, and a correction factor, based on independent measurement of the extent of fermentation, is necessary.

The disposition method has several advantages over the balance and growth curve methods. It is a direct measure of the test substance in question. Since it examines only the test substance and its products by a highly sensitive technique, the method can be employed at doses reflective of human use. Unlike the growth curve method, it can be used in adult animals. Of greatest relevance, the disposition method can be used in humans. Although animal models are useful, particularly in preliminary experiments, greatest reliance should be placed on methods which can also be applied to humans.

APPLICATION OF THE DISPOSITION METHOD

The use of the direct radiolabel method can be illustrated by some examples. Polydextrose has been examined in both rats[3] and man.[2] The time course of evolution of label in CO_2 by rats is shown in Fig. 5,

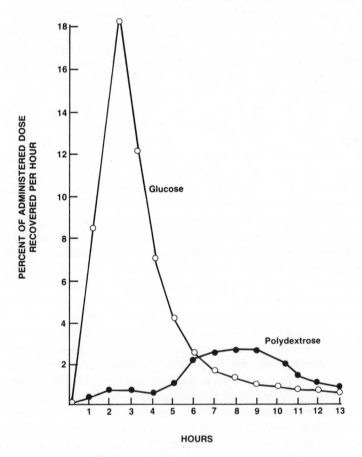

FIG. 5. Recovery of $^{14}CO_2$ from the rat after oral administration of glucose or polydextrose.

TABLE 7
Disposition of Polydextrose in the Rat

Disposition	Percentage of dose
CO_2	20·9
CO_2 adjusted to reflect tissue incorporation	34·8
Urine	1·8
Faeces	
as polydextrose	51·3
as bacterial mass	9·0
	60·3
Unavailable label	
Faecal polydextrose	51·3
Faecal bacteria	9·0
Bacterial CO_2	9·0
Urine	1·8
	71·1
Available label	
CO_2 (total − bacterial)	25·8

where it is compared with that after an oral dose of glucose under the same conditions. Most of the label from glucose appears within the first five hours, a time by which very little label has appeared following the polydextrose. This confirms the resistance of polydextrose to digestive enzymes noted *in vitro*. However, between 5 and 12 hours there is an appreciable appearance of labelled CO_2 indicative of the absorption of labelled fatty acids following fermentation in the lower intestinal tract.

In this experiment in rats, the contents of the entire chamber were collected, so the label represents CO_2 produced directly by the bacteria as well as that resulting from metabolism of absorbed nutrients by the rat. Table 7 quantitates the label in the various excreta. The apparent 35% of the dose converted to absorbed nutrients must be corrected for the contribution from bacterial CO_2. When the faeces were exhaustively extracted with water an amount representing 9% of the dose remained. This is label incorporated into bacteria. Since the conversion of carbohydrate to bacteria is no more than 50% efficient, an additional 9% of the dose must have been converted to CO_2—the 'cost' of the conversion of carbohydrate to bacterial tissue. Subtracting this 9% from the 35% total CO_2 leaves 26% as representative of the utilisation of polydextrose by the rat. Since glucose yields about 4 kcal/g, polydextrose thus has a caloric value of 1 kcal/g. These results were obtained in rats receiving single doses of radiolabelled polydextrose. Virtually identical values were obtained in animals which had received polydextrose (1 or 10 g/kg body weight/day) for 90 days, suggesting the absence of any adaptation by the intestinal flora.

The contribution of bacterial CO_2 to the collected gases is minimal in human experiments, where it is possible to collect respired air uncontaminated with flatus. A small contribution due to passage of

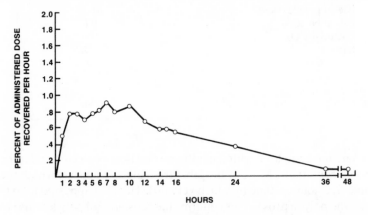

FIG. 6. Recovery of $^{14}CO_2$ from the respired air of man following oral administration of polydextrose.

bacterial CO_2 across the intestinal wall into blood is still possible, however. Figure 6 depicts the recovery of label in samples of respired air from human subjects receiving a dose of labelled polydextrose in a chocolate milk drink after having received 10 g unlabelled material per day for seven days.[2] The total recovery of 16% of the dose as CO_2 over 24 hours was calculated from the values in frequent samples of air and the known volume of air respired over this interval. As in the rat experiment, label in faeces and urine was used to document the loss of energy by these routes. Application of the 60% conversion of glucose to CO_2 leads to a calculated 27% caloric utilisation for polydextrose in man.

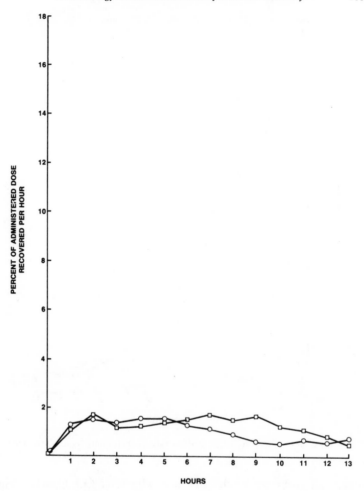

FIG. 7. Recovery of $^{14}CO_2$ from two rats following the oral administration of cellulose.

Similar experiments have been conducted with sorbitol,[30] cellulose,[31] and isomalt[30] in the rat and with maltitol[32] in the rat and man. Figure 7 depicts the recovery of labelled CO_2 following administration of labelled cellulose to the rat. Through 13 hours, about 15% of the dose was recovered as CO_2. With reference to the 60% yield following glucose, this then represents an apparent caloric availability of 25% for cellulose. As with polydextrose, the true value is

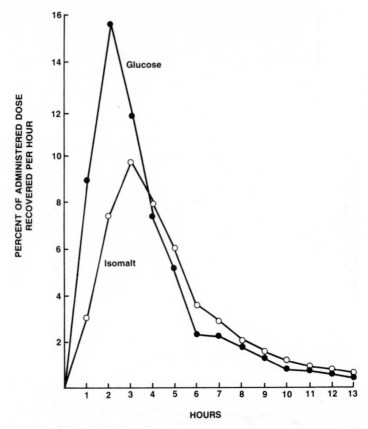

FIG. 8. Recovery of $^{14}CO_2$ from the rat after oral administration of glucose or isomalt.

somewhat lower, due to the presence of bacterial CO_2 from flatus in these samples. The appearance of label as early as one hour following administration is too early to represent fermentation, suggesting that some of the cellulose is directly digested in the upper gastrointestinal tract. Since this seems unlikely, it was concluded that the sample of cellulose may have contained other carbohydrate material such as starch or monomers.

The recovery of labelled CO_2 following isomalt administration to rats is shown in Fig. 8. Unlike polydextrose or cellulose, the label is released rapidly, confirming the susceptibility of isomalt to the digestive enzymes noted in *in vitro* experiments. By comparison with

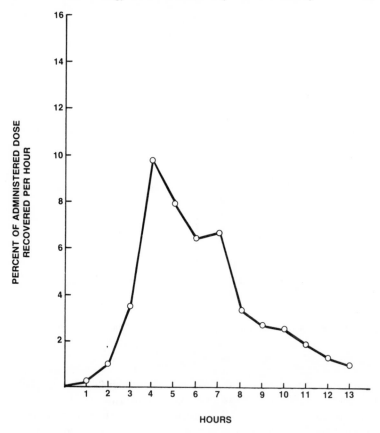

Fig. 9. Recovery of $^{14}CO_2$ from the rat after oral administration of sorbitol.

the label in CO_2 following glucose administration, a caloric availability of 3·2 kcal/g can be calculated for isomalt. No correction for bacterially formed CO_2 is necessary in the case of isomalt, since it is clear from the pattern of CO_2 liberation that isomalt is not fermented to any appreciable extent. The high caloric availability of isomalt was confirmed by the recovery of only 12% of the dose in faeces. A similar experiment in rats with sorbitol[30] (Fig. 9) reveals the high caloric availability of this material. The pattern of CO_2 evolution suggests that sorbitol is made available both by direct absorption in

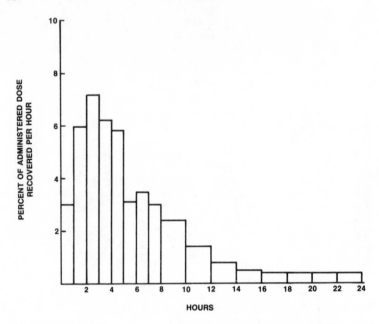

FIG. 10. Recovery of $^{14}CO_2$ from the respired air of man after oral administration of maltitol.

the upper gastrointestinal tract as well as by fermentation in the lower tract. Only 14% of the dose was recovered in faeces. In a human experiment with maltitol (Fig. 10) it is clear that the compound is rapidly absorbed, but may also be fermented. A total caloric availability of 90% is substantiated by recovery of only 8% of the dose in faeces plus urine.

DISCUSSION

Of the various methods available for the determination of caloric availability in this class of materials (Table 8), good accuracy is achievable with two of the partial methods (enzyme susceptibility and recovery in excreta) and with the label disposition method; it is particularly poor in the balance and calorimetry methods, where small differences in large numbers lead to unacceptable confidence

TABLE 8
Attributes of Methods to Measure Caloric Availability

Method	Accuracy	Accounts for all routes	Applicable to all bulking agents	Applicable in humans
Enzyme susceptibility	Good	No	Yes	—
Intestinal absorption	Fair	No	Yes	No
Recovery in excreta	Good	No	Possibly[a]	Yes
Balance method	Poor	No	Yes	Yes
Calorimetry	Poor	No	Yes	Yes
Growth curves	Fair	Yes	Yes	No
Label disposition	Good	Yes	Possibly[b]	Yes

[a] Requires specific assay method.
[b] Requires synthesis of labelled material.

bounds. Only the growth curve and label disposition methods account for all routes by which energy is gained or lost by the animal. Where fermentation is known not to occur, the balance method and calorimetry may be useful in providing crude estimates of caloric availability. All of the methods are potentially applicable to all bulking agents, although a specific assay method may not always be available to quantitate recovery in excreta. Synthesis of labelled material may be difficult for certain bulking agents, particularly those of natural origin. It is preferable to label all of the carbons in the compound, since metabolism may lead to more rapid conversion to CO_2 from some parts of the molecule than from others. Although studies to date have employed ^{14}C, the use of ^{13}C, with isotope ratio mass spectrometric analysis of the respired CO_2, is feasible.

Were it not for its inapplicability to humans, the growth curve method might be a suitable alternative to the label disposition method for determining caloric availability. Sufficient differences exist between animal and human metabolic rates, intestinal flora, digestive enzymes, gastrointestinal transit times, etc. to render inappropriate the extrapolation of findings in animals to availability in man. At the present time, then, the label disposition method appears to be the procedure of choice for determination of caloric availability for this class of products.

REFERENCES

1. NASRALLAH, S. M. and IBER, F. L. (1969). *Am. J. Med. Sci.*, **258**, 80–8.
2. FIGDOR, S. K. and BIANCHINE, J. R. (1983). *J. Agr. Food Chem.*, **31**, 389–93.
3. FIGDOR, S. K. and RENNHARD, H. H. (1981). *J. Agr. Food Chem.*, **29**, 1181–9.
4. GRIESSEN, M., BERGOZ, R., BALANT, L. and LOIZEAU, E. (1986). *Schweiz. Med. Wochenschr.*, **116**, 469–72.
5. CZERKAWSKI, J. W. and BRECKENRIDGE, G. (1969). *Br. J. Nutr.*, **23**, 925–37.
6. LEVITT, M. D. and BOND, J. H. (1970). *Gastroenterol.*, **59**, 921–9.
7. CZERKAWSKI, J. W. (1969). *World Review of Nutr. and Dietetics*, **11**, 240–82.
8. MARTHINSEN, D. and FLEMING, S. E. (1982). *J. Nutr.*, **112**, 1133–43.
9. O'DONNELL, A. U. and FLEMING, S. E. (1984). *Am. J. Clin. Nutr.*, **40**, 48–57.
10. NOCERINI, M. R. and HOBBS, D. C. (1986). Unpublished.
11. PATIL, D. H., GRIMBLE, G. K. and SILK, D. B. A. (1985). *Gut*, **26**, A1114.
12. FIGDOR, S. K. and HOBBS, D. C. (1986). Unpublished.
13. MITCHELL, H. H. (1964). *Comparative Nutrition of Man and Domestic Animals*, Vol. 2, Academic Press, New York.
14. NORGAN, N. G. and DURNIN, J. V. (1980). *Am. J. Clin. Nutr.*, **33**, 978–88.
15. CALLOWAY, D. H. and CHENOWETH, W. L. (1973). *Am. J. Clin. Nutr.*, **26**, 939–51.
16. CALLOWAY, D. H. and KRETSCH, M. J. (1978). *Am. J. Clin. Nutr.*, **31**, 1118–25.
17. GÖRANZON, H., FORSUM, F. and THILEN, B. (1983). *Am. J. Clin. Nutr.*, **38**, 954–63.
18. PESTI, G. M. and WARE, G. O. (1986). *J. Nutr.*, **116**, 1385–9.
19. BLAXTER, K. L. (1971). *Fed. Proc.*, **30**, 1436–43.
20. DAUNCEY, M. J. (1980). *Br. J. Nutr.*, **43**, 257–69.
21. DAUNCEY, M. J. (1981). *Br. J. Nutr.*, **45**, 257–67.
22. HURNI, M., BURNAND, B., PITTET, P. and JEQUIER, E. (1982). *Br. J. Nutr.*, **47**, 33–43.
23. RAVUSSIN, E., BURNAND, B., SCHUTZ, Y. and JEQUIER, E. (1982). *Am. J. Clin. Nutr.*, **35**, 566–73.
24. WEBB, P. (1981). *Am. J. Clin. Nutr.*, **34**, 1816–26.
25. VAN ES, A. J. H., VOGT, J. E., NIESSEN, C., VETH, J., RODENBURG, L., TEEUWSE, V., DHUYVETTER, J., DEURENBERG, P., HAUTVAST, J. G. A. J. and VAN DER BEEK, E. (1984). *Br. J. Nutr.*, **52**, 429–42.
26. RICE, E. E., WARNER, W. D., MONE, P. E. and POLING, C. E. (1957). *J. Nutr.*, **61**, 253–66.
27. JUST, A. (1984). *J. Animal Sci.*, **58**, 740–52.
28. STETTEN, M. R. and STETTEN, D. (1951). *J. Biol. Chem.*, **193**, 157–65.

29. ZILVERSMIT, D. B., CHAIKOFF, I. L., FELLER, D. D. and MASORO, E. J. (1948). *J. Biol. Chem.*, **176**, 389–400.
30. FIGDOR, S. K., ALLINGHAM, R. P. and KITA, D. A. (1983). *Abstracts of Papers, Amer. Chem. Soc. Annual Meeting*, AGFD-200.
31. FIGDOR, S. K. (1982). Unpublished.
32. RENNHARD, H. H. and BIANCHINE, J. R. (1976). *J. Agr. Food Chem.*, **24**, 287–91.

18

Legislation and Low-Calorie Products

D. P. ATKINS

Food Science Division, Ministry of Agriculture, Fisheries and Food,
London, UK

ABSTRACT

In the United Kingdom there are two distinct areas of regulatory control which relate to low-calorie products. Firstly, food additives such as sweeteners, bulking aids, emulsifiers and stabilisers, whose technological properties are necessary for the manufacture of many low-calorie products, are controlled by specific statutory regulations which list and specify those additives permitted. Secondly, the final food is itself subject to the provisions of the Food Act 1984 and to the Food Labelling Regulations 1984, which include specific controls over 'slimming claims' and contain statutory definitions of low-energy and reduced-energy foods. Currently there are also Codex proposals in negotiation on the labelling of low-calorie products and there is the intention of a specific EEC Directive to harmonise labelling regulations for these foods.

In order to gain approval for a new food additive in one of the above categories, the Food Advisory Committee (FAC) has to be convinced of a genuine need for this food additive against the requirement made by Section 4(2) of the Food Act 1984, that:

'Ministers shall have regard to the desirability of restricting, so far as practicable, the use of substances of no nutritional value as foods or as ingredients of foods.'

A new food additive therefore has to demonstrate technological and commercial advantages over those additives already permitted. The food additive submission is initially made to Food Science Division of the Ministry of Agriculture, Fisheries and Food, who advises the applicant on the technical aspects of their case and the regulatory machinery. When the applicant is confident that the criteria for a case-of-need have been established, the opinion of the FAC is then sought.

The FAC has recently published guidelines on establishing a case-of-need, which emphasise consumer benefit as an important criterion. Following the dietary recommendations made by the Committee on Medical Aspects of Food Policy (COMA) on the intakes of fats and simple sugars, it may be pertinent in a case-of-need submission to consider the potential benefits to consumers of a wide choice of low-calorie products. If the FAC agrees that the conditions of a case-of-need have been met then the Committee on Toxicity (COT) is asked to evaluate the safety of the food additive. Food Science Division assists in this evaluation by providing the COT with estimates of the likely levels of intake of the food additive. The outcome of the safety evaluation is referred to the FAC who then advise Ministers.

INTRODUCTION

Evidence from the USA[1] suggests that the market for low-calorie products in the United Kingdom has yet to reach its full potential. Undoubtedly the market will further develop as and when new food additives are produced which present technological improvements to the manufacturers of low-calorie products and which benefit consumers. Low-calorie products present unique opportunities for the manufacturers of food additives, since many of these products rely for their efficacy almost entirely upon the technological and nutritional qualities of their food additive components. This is particularly true for low-calorie soft drinks whose market has increased remarkably since 1983 due to the high quality of sweetness which can now be achieved with a negligible calorie cost. The role that food and food additives regulations play in the development of new low-calorie products is to ensure that both the food and the food additives are safe and, in addition, that new food additives are permitted only when genuine commercial and consumer needs exist for them.

LEGISLATION

The Food Act 1984 provides the legal framework for the control of food safety and food labelling in England and Wales; parallel legislation exists for Scotland and Northern Ireland. Ministers are empowered by Section 4 of the Act to create statutory controls for specific categories of food additives. Most food additive categories are subject to specific statutory controls under which only those substances listed and specified may be used. The categories of food additives which are central to the production of low-calorie products, sweeteners, bulking aids, emulsifiers and stabilisers are regulated by the following specific Statutory Instruments (S.I.): the Sweeteners in Food Regulations 1983 (S.I. 1983 No. 1211), the Miscellaneous Additives in Food Regulations 1980 as amended 1982 (S.I. 1980 No. 1843 and 1982 No. 14) and the Emulsifiers and Stabilisers in Food Regulations 1980 as amended 1982 and 1983 (S.I. 1980 No. 1833, 1982 No. 16, 1983 No. 1810). Although not all categories of food additives are regulated by specific Statutory Instruments, the general provisions of the Food Act 1984 do provide the means for indirect control by requiring that nothing injurious to the health of the consumer is added to food (Section 1) and that food is of the nature, of the substance and of the quality expected by the consumer (Section 2). The Ministry of Agriculture, Fisheries and Food has recently prepared a series of information sheets known as Food Facts which provide basic information on the evaluation and regulation of food additives.[2]

LABELLING

Section 7 of the general provisions of the Food Act 1984 empowers Ministers to create regulations relating to the labelling of food intended for human consumption. Section 6 of the same Act provides protection to the consumer from false and misleading claims made for food. The Food Labelling Regulations 1984 (S.I. 1984 No. 1305) make specific references to low-calorie products under Part II of Schedule 6 which contains the controls over slimming claims and the statutory definitions of 'low-energy' and 'reduced-energy' claims of food products. If a claim is made in the labelling or advertising of a food that it is an aid to slimming or weight control or weight reduction then the following qualifying statement has to accompany it—'can help slimming or weight control only as a part of a controlled (calorie, Joule or energy) diet'. The food of course has also to be capable of contributing to weight control and weight reduction. A food for which a reduced-energy claim is made is required to have an energy value of not more than three-quarters, weight for weight or volume for volume, of a similar food for which no such claim is made, unless that food is an intense sweetener or an intense sweetener product significantly sweeter than sucrose on a weight-for-weight basis. A food for which a low-energy claim is made is required to have an energy value of not more than 167 kJ (40 kcal) per 100 g or 100 ml, unless the product is an intense sweetener or product based on an intense sweetener which is significantly sweeter than sucrose on a weight-for-weight basis.

Currently there are Codex Alimentarius proposals in negotiation for the labelling of low-calorie products, in which agreement on definitions of reduced energy and low energy is being sought. It appears that low energy will be defined as 40 kcal per 100 g serving of solid food or 20 kcal per 100 ml serving of liquid food. The outcome of negotiations on the definitions of a reduced-energy claim is less clear. Figures from 60% to 75% of the energy value of the normal food have been suggested. It is the intention of the European Commission to introduce, within the near future, a specific directive to harmonise the labelling of low-calorie and reduced-calorie products.

THE MECHANISM OF FOOD ADDITIVE APPROVAL

In order for a new food additive to be approved, the Food Advisory Committee (FAC) has to be convinced that there is a need for this additive and that it is safe for use in food.

The submission of technical data on a new food additive is initially made to Food Science Division of the Ministry of Agriculture, Fisheries and Food. Officers of Food Science Division and Food Standards Division, after considering the submission, then advise the applicant on their case and request any further data considered to be necessary before approaching the FAC for an opinion. At this stage the FAC has to be convinced of a genuine need for this food additive against the requirement made by Section 4(2) of the Food Act 1984, that:

'Ministers shall have regard to the desirability of restricting, so far as practicable, the use of substances of no nutritional value as foods or as ingredients of foods.'

The applicant has therefore to demonstrate that the new food additive has technological or commercial advantages over existing food additives which have a clear benefit for the consumer. Support from the food industry for the use of the food additive is taken into account at this stage. Information is particularly sought from food manufacturers who have assessed the technological functions of the food additive through trial formulations, from which comparisons can be made against currently permitted food additives. In deciding whether there is benefit to the consumer the FAC takes into account the following points:

(a) the need to maintain the wholesomeness of food products up to the time they are consumed;
(b) the need for food to be presented in an attractive and palatable manner;
(c) convenience in purchasing, packaging, storage, preparation and use;
(d) the extension of dietary choice;
(e) the need for nutritional supplementation;
(f) any economic advantage

If the FAC decides that a case-of-need has been established and that the specification of the food additive conforms with an appropriate specification of purity which also relates to the material which has been toxicologically tested, it will be referred to the DHSS Committee on Toxicity of Chemicals in Food, Consumer Products and the Environment (COT) for advice on its safety in use. Officers of Food Science Division assist the COT secretariat in this evaluation by providing estimates of the range of likely intakes of this food additive based on the technical information provided by the applicant and by the food industry reports. The COT evaluate all of the available data relating to the safety in use of the proposed food additive and define its status according to the classification:

Group A: Substances that the available evidence suggests are acceptable for use in food.
Group B: Substances that on the available evidence may be regarded as provisionally acceptable for use in food but about which further information is necessary and which must be reviewed within a specified period of time.
Group C: Substances for which the available evidence suggests

possible toxicity and which ought not to be allowed in food without further evidence establishing their acceptability.

Group D: Substances for which the available evidence suggests probable toxicity and which ought not to be allowed in food.

Group E: Substances for which inadequate or no toxicological data are available and on which it is not possible to express an opinion as to their acceptability for use in food.

The outcome of the COT evaluation of safety is then referred back to the FAC who will then advise Health and Agriculture Ministers that approval of the food additive should be granted only if the following criteria have been satisfied:

(a) There is a genuine demonstrable need;
(b) it can be established to the satisfaction of the Committee on Toxicity of Chemicals in Food, Consumer Products and the Environment (COT) that its use would not prejudice the health of the consumers;
(c) there is satisfactory evidence that its presence would not adversely affect the nutritive value of food;
(d) it conforms with an adequate and appropriate specification of purity;
(e) the quantity of any additive permitted in food should, where necessary, be restricted to that which, in the judgement of the Committee, is needed to achieve its effect; and
(f) the addition of any additive to a food should be identified to the consumer to enable an informed choice to be made.

If Ministers then agree that the new substance may be added to the Regulations, they must first consult the whole spectrum of interests including consumer organisations, enforcement authorities and the food industry. After taking account of the views expressed during the consultation process, Ministers may propose new legislation which, before it can operate, has to be laid before Parliament.

In the case of food additives with a Group B safety evaluation the applicants are required to provide further data to the COT within a specified period. The FAC and COT are currently reviewing all additives in Group B and, where the required work has not been performed, consideration will be given to removing approval. Group A additives are also periodically reviewed by the COT as and when further toxicological data become available, which may have an influence on the previous evaluation. In the case of the intense and bulk sweeteners, the FAC and COT have required information on the actual intakes of all sweeteners by specific population groups within five years of the approval of the Sweeteners in Food Regulations 1983.[3] This work is currently being commissioned by Food Science Division in co-operation with the British Diabetic Association.

PERCEPTIONS OF RISK AND BENEFIT

The issues involved in balancing benefit against risk in the regulation of food additives can become confused by differences between regulators and consumers in their perception of acceptable risk.

Consumer Benefits

Low-calorie carbonated drinks have become one of the most successful low-calorie products. Since 1983, when the Sweeteners in Food Regulations came into operation, the market for low-calorie carbonated drinks has developed enormously. This has been largely due to the high quality of sweetness and low cost which is provided by the combination of aspartame and saccharin. Such products have a negligible energy value compared with the traditional product sweetened with sugars which contribute about 360 kcal/litre. It has been estimated that the market for low-calorie soft drinks increased by 34% between 1984 and 1985 at which time it was worth £150 million and accounted for 8·8% of the soft drinks market.[4] Undoubtedly the corresponding figures for 1986 and 1987 will reflect the continued growth of this sector of the market. The success of low-calorie drinks reflects the evident consumer benefits of a negligible calorific penalty and negligible cariogenic activity. If one accepts that such low-calorie products assist in the control of calorie intake, the restriction of the intake of simple sugars and reduction of total fat intake, then there is evidence for potential health benefits as described by the Committee on Medical Aspects of Food Policy (COMA) in their report on Diet in Relation to Cardiovascular Disease.[5]

The food additives responsible for the production of low-calorie products provide consumers with an opportunity to make some appropriate nutritional changes to their diets without radical changes to the type or the organoleptic nature of their food which might otherwise be necessary and would therefore be unacceptable for some consumers.

Consumer Risks

In the hierarchy of quantifiable risks to consumers from the food supply, microbiological, nutritional, environmental contaminant, natural toxicant and pesticide residue hazards have all been estimated to have a higher priority than food additives.[6] It may be of comfort to consider how safe food additives appear when compared with some of the foods which are eaten. When faced with the poor microbiological quality of some herbs and spices,[7] the prevalence of *Salmonella* species in frozen poultry[8] and the presence of natural toxicants in the diet,[9] the risks from food additives can appear to be of little consequence. Contrary to this it would appear that many consumers are greatly concerned about any risk from food additives and would argue that the comparison with food-related hazards is irrelevant. Although appropriate food labelling, according to the Food Labelling Regulations 1984, does provide a means for the consumer to identify certain food additives, one suspects that, whereas food-related hazards are largely seen as voluntary and therefore acceptable, any risks from food additives are perceived to be involuntary[10] and therefore are completely unacceptable.[11]

Safety Evaluation

The safety in use of a food additive or the risk to the consumer from a food additive is evaluated by feeding trials using animal models. The acceptability of a food additive is then usually determined by calculating from the results of these studies an acceptable daily intake figure (ADI) for man. An ADI is defined by the FAO and WHO Joint Expert Committee on Food Additives (JECFA) as being the daily intake of a food additive which may be consumed over a lifetime without risk, on the basis of all the known facts at the time of the evaluation. The ADI is in fact an arbitrary figure derived from the experimentally determined no-observed-effect level (NOEL), the maximum dose fed to at least two species of laboratory animals which did not result in an observable effect. To derive the ADI a safety factor of ten is usually applied to take account of the uncertainty of extrapolating data from animals to man and a further factor of ten is applied to take account of heterogeneity of sensitivity within the human population. The ADI is therefore usually one-hundredth of the daily dose range which did not cause an observable effect in laboratory animals.

The acceptability of the food additive is then usually judged by the extent to which dietary intakes are likely to exceed the ADI. Controversy over the safety evaluation of a food additive can result from disagreement over the statistical design of a study and the confidence placed in its results, the establishment of an observed effect level and the significance of the observed biological effects. The latter case is illustrated by food additives for which certain animal studies using high dose levels have demonstrated a carcinogenic effect. The decision concerning their acceptability for use in food is then determined by an assessment of the relevance of these studies to man. This requires substantial pharmacokinetic and metabolism studies in man and laboratory animals to elucidate the mechanism of the observed high dose effect and to determine its relevance both to the test animal at lower dose levels and to man.

As toxicological testing methodologies become more sensitive, the dose of a food additive necessary to cause an effect in the test animal decreases and so the ADI decreases.[12] In the case of certain intense sweeteners, their very success has created a situation where it is not difficult for the consumers of low-calorie products to exceed their ADIs. This situation is illustrated by considering the intake of three intense sweeteners, acesulfame-K, aspartame and saccharin from two sources: low-calorie drinks and tea or coffee sweetened by a table-top sweetener at a level equivalent to two teaspoons of sugar. Table 1 provides estimates of the intakes from these individual sources which would result in 60 kg individuals exceeding their ADI for each sweetener. These estimates indicate the possibility that the ADIs for acesulfame-K and saccharin can be exceeded by a small proportion of consumers. Before one considers risk from such a situation it is prudent to consider the meaning and derivation of the ADI. Firstly it is a daily intake acceptable over a whole lifetime and secondly it is a figure derived with an inherent and arbitrary 100-fold safety factor. As such the ADI could not be expected to delineate precisely between what is safe and what is unsafe. Nonetheless, concern over exceeding the ADI for an individual sweetener has been used as an argument in favour of the multi-sweetener concept

TABLE 1
Estimated Intake of Intense Sweeteners

Sweetener	ADI (mg/kg/day)	Product intake to exceed ADI for a 60 kg individual	
		Low-calorie drink (litre)	Sweetened[a] tea or coffee (cups)[b]
Acesulfame-K	0–9	0·58	8·1
Aspartame	0–40	16·1[c]	48·0
Saccharin	0–2·5	1·0[c]	4·5

[a] Equivalent to 2 teaspoons of sugar.
[b] 1 cup = 225 ml.
[c] Sweetened by saccharin and aspartame, 1:1 by weight.

and undoubtedly this argument can be used in a case-of-need submission for a new sweetener, particularly where there is evidence of synergy with currently permitted sweeteners.

A recent market research survey commissioned by the Ministry of Agriculture, Fisheries and Food (MAFF) into public awareness of food additives[13] has revealed that about one-third of consumers believe that there is no need for any food additives. It also revealed that only 15% of consumers were definitely aware that there were any controls at all on what is used in food. These findings demonstrate the need for both the food industry and MAFF to inform customers about the benefits to them from the use of food additives and the controls over their use in food which ensure safety. In an attempt to remedy this situation MAFF has recently published a free booklet, *Food Additives—The Balanced Approach*.[14] It is also important for food manufacturers, food additive manufacturers and retailers to inform consumers of the technical needs and benefits from the use of food additives. Low-calorie products provide good examples of technological need and consumer benefit from the use of food additives and would therefore provide an excellent vehicle for such an informative exercise.

CONCLUSIONS

The technological need for food additives in certain foods and their benefits is a case which has yet to be demonstrated effectively to consumers. A recent market research survey commissioned by the Ministry of Agriculture, Fisheries and Food has revealed that about one-third of consumers feel that there is no need for any food additives.[13] This belief is unfortunately reinforced by the current climate of 'additive-free' foods. The use of food additives in the manufacture of low-calorie products can be seen to provide an example of demonstrable consumer benefit, an example which if effectively communicated can only benefit the long-term interests of the food industry.

REFERENCES

1. HENDLEY, B. (1986). *Food Processing*, May, 23–6.
2. MINISTRY OF AGRICULTURE, FISHERIES AND FOOD (1986). *Food Facts No. 1 Main types of additives; No. 2 Evaluation of permitted additives; No. 3 Procedure for considering and regulating food additives; No. 4 Allergies and additives; No. 5 Systems of control of food additives in the UK and European Community; No. 6 Control of flavourings; No. 7 Assessment of food additives by the Food Advisory Committee*, MAFF Publications, Lion House, Alnwick, Northumberland.
3. MINISTRY OF AGRICULTURE, FISHERIES AND FOOD (1983). *Food Additives and Contaminants Committee Report on the Review of Sweeteners in Food*, FAC/REP/34, HMSO, London.
4. HILLIAM, M. A. (1986). *Sweeteners in the UK*, Leatherhead Food R.A. Food Market Updates No. 18, Leatherhead, England.
5. DEPARTMENT OF HEALTH AND SOCIAL SECURITY (1984). *Report on Health and Social Subjects 28. Committee on Medical Aspects of Food Policy Report of the Panel on Diet in Relation to Cardiovascular Disease*, HMSO, London.
6. WODIKA, V. O. (1977). *Fd Technol.*, **31** (9), 75–9.
7. LINDBERG, A. M. and NICKELS, C. (1976). *Lius Medelsteknik*, **4**, 160–4.
8. COMMUNICABLE DISEASE SURVEILLANCE CENTRE (1985). *Br. Med. J.*, **291**, 394–6.
9. AMES, B. N. (1983). *Science*, **222**, 1256–64.
10. STARR, C. (1969). *Science*, **165**, 1232.
11. COOMES, T. J. (1983). In: *Control of Food Quality and Food Analysis*, Eds Birch, G. G. and Parker, K. J., Elsevier Applied Science, London, 81–95.
12. GANGOLI, S. D. (1983). *Food Chem.*, **11** (4), 339–46.
13. MINISTRY OF AGRICULTURE, FISHERIES AND FOOD (1986). *Survey of Consumer Attitudes to Food Additives*, HMSO, London.
14. MINISTRY OF AGRICULTURE, FISHERIES AND FOOD (1987). *Food Additives—The Balanced Approach*, HMSO, London.

Index

Abdominal fat, 206
Abdominal obesity, 207
Absorption, effects of acute or chronic
    carbohydrate (CHO)
    overfeeding versus fat
    overfeeding, 174–5
Acceptable daily intake (ADI), 21,
    276, 277
Acesulfame K, 16, 67, 101–12, 159–62,
    277
  ADI, 106
  applications, 107–11
  bakery products, in, 110–11
  confectionery, in, 111
  intended uses of, 107
  losses after storage, 103
  metabolic investigations, 106
  physical and chemical properties,
    102–4
  physiology, 105–6
  products requiring heat stability, in,
    110–11
  sensory properties, 104–5
  soft drinks, in, 108–10
  solubility in water, 103
  stability in aqueous media, 103
  synergism with aspartame and
    cyclamate, 105
  table-top products, in, 110
  taste characteristics of, 104–5
  toxicology, 105–6
ACTH, 207

Additives, 21, 30, 96, 147, 271
  approval mechanism, 272–5
Adopted children, obesity studies,
  188–9
Alitame, 16, 19
American Cancer Society Study, 202,
  204
Anti-cholesterol drugs, 57
Appetite
  effects of artificial sweeteners, 147–
    70
  effects of aspartame and sucrose,
    157–9
  mechanisms controlling, 168–9
  suppressants, 2
Aseptic drinks, 121
Aseptic packaging, 122
Aspartame, 12, 14, 16, 17, 20, 21, 67,
  108, 113, 115–16, 142, 159–63,
  275, 277
  conversion products, 119
  dry stability of, 119
  effects on appetite, 157–9
  heat applications, 119
  paradoxical effects of, 152–7
  see also NutraSweet
Ayds, 2

Bakery products, 98, 110–11
Balance method for caloric availability
  measurement, 252–4